MICROBIAL ECOLOGY

MICROBIAL ECOLOGY

SEVENTH SYMPOSIUM OF THE
SOCIETY FOR GENERAL MICROBIOLOGY
HELD AT THE
ROYAL INSTITUTION, LONDON
APRIL 1957

CAMBRIDGE

Published for the Society for General Microbiology

AT THE UNIVERSITY PRESS

1957

PUBLISHED BY

THE SYNDICS OF THE CAMBRIDGE UNIVERSITY PRESS

Bentley House, 200 Euston Road, London, N.W. 1
American Branch: 32 East 57th Street, New York 22, N.Y.

Printed in Great Britain at the University Press, Cambridge
(Brooke Crutchley, University Printer)

CONTRIBUTORS

ANDERSON, E. S., Central Enteric Reference Laboratory and Bureau, Public Health Laboratory Service, Colindale, London.

ANDREWES, C. H., National Institute for Medical Research, Mill Hill, London.

BAWDEN, F. C., Rothamsted Experimental Station, Harpenden, Herts.

BRIAN, P. W., Imperial Chemical Industries Ltd, Akers Research Laboratories, Welwyn.

COHEN-BAZIRE, GERMAINE, Department of Bacteriology, University of California.

DUDDINGTON, C. L., Biological Laboratory, The Polytechnic, Regent Street, London.

GIBSON, JANE, Agricultural Research Council Unit for Microbiology, University of Sheffield.

HAWKER, LILIAN E., Department of Botany, University of Bristol.

HEWITT, L. F., Serum Research Institute, Carshalton, Surrey.

INGRAM, M., Low Temperature Research Station, University of Cambridge.

JOHNSON, F. H., Biology Department, Princeton University, New Jersey.

KITCHING, J. A., Department of Zoology, University of Bristol.

LOVELL, R., Royal Veterinary College, London.

SHEPHERD, C. J., Medical Research Council Unit for Chemical Microbiology, University of Cambridge.

SMITH, K. M., Virus Research Unit, Agricultural Research Council, Cambridge.

STANIER, R. Y., Department of Bacteriology, University of California.

TRIBE, H. T., School of Agriculture, University of Cambridge.

WILSON, G. S., Public Health Laboratory Service, London.

CONTENTS

EDITORS' PREFACE

The papers in this volume form the basis of a Symposium on Microbial Ecology, arranged by the Society for General Microbiology through its Meetings Secretary, Dr E. F. Gale, to be held in London in April 1957.

The introductory paper deals with the genetic basis of microbial variation. There follow a group of five papers on the interaction of microbes with their inanimate environment and a set of three papers on interactions between microbes. The remaining papers discuss the ecology of various groups of microbes, in several cases with special reference to their interaction with higher organisms.

Microbial ecology is, in its present stage of development, less quantitative than the ecology of animals and plants, but the papers in this volume reveal the extensive development of qualitative investigation that has been carried out in recent years and will form a valuable basis, not only for the discussions at the Symposium, but also for further studies.

R. E. O. WILLIAMS
C. C. SPICER

Central Public Health Laboratory,
Colindale Avenue,
London, N.W. 9

THE GENOME AS A COMPONENT OF THE ECOSYSTEM

C. J. SHEPHERD

Medical Research Council Unit for Chemical Microbiology,
Department of Biochemistry, University of Cambridge

'The fault, dear Brutus, is not in our stars, but in ourselves.'

Ecology is a study of the interactions of organisms and environments. In many of the papers that follow in this Symposium, authors discuss the selective action of environmental factors on microbial populations. If all organisms possessed the same chemical, physical and biological potential, no such selection could occur and ecology would not exist as a field for study. Consequently, any discussion of selective actions of environments must be prefaced by a description of variability, its nature, origin and scope, in the organisms affected. The purpose of this contribution is to set out what is known of the genetic constitution of organisms and how gene diversities may arise and affect the interaction of those organisms with their environments.

The ultimate expression of the biological behaviour of any organism must be in terms of the properties and structures of molecules, those of outstanding biological importance in direct relation to the external and internal environments being the proteins. The mechanism of control of the synthesis of these specific molecules is not yet clear, but that this control involves genetic material of the organism is certain. In this contribution, an attempt has been made to outline the possible types of interaction between this genetic material and the environment, since the study of ecology, from the point of view of the geneticist, may be said to be the study of the relationship between the intrinsic, genetic, characters of the organism and the extrinsic characters of the environment.

While it is not possible at the present time to relate ecological behaviour to molecular structure and organization, some correlation with the factors determining such organization can be attempted.

For the benefit of those who may not be familiar with the nomenclature of genetics, it may be desirable to define a few of the terms to be used. The *gene* is a hypothetical entity postulated to explain the results of breeding experiments, and may be defined as a self-reproducing body, passed from generation to generation, that has a specific function in the production of the phenotype. In referring to Mendelian genes, we may say that these are located on larger units, the chromosomes. It must not be assumed that other parts of the cell have no role in heredity, but simply that most of what is known of the hereditary mechanism at the present time is associated with the chromosomal genes. Particulate units, having the properties of genes, may exist in the cytoplasm, but they are not attached to chromosomes and do not show Mendelian segregation.

The individual's genetic constitution is called its *genotype*, which describes its genetic formula and breeding behaviour. The term *phenotype* refers to the external appearance produced by reaction of an organism of given genotype with a given environment. Within the term, *genome*, in the following discussion, are included not only chromosomal genes, but any particles in the nucleus or cytoplasm having the properties of hereditary determination and an autonomy in replication.

The term *ecosystem* includes the interrelationships between the organism as a whole and its immediate physico-chemical and biotic environment, both internal and external, and also includes alterations of these relationships with time. Thus *ecology* may be defined in these terms as a study of genome-controlled phenotypes in relation to their environments.

It is important to realize that the characteristics of organisms are not inherited as such, but that heredity is transmitted in the form of genes. These entities determine the potentialities which can be fulfilled by the organism, the realization of these potentialities being dependent on the environment in which the genes perform their functions. However, the potentialities possessed by the phenotype are set within rigorous limits characteristic of the genotype. It is necessary to emphasize that no gene acts alone, but in an environment and, to a greater or lesser degree, the functioning of a gene always depends on its environment. The ability to adapt to an environment is inherited, but the phenotypic state resulting from the adaptation may, or may not, be inherited.

The survival of an individual, or species, requires adaptation both to long-term variations (evolutionary adaptation) and short-term variations (physiological adaptation). Evolutionary adaptation involves the change of genotype by selection, while physiological adaptation represents the response of the organism, or population, to changes having a much shorter time base. This latter may, or may not, involve the selection of different genotypes.

Sometimes a fortuitous change of genotype will result in the organism inhabiting a completely different environment, e.g. tall to dwarf mutations in plants.

Although the title of this Symposium is 'Microbial Ecology', I have had no hesitation in drawing on higher classes of organisms to illustrate certain points, as the ecological relationships between the higher and lower classes will be, I am sure, fully covered by later papers.

The various types of interaction of genome and environment fall into four groups:

(1) The fixed genome in a fixed environment.
(2) The fixed genome in a variable environment.
(3) The variable genome in a fixed environment.
(4) The variable genome in a variable environment.

I shall now proceed to discuss each of these types in detail, with particular reference to the importance in ecological relationships of the interactions described.

FIXED GENOME IN A FIXED ENVIRONMENT

This system, while being of interest to some biochemists and those of us who play with chemostats, is of no interest from an ecological point of view, as no interaction is possible.

FIXED GENOME IN A VARIABLE ENVIRONMENT

It is necessary in this instance to differentiate between the reaction of a single organism and the reaction of a population to its environment. Clearly, a greater degree of elasticity of response is observed in the latter case, even when the observations are confined to a single generation, due to the varied genetic constitution of the members of any natural population.

Within a given individual organism, providing no mutation of any gene takes place, the genome is a constant factor and the genetic constitution merely limits the degree and type of adaptation to any environment. Nevertheless, even with a fixed genome there is, in many cases, a remarkable plasticity to changes in either the external or internal environment of the organism. The response of the individual to the environment when there is no change of genotype is, by definition, phenotypic adaptation, and recognition of a purely phenotypic adaptation is often experimentally difficult. Frequently such adaptation is relatively rapid and the organism can de-adapt to the original phenotype immediately on restoration to the original environment. This does not, however, constitute critical evidence that mutation has not occurred, but there are tests, such as those of Luria & Delbruck (1943), Newcombe (1949) and Lederberg & Lederberg (1952), which can be used successfully to distinguish between adaptation and simple mutation. In dealing with populations of micro-organisms, such difficulties may be sidestepped by using non-growing cells, but this technique cannot be used in all cases, since many phenotypic adaptations have not as yet been demonstrated in the absence of growth.

A considerable amount of evidence supports the conclusion that genes work in terms of the chemistry of the organism and it is not surprising, therefore, that characteristics determined by genes are affected by agents known to influence chemical reactions in general. As illustration, let us first consider the interaction of the external environment with the genome.

Temperature

As long ago as 1920, Krafka clearly demonstrated that temperature affects the expression of the *bar-eye* mutation in *Drosophila*, since the number of facets found in bar-eyed flies markedly decreases as the temperature of growth is raised (Table 1).

Table 1. *The effect of temperature on the expression of 'bar-eye' mutation in* Drosophila (*Krafka*, 1920)

	No. of facets per eye when grown at			
Stock	15°	20°	25°	30°
Bar-eyed ♂♂	270	161	121	74
Bar-eyed ♀♀	214	122	81	40

Similar effects of temperature of growth on gene expression have been shown by Stern (1948) for the mutation *cubitus interruptus* in *Drosophila* and by Harnly & Harnly (1936) for the mutation *vestigial* in the same organism. The results of these studies with *Drosophila* indicate that such temperature sensitivity effects are not necessarily a general property of groups of genes, but are confined to particular genes within each allelic series.

A considerable number of nutritional mutants of micro-organisms are known which require the addition of growth factors at certain temperatures, but not others. A relatively simple example of this class is provided by mutant 70,004 of *Neurospora crassa*, which will grow without any external supply of adenine at temperatures up to 26°, but at 33° will not grow at all without an external supply of adenine. As an example of extremely complex temperature effects we may take the work of Doudney

& Wagner (1952, 1953), again with *Neurospora*. Mutants of this fungus were selected which were phenotypically wild type, except that they showed inhibition of growth on media containing threonine or histidine. One mutant showed no inhibition of growth by threonine at 20°, but its growth was greatly stimulated by thiazole. At 25°, growth inhibition by threonine was only slight, but growth stimulation by thiazole plus choline, or methionine, was marked. At 30° the mutant had a completely wild-type phenotype and showed no inhibitions or stimulations, but at 35° in the presence of threonine, the mutant required methionine, homocysteine, homoserine or sulphanilamide for growth, and this was further stimulated by the addition of choline or thiamine. The precise explanation of these phenomena is not known, but it is clear that the nutritional requirements are dependent simultaneously on gene action and environment.

As a last example of temperature effects we may take the work of Sonneborn (1950) and Beale (1952) on serotype transformations in *Paramecium aurelia*. From stock arising by asexual reproduction (autogamy) from a single homozygous individual, any one of a number of antigenic types may be produced, depending on the growth temperature. The transformations from one type to another are readily reversible, but occur only after a number of fissions have taken place at the new temperature, although the transformation itself is relatively rapid. It has been demonstrated beyond all reasonable doubt that no genic changes accompany the transformation.

The effects of temperature so far considered have concerned mutant organisms, but similar drastic effects have been shown in the case of wild-type organisms. Goldschmidt (1938) has produced a number of phenotypic variants of *Drosophila* by subjecting the flies to high temperatures for varying periods of time; these 'phenocopies' resemble to a remarkable degree certain known inherited mutant phenotypes. For example, exposure of 5-day-old larvae to a temperature of 35° for 24 hr. produced phenocopies resembling the mutant *scalloped*, while treatment of 7-day-old larvae at 37° for 24 hr. produced phenocopies resembling the mutant *trident*.

Many of the temperature-sensitive mutants and phenocopies in *Drosophila* have a definite time of induction during the life cycle of the organism, indicating a sensitive period in development at which a particular abnormality is produced. It is possible that this phenomenon is in some way analogous to differentiation in embryonic tissues. No comparable effects are known for micro-organisms.

Hydrogen-ion concentration

In a manner similar to that described for temperature, the pH of the external medium can affect the phenotypic expression of various genes, although such effects are rather more uncommon. Stokes, Foster & Woodward (1943) have described a pyridoxin-requiring mutant of *Neurospora*, which is B_6-dependent at pH levels below 5·8, but can synthesize pyridoxin at higher pH values. Srb & Horowitz (1944) have described a similar situation in the case of a citrullineless strain of *Neurospora*.

One of the most striking effects of pH change can be seen in the determination of flower colour in higher plants, where anthocyanin pigments act as pH indicators. The acidity of the cellular environment in which a genotypically determined anthocyanin exists may be affected by the external environment, such as the pH of the soil, or it may vary with the genotype of the organism itself, e.g. Scott-Moncrieff (1936) has shown that in *Primula sinensis*, pH differences of the petal sap are inherited in simple Mendelian fashion and are thus gene-controlled.

Gale & Epps (1942) have reported on the effects of pH of the medium during growth on the enzymic activities of *Escherichia coli* and *Micrococcus lysodeikticus*. They have found that change in the external pH during growth is followed by an alteration in the enzyme content of the cells. The various enzymes studied fell into two groups according to the type of their variation with the pH of the growth medium. The formation of one group of enzymes undergoes a variation so that their activity per cell is constant whatever the pH of the medium. The other group comprises enzymes whose formation is greatest when the growth pH approaches their optimum activity pH. Gale & Epps concluded that bacteria react to a change in their external environment in such a way that the resultant change in their internal environment is at a minimum

Other environmental factors

Emerson (1921) showed that maize plants containing the appropriate genes would only develop the 'sun-red' colour if the plants were exposed to direct sunlight. More recently (Carlile, 1956), light has been shown to affect the synthesis of carotenoids and the production of macrospores in *Fusarium oxysporum*. Table 2 summarizes the effects of light on non-genetic variation in *Fusarium*. The results of Carlile (1956) also show that phenotypic modification may be caused by changes in the nutrient composition of the growth medium.

Sonneborn (1950) showed that it was possible to change the serotypes of *Paramecium aurelia* by nutritional changes, as well as temperature changes.

Rogosa & Mitchell (1950) have demonstrated that variations of colonial morphology of *Lactobacillus* species, copying in all details the appearance of certain mutants, may be produced by environmental changes. Species normally developing into rough colonies on tomato-juice agar will produce smooth colonies when sorbitan mono-oleate is added to the medium. The smooth phenotype disappears immediately upon subculturing on media without sorbitan mono-oleate. Similarly, Braun, Kraft, Mead & Goodlow (1952) have shown that genetically smooth strains of *Brucella* species produce rough or mucoid colonies when grown in the presence of penicillin, the actual phenotype depending on the strain of organism and concentration of penicillin used. Addition of penicillinase, or subculture on media without penicillin, will re-establish the smooth type immediately.

Table 2. *The effect of light on non-genetic variation in* Fusarium oxysporum (*Carlile*, 1956)

Age in days	Light	Darkness
4	Carotenoids formed	No carotenoids
	Macrospores abundant	Macrospores absent
	No sclerotia	No sclerotia
	No chlamydospores	No chlamydospores
20	Carotenoids formed	Naphthoquinone pigments formed on some media, no carotenoids
	Macrospores formed on some media	No macrospores
	Sclerotia formed on some media	No sclerotia
	No chlamydospores	Chlamydospores abundant on some media

In certain strains of *Drosophila*, the normal banded pattern on the abdomen may be altered by a simple gene change (Morgan, 1919). The degree of deviation from the normal is, however, dependent on the cultural conditions. When the flies are reared on fresh, moist culture medium the effect is shown in its most extreme form. With increasing dryness of the medium, flies are more normal, until they are indistinguishable from the wild type. This again emphasizes that the genes themselves do not produce characteristics, but do so only through interaction with the environment.

The effects of environmental changes on the formation of adaptive (inducible) enzymes have been fully discussed in a previous Symposium (1953) in this series, so will not be dealt with here.

The most marked examples of interaction of a fixed genome with a changing environment can be seen in embryonic differentiation, but this is outside the scope of the present Symposium. For an interesting discussion of this problem, reference should be made to Waddington (1939, 1954).

The subject of morphological differentiation is, however, of great importance with regard to some classes of micro-organisms (fungi, algae, Protozoa). The little evidence to date indicates that such changes are caused by the effects of a changing environment on a constant genome. For example, Parke, Manton & Clarke (1955) have shown that the flagellate, *Chrysochromulina kappa*, changes into an amoeboid form in old cultures, when the medium becomes exhausted. Cantino (1956) has shown that the presence or absence of bicarbonate ion influences the direction of morphogenesis in *Blastocladiella* in the direction of formation or inhibition of resting sporangia.

Limitation of phenotype

The essential fact brought out by the above survey is that different genes respond differently to environmental stimuli. This observation is contained within the concept of 'reaction norm', proposed by Johannsen (1911), which states that the modification of expression of the genotype is set within limits characteristic of the genotype. The precise phenotypic effects are determined by the environmental conditions. Different genes may have overlapping reaction norms; e.g. any mutant genes, such as the temperature-sensitive alleles, can under certain environmental conditions overlap in phenotypic expression with their wild-type alleles. Modification of the environment, by external or internal factors, or by the influence of other genes, may be expected to change the expression of any specific gene within the limits characteristic of that gene's ability to act. Thus the genotype sets the limits of possible phenotypes.

VARIABLE GENOME IN A FIXED ENVIRONMENT

The genome was considered previously as a constant factor; in this section it is variable while the external factors remain constant. A simple, single-character, variation of the genome in an individual may be brought about in various organisms by several mechanisms, including spontaneous and induced mutations, transformation, transduction or heterokaryosis.

Spontaneous mutation

The spontaneous mutation rate is that rate which occurs in the absence of abnormal external conditions, although this does not necessarily imply that spontaneous mutations occur completely independently of influences outside the genetic material. The spontaneous mutation rate is that which is assumed to approximate the mutation rate in any natural population of organisms. The total frequency of spontaneous mutation in a species cannot be accurately measured, due to the fact that many small mutations may escape detection, but the rates of mutation at specific loci have been determined for a number of genes in various organisms. For each gene, mutation is a rare event; the rate is constant for any particular gene, but varies from one gene to another, whereas the overall rate for the organism, if all possible mutations are considered, has been estimated at about one mutation per 10–30 gametes (Race, Sanger & Lawley, 1948). Furthermore, the overall rate is different for different species and may even vary within different populations of the same species. It would also appear that the spontaneous mutation rate may vary within different tissues of a single organism (Stadler, 1942).

If a 'mutant' gene is already present in a population, this can spontaneously back-mutate to the wild-type allele and the same considerations hold as for forward mutation.

The cause, or causes, of spontaneous mutation are obscure and much speculation has been indulged in regarding the role of natural radiations, such as cosmic radiation, but it seems likely that a number of different factors may be involved. Any mutation caused by applied physical or chemical treatments is known as an 'induced mutation', but there would appear no reason to suppose that mutations caused by such artificial means differ in any way from spontaneously occurring mutations.

A number of physical, chemical and genetic factors are known which influence the spontaneous mutation rates of certain genes in various organisms, and consideration of these will allow speculation on the mechanisms of origin of spontaneous mutations.

Influence of physical factors on the mutation rate

The effect of temperature on mutation rate has been described by Plough (1941) and Birkana (1938) for lethal mutations on the second chromosome in *Drosophila*. Between 6 and 18° there was no effect of changing temperature on mutation rate, but above (18–31°) and below (– 6°) this temperature range the rate of lethal mutation was increased between two and three times. Genes with high mutation rates respond differently to temperature change from wild-type genes mutating to lethals in *Drosophila*, there appearing to be an inverse relationship between mutation rate and temperature (Gowen & Gay, 1933).

No satisfactory generalizations can be made at present from the known data concerning the effect of temperature on mutation rate, although an attempt has been made by Muller (1950) to reconcile the differences in response shown by 'stable' genes to temperature by application of the quantum theory.

As an example of the effect of temperature on mutation rate in microorganisms, we may take the work of Lincoln (1947), who studied the mutation rates in two stocks of *Phytomonas stewartii*, grown at various temperatures between 12 and 36°. Mutations were observed in colony colour, size and surface appearance and it was found that the rate of mutation at 36° was ten times that at 12°, with intermediate rates at intermediate temperatures.

Practically nothing is known regarding the effects of pressure on mutation rate, but McElroy & de la Haba (1949) have reported that the application of high pressure depresses the number of mutants obtained by treating *Neurospora* conidia with nitrogen mustard. The reduction of the mutation rate was directly proportional to the pressure applied, 9000 lb./sq.in. giving a 50 % reduction in the number of mutants produced by the nitrogen mustard treatment, 2000 lb./sq.in. giving a 10 % reduction. No particular types of mutants were preferentially suppressed. However, most of these morphological mutants appeared to be due to gross chromosomal changes, rather than true gene mutations. If the pressure is applied 30 min. after the treatment with nitrogen mustard, then there is no reduction of the mutation rate. In contrast to the reduction of the numbers of morphological mutants with increasing pressure, the number of biochemical mutants increases. It is suggested that the latter are due to true gene mutation, which is accompanied by a volume decrease, such as might be expected to occur with a simple bimolecular reaction.

Radiation in the form of X-, α-, β-, γ- and ultra-violet radiation brings about increased mutation by causing changes affecting both genes and chromosomes. In nature, cosmic radiation and radiation from natural radioactive sources have been suggested as possible causative agents for spontaneous mutation (Muller, 1927), and, in fact, slight increases in mutation rates have been found in regions with a high natural radiation intensity. However, estimates of the amount of natural radiation show that the dosage is far too small to account for observed spontaneous mutation rates. Recently (*Report*, 1956), owing to the considerable public and scientific interest aroused in radiation hazards due to the various uses and misuses of atomic energy, accurate measurements have been made of this 'background' radiation. The total dose of radiation accumulated by an average person over a 30-year period amounts to 4·3 roentgens at average altitudes, or 5·5 r. at high altitudes. It is difficult to assess the significance of this dosage in terms of possible mutations produced. An estimate, perhaps better described as a guess, of the effect for mice is that a dosage of between 5 and 150 r. would lead to a doubling of the spontaneous rate. A closer but probably no more accurate guess of the doubling dosage is 30–80 r. It seems likely therefore that radiation from cosmic and natural radioactive sources cannot account for more than a small part of the normal 'spontaneous' mutation rate.

Hollaender & Emmons (1946) have shown that solar radiations of wavelengths shorter than 3150 Å. are effective in producing mutations in *Aspergillus terreus* conidia. The rate is quite significant: e.g. solar radiation during a day of unobstructed Washington sunlight in June is able to produce a mutation rate of 6 % in *A. terreus* spores. Moreover, it has been shown that pre-treatment with light of longer wavelengths (near infra-red), while producing no mutagenic effect itself, will significantly increase the effect of subsequent active radiation by X-rays (Kaufmann, Hollaender & Gay, 1946).

Influence of chemical factors

The pioneer work of Auerbach & Robson (1947) clearly established that chemical treatments could be as effective as radiations in inducing mutations. Subsequent work by these and other workers has made it apparent that a great variety of chemicals are mutagenic, including many naturally occurring products, such as formaldehyde, various purines and hydrogen peroxide. Indirect evidence that hydrogen peroxide produced during respiration may be a factor in determining part of the spontaneous mutation rate is provided by the results of experiments with catalase and catalase inhibitors (Jensen, Kirk, Kolmark & Westergaard, 1951). If catalase is added together with peroxide to *Neurospora* conidia or bacteria the mutagenic activity of the peroxide ceases. If catalase inhibitors, such as cyanide or azide, are added the mutation rate increases. Even in the absence of added peroxide the presence of catalase inhibitors causes an increase in the spontaneous mutation rate, presumably due to accumulation of peroxide produced by the organism's own metabolism. Similarly, Mittler & Laverty (1953) have shown that the expression of the effect of oxygen in increasing irradiation damage depends on the absence of anti-peroxide agents, and differences in the ultra-violet sensitivity of bacteria may be attributed to differences in their catalase contents.

There is now available a considerable amount of evidence to show that the effect of ionizing radiation is not always a direct effect on the gene itself. Hollaender, Baker & Anderson (1951) have demonstrated that increased oxygen tensions increase the X-ray sensitivity of a number of organisms, and that these organisms can be protected against the effect by the addition of reducing compounds, or such metabolites as succinate and formate. They have postulated that the formation of free radicals such as H, OH, HO_2 and H_2O_2 are responsible for at least part of radiation damage. In a similar way the effects of different media on survival after irradiation may also be attributed to peroxide effects. Thus incubation in iodoacetate prior to ultra-violet treatment was found to increase the survival of *Streptomyces* spores, an effect which was antagonized by peptone (Wainwright & Nevill, 1955).

The conclusion that genetic specificity may reside primarily in deoxyribose nucleic acid has become widely accepted in recent years, although the absence of such nucleic acid from plant viruses indicates that it cannot be the only genetic material. Novick & Szilard (1952) have shown that caffeine and related purines can act as mutagens to bacteria and fungi, and that, in the case of *Escherichia coli*, these mutagenic effects can be antagonized by guanosine, adenosine or inosine. It would thus appear reasonable to postulate that occasional faulty purine synthesis and incorporation of the purine analogues so produced into nucleic acid might account for a part of the spontaneous mutation rate.

Thus there is some evidence that cells may provide for their own spontaneous mutation through certain of their metabolic products reacting with their own genetic material. Indeed, the fact that mutation is itself under genetic control (see below) is strong evidence that extragenic chemicals in the cell can bring about mutations, otherwise there can be no reasonable explanation for the phenomenon of one gene having an effect on the mutation of another.

Moreover, these phenomena may also explain the observation that some mutations occur more frequently at one stage of the life cycle than another, in that there may be a relation between the metabolic state and the mutation rate; e.g. mature sperm of *Drosophila* is more sensitive to X-radiation than spermatogonia (Muller, 1950).

Besides the above examples, many other observations have been made on factors that influence the action of mutagens. Thus reduction of the oxygen tension of the atmosphere during irradiation greatly reduces the production of sex-linked lethals in *Drosophila* (Anderson, 1951), and increasing hydration of barley seeds can be correlated with increasing mutagenic effect (Kaplan, 1951). The action of such factors in altering mutation effects may be due to modification of metabolism so that lower numbers of lethals are produced and hence more mutations observed; or they may act more directly by sensitizing the genes in some way; or they may allow the production of secondary mutagenic substances during treatment of the organism with the primary mutagen. Since there is no method of determining quantitatively the direct and indirect effects of the various mutagens, interpretation of the mode of action of any particular mutagenic agent is little short of impossible.

It therefore seems that spontaneous mutagenesis may be primarily a biochemical rather than a biophysical process. Some effects of radiation may be due to direct hits on the genic substance with subsequent loss mutation, but most appear to be due to the formation of mutagenic compounds. We may therefore speculate that the mutational process is one involving ionization. Probably an electron is not lost, but is transferred to a new position within the gene molecule. Such spontaneous transfer of an electron would be directly affected by heat, as shown above. We can postulate, then, that mutation occurs by the single alteration in the equilibrium position of an atom, or electron, in the gene molecule, and this change may occur spontaneously as a result of heat or ionization. Any complex molecule, such as we suppose a gene to be, must have a number of equilibrium positions, and it is possible that some of these may cause the production of a product with slightly altered physical properties or specificities. As the postulated change is not large, it is conceivable that the altered gene may be copied as such in future generations and could possibly return to its original equilibrium state. If a somewhat more drastic alteration is postulated, we could get a complete loss of function and perhaps even the copying process might be blocked. Either of these events would explain a 'loss' mutation, without the necessity of having to postulate that a piece is knocked right out of the chromosome, although this might occur in some cases.

Influence of genetic factors

The mutation rate itself may also be affected by particular genes. Perhaps the most specific example of this type of control of mutation is shown by the *dotted* gene in corn (Rhoades, 1941, 1945; McClintock, 1951, 1953). Here the gene *a* is caused to mutate to the dominant allele *A* in the presence of the gene *Dt*, and, moreover, the percentage of mutations produced increases with an increase in the number of *Dt* alleles present. Similar results have been described for *Drosophila* by Neel (1942) and Ives (1950).

Chromosome alterations

So far we have regarded mutation as involving gene change, but the term can also include changes in the number and structure of the chromosomes. Stadler & Roman (1948) have shown that it is probable that ionizing radiations can cause deletions of portions of the chromosomes. Other changes, such as duplication, translocation and inversion of chromosome fragments, may also occur. A more indirect type of interference with the reduplication of the chromosomes as a whole has been shown for the antibiotic actidione (Wilson & Bowen, 1954), which will inhibit mitosis in *Pisum sativum*.

Transformation and transduction

These are relatively simple changes that can effect a change of genome within a fixed environment. The genotype and phenotype of certain strains of bacteria can be transformed by subjecting strains of one genotype to the influence of extracts of cells of a different genotype. This was first described in Pneumococci by Griffith (1928) and later studied in more detail by Avery, McLeod & McCarty (1944) and Ephrussi-Taylor (1951). The change is inherited and will continue indefinitely in the new strain unless and until it is lost or modified by spontaneous mutation. The simplest explanation of the transformation phenomenon is that the transforming material, which has been shown to be deoxyribosenucleic acid by McCarty & Avery (1946), becomes part of the genetic material of the transformed cell. It would appear to be an addition to the genotype rather than a change in the existing genetic material. Transformation has been demonstrated for other characters than capsular changes in *Pneumococcus*; e.g. penicillin resistance (Hotchkiss, 1951) and colonial morphology (Ephrussi-Taylor, 1951) and also for other organisms such as *Haemophilus influenzae* (Alexander & Leidy, 1951), *Escherichia coli* (Boivin, 1947) and *Shigella paradysenteriae* (Weil & Binder, 1947).

It is not possible to assess the importance of transformation with respect to genetic variation in any one group of bacteria, but it is possible that it is a rather general phenomenon in competent species, as any natural population which is capable of transformation must be exposed from time to time to the nucleic acid fragments from lysed and autolysed organisms.

A parallel phenomenon is found in the process of transduction, by which hereditary characters may be transferred to certain bacteria by phage infection, as demonstrated by Stocker, Zinder & Lederberg (1953).

Heterokaryosis

Heterokaryosis, as Stanier (1953) has pointed out, is a mechanism unique to fungi and results in two genomes coming to occupy a common cytoplasm. This, as Jinks (1952) has demonstrated with heterokaryons in nature, allows great plasticity to the growing mycelium. The phenomenon has been reviewed in detail by Pontecorvo (1946, 1953). Nuclei from two or more strains of fungus multiply side by side in a common cytoplasm which is affected by both kinds of nuclei. The proportions of the two kinds of nuclei are selectively adjusted to external conditions by differential multiplication.

Experimentally, this plasticity can be demonstrated by synthesizing balanced heterokaryons between strains requiring various growth factors. The rate of synthesis relative to the rates of utilization of the metabolites change differently as the medium is depleted of nutrients and the adaptive equilibrium between the nuclei is changed accordingly.

The heterokaryon is essentially a temporary structure confined to a single growth cycle as, in species where uninucleate conidia are formed, the various kinds of nuclei are separated from each other at the time of sporulation. In addition, heterokaryons sometimes show dissociation during growth, spontaneous segregation of the nuclear components occurring; this is one of the causes leading to the typical sectored appearance of colonies of some fungi.

Heterokaryon formation is, itself, genetically controlled, as has been demonstrated by Garnjobst (1953) for *Neurospora*.

As Pontecorvo & Roper (1953) have shown in *Aspergillus nidulans*, heterokaryosis permits the phenomenon of mitotic recombination which thus forms an additional mechanism for genetic variation in some fungi. A further peculiar phenomenon, termed 'heterokaryotic mutagenesis', occurs in which a 100,000-fold increase in mutability with respect to certain characters is observed on establishing heterokaryons (Raper, 1953).

Variations of chromosome number

The phenotype of any organism results from the balanced activities of all the genes in the genome and for 'normal' function of the organism it must be in 'genic balance'. Various mechanisms will disturb this balance, such as reduplication, or loss of whole chromosomes, or parts of chromosomes. Bridges (1939) has described in detail the effects on sex in *Drosophila* of changing the ratio of autosomes to *X*-chromosomes and similar investigations have been made on many other organisms. In some plant species, individuals frequently arise with one or more extra chromosomes in addition to the normal complement (aneuroploids). The effect of addition, or loss, of whole sets of chromosomes, or single chromosomes, or parts of a chromosome, has been demonstrated by Satina, Blakeslee & Avery (1937) in *Datura*. Here, quite a small change, such as the addition of a single extra chromosome, may alter the phenotype of the plant so drastically that effectively it is placed in a new environment; e.g. the addition of a single chromosome may result in the plant becoming an extreme dwarf form, which will be growing in a completely different environment, climatically and biotically, from the parent type. For the most part, aneuroploids do not breed true and such abnormalities are likely to have but little evolutionary significance, although sometimes they are of considerable significance to the individual.

VARIABLE GENOME IN A VARIABLE ENVIRONMENT

From the point of view of the individual organism, the reaction of the variable genome to a variable environment is a measure of the adaptability of the genetic system, by mechanisms such as mutation and/or heterokaryosis, to a changing environment. From the point of view of a population, the most important factor to be considered is selection. Our present concepts of the mechanisms of evolution are based in large part on the recognition that change in gene frequency is the elementary process of evolution. From this point of view, the subject-matter of the preceding section is continuous with that of the present. It is the reaction of the variable genome to the variable environment that is germane to the purpose of this Symposium, for it is within the framework of the genetic capabilities of the individual, or the genetic potentialities of the population, that any environmental factors must act on that individual, or population, and it is the description of such interactions that must constitute the fundamentals of any approach to ecology.

In populations containing various genomes, it is the variation of the environment that is the primary cause of change, due to selection, with its consequent evolutionary significance. The results of Lincoln (1947), with *Phytomonas stewartii*, provide a model for the principles of selection. The ability of a number of different mutants to compete with each other, and with the parent stock, was determined on a number of different media. In broth medium, none of the mutants was as competent as the parent strain. It may be seen from Table 3 that a mutation, which was non-competent in broth, may well be competent in a different medium.

Table 3. *Environmental selection of strains of* Phytomonas stewartii *from mixed cultures* (*Lincoln*, 1947)

Additions to nutrient broth	Temp. (° C.)	Hr. growth	Proportion of respective types (%)			
			500	520	400	427
—	—	0	54	25	19	2
None	24	606	100	0	0	0
1% glucose	12	798	1	0	27	72
1% glucose	24	462	0	0	100	0
1% glucose	36	272	0	100	0	0
1% glucose +5% NaCl	24	798	0	0	52	48
1% lactose	24	798	47	0	44	9
10% glucose	24	366	78	4	20	2

One strain (520) replaced all others when grown at high temperatures, yet was markedly less competent than the other strains in all other environments tested. Had such a mutation occurred during growth in this particular environment in nature, it might be expected that this mutant would become the predominant type in the population. Occurrence in any other environment would have caused the mutant type to be lost.

The work of Goodlow, Mika and Braun (1950) again exemplifies mutant selection by the environment. They showed that a culture of smooth *Brucella* sp. growing in a medium with DL-asparagine as the sole nitrogen source displayed typical logarithmic growth, which ceased after 4 days. During the subsequent 5 days, the viable count fell until growth of a progeny of rough mutants commenced. The rate of this change could be increased by the addition of culture filtrates from old cultures, and analysis of the medium showed the accumulation of D-alanine, which inhibited the smooth parent cells, but not the rough mutants. Subsequently, Goodlow, Tucker, Braun & Mika (1952) demonstrated that the parental type can influence the direction in which a population may change, since its metabolic products can determine which of many mutants will have the greatest survival value. When cells of a smooth *Brucella* strain were used as inocula for media containing either D- or L-asparagine, alanine accumulated in the D-asparagine cultures, leading to the progressive establishment of an alanine-resistant, rough, population, while with L-asparagine, valine accumulated, with the subsequent growth of a population of valine-resistant, mucoid, mutants.

In any environment the least competent genotype is lost, or occurs at a low frequency. After environmental changes, mutants of low frequency that arise during growth may replace types competent in the earlier environment. This topic has been discussed in detail by Stanier and others in a previous Symposium (1953) of this Society.

Mutation and selection are important forces in changing microbial populations, and it is hoped that this survey will assist appreciation of the importance of these factors in the further discussions of the subject of microbial ecology.

REFERENCES

ALEXANDER, H. E. & LEIDY, G. (1951). Determination of inherited traits of *H. influenzae* by desoxyribonucleic acid fractions isolated from type-specific cells. *J. exp. Med.* 93, 345.

ANDERSON, E. H. (1951). The effect of oxygen on mutation induction by X-rays. *Proc. nat. Acad. Sci., Wash.*, 37, 340.

AUERBACH, C. & ROBSON, J. M. (1947). The production of mutations by chemical substances. *Proc. roy. Soc. Edinb.* B, 62, 271.

AVERY, O. T., McLEOD, C. M. & McCARTY, M. (1944). Studies on the chemical nature of the substance inducing transformation of pneumococcal types. Induction of transformation by a desoxyribonucleic acid fraction isolated from *Pneumococcus* Type III. *J. exp. Med.* 79, 137.

BEALE, G. H. (1952). Antigen variations in *Paramecium aurelia* variety 1. *Genetics*, 37, 62.

BIRKANA, B. N. (1938). *Biol. Zh.* 7, 653. Cited in Wagner, R. P. & Mitchell, H. K. (1955). *Genetics and Metabolism*. New York: John Wiley and Sons, Inc.

BOIVIN, A. (1947). Directed mutation in colon bacilli, by an inducing principle of desoxyribosenucleic nature: its meaning for the general biochemistry of heredity. *Cold Spr. Harb. Symp. quant. Biol.* 12, 7.

BRAUN, W., KRAFT, M., MEAD, D. P. & GOODLOW, R. J. (1952). The effect of penicillin on genetic changes and temporary modifications in populations of *Brucella*. *J. Bact.* 64, 41.

BRIDGES, C. B. (1939). Cytological and genetic basis of sex. In *Sex and Internal Secretions*, 2nd ed. Baltimore: Williams and Wilkins.

CANTINO, E. C. (1956). The relation between cellular metabolism and morphogenesis in *Blastocladiella*. *Mycologia*, 48, 225.

CARLILE, M. J. (1956). A study of the factors influencing non-genetic variation in a strain of *Fusarium oxysporum*. *J. gen. Microbiol.* 14, 643.

DOUDNEY, C. O. & WAGNER, R. P. (1952). Threonine inhibition in a strain of *Neurospora*. *Proc. nat. Acad. Sci., Wash.*, 38, 196.

DOUDNEY, C. O. & WAGNER, R. P. (1953). A relationship of homocysteine metabolism to thiamin, serine and adenine biosynthesis in a mutant strain of
Neurospora. Proc. nat. Acad. Sci., Wash., **39**, 1043.

EMERSON, R. A. (1921). The genetic relations of plant colors in maize. Mem.
Cornell agric. Exp. Sta. **39**, 1.

EPHRUSSI-TAYLOR, H. (1951). Genetic mechanisms in bacteria and bacterial viruses.
III. Genetic aspects of transformations in Pneumococci. Cold Spr. Harb. Symp.
quant. Biol. **16**, 445.

GALE, E. F. & EPPS, H. M. R. (1942). The effect of the pH of the medium during
growth on the enzymic activities of bacteria (Escherichia coli and Micrococcus
lysodeiktikus) and the biological significance of the changes produced. Biochem. J. **36**, 600.

GARNJOBST, L. (1953). Genetic control of heterokaryosis in Neurospora crassa.
Amer. J. Bot. **40**, 607.

GOLDSCHMIDT, R. (1938). Physiological Genetics. New York: McGraw-Hill
Book Co.

GOODLOW, R. J., MIKA, L. A. & BRAUN, W. (1950). The effect of metabolites upon
growth and variation of Brucella abortus. J. Bact. **60**, 291.

GOODLOW, R. J., TUCKER, L., BRAUN, W. & MIKA, L. A. (1952). Effect of the
isomeric configuration of the source of nitrogen on changes in population and
metabolism in cultures of Brucella. J. Bact. **63**, 681.

GOWEN, J. W. & GAY, E. H. (1933). Effect of temperature on ever-sporting eye
colour in Drosophila melanogaster. Science, **77**, 312.

GRIFFITH, F. (1928). The significance of pneumococcal types. J. Hyg., Camb., **27**, 113.

HARNLY, M. H., & HARNLY M. L. (1936). The effects of the gene on growth and
differentiation as shown by the temperature responses of pennant and its
heterozygote in D. melanogaster. J. exp. Zool. **74**, 41.

HOLLAENDER, A. & EMMONS, C. W. (1946). Induced mutations and speciation in
fungi. Cold Spr. Harb. Symp. quant. Biol. **11**, 78.

HOLLAENDER, A., BAKER, W. K. & ANDERSON, E. H. (1951). Effects of oxygen
tension and certain chemicals on the X-ray sensitivity of mutation production
and survival. Cold Spr. Harb. Symp. quant. Biol. **16**, 315.

HOTCHKISS, R. D. (1951). Transfer of penicillin resistance in Pneumococci by the
desoxyribonucleate derived from resistant cultures. Cold Spr. Harb. Symp.
quant. Biol. **16**, 457.

IVES, P. T. (1950). The importance of mutation rate genes in evolution. Evolution,
4, 236.

JENSEN, K. A., KIRK, I., KOLMARK, G. & WESTERGAARD, M. (1951). Chemically
induced mutations in Neurospora. Cold Spr. Harb. Symp. quant. Biol. **16**, 245.

JINKS, J. L. (1952). Heterokaryosis in wild Penicillium. Heredity, **6**, 77.

JOHANNSEN, W. (1911). The genotype conception of heredity. Amer. Nat. **45**, 129.

KAPLAN, R. W. (1951). Z. indukt. Abstamm.- u. VererbLehre, **83**, 347. Cited in
Wagner, R. P. & Mitchell, H. K. (1955). Genetics and Metabolism. New York:
John Wiley and Sons, Inc.

KAUFMANN, B. P., HOLLAENDER, A. & GAY, H. (1946). Modification of the frequency
of chromosomal rearrangements induced by X-rays in Drosophila. 1. Use of
near infrared radiation. Genetics, **31**, 349.

KRAFKA, J. (1920). The effect of temperature upon facet number in bar-eyed
mutant of Drosophila. J. gen. Physiol. **2**, 409.

LEDERBERG, J. & LEDERBERG, E. M. (1952). Replica plating and indirect selection of
bacterial mutants. J. Bact. **63**, 399.

LINCOLN, R. E. (1947). Mutation and adaptation in Phytomonas stewartii. J. Bact.
54, 745.

LURIA, S. E. & DELBRUCK, M. (1943). Mutations of bacteria from virus sensitivity to virus resistance. *Genetics*, **28**, 491.

MCCARTY, M. & AVERY, O. T. (1946). Studies on the chemical nature of the substance inducing transformation of pneumococcal types. 2. Effects of desoxyribonuclease on the biological activity of the transforming substance. *J. exp. Med.* **83**, 89.

MCCLINTOCK, B. (1951). Chromosome organization and genic expression. *Cold Spr. Harb. Symp. quant. Biol.* **16**, 13.

MCCLINTOCK, B. (1953). Induction of instability at selected loci in maize. *Genetics*, **38**, 579.

MCELROY, W. D. & DE LA HABA, G. (1949). Effect of pressure on induction of mutations by nitrogen mustard. *Science*, **110**, 640.

MITTLER, S. & LAVERTY, J. A. (1953). Susceptibility of catalase-negative bacteria to ultra-violet irradiation. *Nature, Lond.*, **171**, 793.

MORGAN, T. H. (1919). *The Physical Basis of Heredity.* Philadelphia: Lippincott Co.

MULLER, H. J. (1927). Artificial transmutation of the gene. *Science*, **66**, 84.

MULLER, H. J. (1950). Some present problems in the genetic effects of radiation. *J. cell comp. Physiol.* **35** (Suppl. 1), 9.

NEEL, J. V. (1942). A study of a case of high mutation rate in *Drosophila melanogaster*. *Genetics*, **27**, 519.

NEWCOMBE, H. B. (1949). Origin of bacterial variants. *Nature, Lond.*, **164**, 150.

NOVICK, N. & SZILARD, L. (1952). Antimutagens. *Nature, Lond.*, **170**, 926.

PARKE, M., MANTON, I. & CLARKE, B. (1955). Studies on marine flagellates. 2. Three new species of *Chrysochromulina*. *J. Mar. biol. Ass. U.K.* **34**, 579.

PLOUGH, H. H. (1941). Spontaneous mutability in *Drosophila*. *Cold Spr. Harb. Symp. quant. Biol.* **9**, 127.

PONTECORVO, G. (1946). Genetic systems based on heterokaryosis. *Cold Spr. Harb. Symp. quant. Biol.* **11**, 193.

PONTECORVO, G. (1953). The genetics of *Aspergillus nidulans*. *Advanc. Genet.* **5**, 141.

PONTECORVO, G. & ROPER, J. A. (1953). The genetics of *Aspergillus nidulans*. 7. Diploids and mitotic recombination. *Advanc. Genet.* **5**, 218.

RACE, R. P., SANGER, R. & LAWLEY, S. D. (1948). Allelomorphs of the *Rh* gene *C*. *Heredity*, **2**, 237.

RAPER, J. R. (1953). Tetrapolar sexuality. *Quart. Rev. Biol.* **28**, 233.

Report (1956). *The Biological Effects of Atomic Radiation.* National Academy of Sciences; National Research Council. Washington.

RHOADES, M. M. (1941). The genetic control of mutability in maize. *Cold Spr. Harb. Symp. quant. Biol.* **9**, 138.

RHOADES, M. M. (1945). On the genetic control of mutability in maize. *Proc. nat. Acad. Sci., Wash.* **31**, 91.

ROGOSA, M. & MITCHELL, J. A. (1950). Induced colonial variation of a total population among certain Lactobacilli. *J. Bact.* **59**, 303.

SATINA, S. A., BLAKESLEE, A. F. & AVERY, A. G. (1937). Balanced and unbalanced haploids in *Datura*. *J. Hered.* **28**, 193.

SCOTT-MONCRIEFF, R. (1936). A biochemical survey of some Mendelian factors for flower colour. *J. Genet.* **32**, 117.

SONNEBORN, T. M. (1950). The cytoplasm in heredity. *Heredity*, **4**, 11.

SRB, A. M. & HOROWITZ, N. H. (1944). The ornithine cycle in *Neurospora* and its genetic control. *J. Biol. Chem.* **154**, 129.

STADLER, L. J. (1942). *Some observations on gene variability and spontaneous mutation. Spragg Lect. Pl. Breed.* (3rd series), Michigan State College.

STADLER, L. J. & ROMAN, H. (1948). The effect of X-rays upon mutation of the gene *A* in maize. *Genetics*, **33**, 273.

STANIER, R. Y. (1953). Adaptation, evolutionary and physiological: or Darwinism among the micro-organisms. *Third Symp. Soc. gen. Microbiol.* p. 1.

STERN, C. (1948). The effects of changes in quantity, combination and position of genes. *Science*, **108**, 615.

STOCKER, B. A. D., ZINDER, N. D. & LEDERBERG, J. (1953). Transduction of flagellar characters in *Salmonella. J. gen. Microbiol.* **9**, 410.

STOKES, J. L., FOSTER, J. W. & WOODWARD, C. R. (1943). Synthesis of pyridoxin by a 'pyridoxinless' X-ray mutant of *Neurospora sitophila. Arch. Biochem.* **2**, 235.

Symposium (1953). *Adaptation in Micro-organisms. Third Symp. Soc. gen. Microbiol.*

WADDINGTON, C. H. (1939). *Introduction to Modern Genetics.* London: George Allen and Unwin Ltd.

WADDINGTON, C. H. (1954). Recent developments in cell physiology. In *Proc. 7th Symp. Colston Res. Soc.* London: Butterworths Scientific Publications.

WAINWRIGHT, S. D. & NEVILL, A. (1955). Modification of the biological effects of ultra-violet irradiation by post-radiation treatment with iodoacetate and peptone. *J. gen. Microbiol.* **12**, 1.

WEIL, A. J. & BINDER, M. (1947). Experimental type transformation of *Shigella paradysenteriae* (Flexner). *Proc. Soc. exp. Biol., N.Y.,* **66**, 349.

WILSON, G. B. & BOWEN, C. C. (1954). The study of mitotic poisons. *VIIIᵉ Cong. Int. Bot.* **31**.

NUTRITIONAL ASPECTS OF MICROBIAL ECOLOGY

JANE GIBSON

*Agricultural Research Council Unit for Microbiology,
University of Sheffield*

The nutritional factors which govern the nature and magnitude of a microbial population are extremely complex. Among higher animals and plants, the nutritional chain starts with the elaboration of complex molecules from carbon dioxide and other inorganic compounds by photosynthetic organisms, and ultimately all animals rely on plants for their energy requirements, though it may be at one or more steps removed. Among micro-organisms, a wide variation in types of metabolism which has no parallel among higher organisms makes it possible for many nutritional chains to intertwine. Light is not the sole source of energy, since organisms capable of using chemical energy released by the oxidation of inorganic compounds are known. A delicate balance is therefore reached in any given habitat between synthesis and degradation, between oxidation and reduction, of the chemical compounds present.

It is generally recognized that certain steps in the nitrogen cycle are carried out exclusively by micro-organisms. Their quantitative importance in other steps of this and the carbon cycle is less generally appreciated. It has been calculated, for instance, that the total carbon dioxide in the atmosphere together with that made available by the metabolism of higher animals and plants would only serve to maintain the present level of photosynthesis for about forty years, were it not supplemented by CO_2 released by bacteria (Lundegardh, 1924). The chemical potentialities of micro-organisms are also so wide that they themselves are capable of carrying on the circulation of all the elements found in organic molecules. The same is true of the more restricted group of bacteria, with the important exception of oxygen; since bacterial photosyntheses do not lead to the release of molecular oxygen, the exhaustion of this gas would very soon occur if by some means all living organisms with the exception of bacteria were suddenly to be eliminated.

It is no more than a truism to say that knowledge in any field is governed by the techniques applicable to its study, and that progress is intimately linked to the development of new approaches and methods. It is thus necessary to consider the methods which have been used in studies of microbial ecology, and to try, very tentatively, to see where advances may be made in the near future.

The relationship between an organism and its nutrient environment may be studied at several of the levels of investigation which Marjory Stephenson enumerated (Woods, 1953). At the first level, the chosen habitat may be investigated as closely as possible for the nutrient substances available, and for the organisms which are present. Also the effect of some change, such as the addition of a new nutrient source, on the microbial population may be determined. At the next level, pure cultures of organisms derived from the habitat may be studied, and their nutritional requirements worked out. The third level is also concerned with pure strains, and either growing cultures or washed suspensions. The course of metabolism may be followed in overall pattern, and the end-products determined; these may themselves be the starting material for an organism lying next in the nutritional chain. With the last level of investigation, in which cell-free preparations of greater or lesser complexity are used, the microbial ecologist is not, perhaps, concerned at present. From studies at the other levels some predictions can be made about the situations in which the organism under investigation should be found, and its possible relationship to others, and it is, naturally, by attack at several different levels that problems in ecology are most easily solved.

The microbial ecologist, seeking to discover what types of organism are to be found in the environment he has chosen, is faced with a very different problem from the investigator of a population of higher animals or plants. In the latter case, differentiation of the inhabitants is based almost entirely on morphological grounds, and therefore close inspection is usually sufficient to enable the organisms to be identified and classified. Although, of course, morphologically distinct microbes will be found, the possible variations are very small compared with the range of metabolic types, and one cannot analyse a microbial population simply by looking at it. Not only have many different types of bacteria roughly the same shape and size, but their characters may vary appreciably under different cultural conditions, and the morphology characteristic of an organism in the laboratory may be unrecognizable in its natural environment.

It is not altogether surprising, therefore, to find that the higher levels of investigation have been much more favoured as an approach to ecological problems than the lowest or analytical. Among the exponents of the latter, Winogradsky was one of the earliest and most persistent. When he first started his investigation of the sulphur bacteria, it was the careful observation of natural collections of these organisms, coupled with a few simple physiological experiments, which led him to the conclusion that they were able to obtain their energy by the oxidation of inorganic substances. Years later, when he was established in France, he applied himself to the subject of soil microbiology using a similar approach (Winogradsky, 1948). Previously to this, Conn (1918) in America had started making preparations from soil in which it was possible to make direct counts of the bacteria present. The technique consisted of suspending the soil sample in gelatin, and afterwards staining the micro-organisms with an acidic dye, such as phenyl erythrosin, which had the advantage that it did not stain the soil colloids. By such means it was possible to show that the many plating techniques being used for bacterial counts in soil were allowing at the very most one-tenth of the organisms present to develop into colonies. Winogradsky developed this technique, adding such refinements as the removal of coarse particles before making the preparation, and used it to study systematically the normal microbial flora of fallow land, and of land which had been treated in some way. He found a characteristic population in untreated land, consisting in the main of small cocci and short rods, the latter often joined together in veils, together with some larger cocci, tentatively identified with *Azotobacter*. Spore-formers were notable by their absence, and, rather surprisingly, actinomycetes were rarely seen in any number, although corynebacteria appeared quite often. The addition of soluble nutrient substances to soil samples was investigated both by direct microscopical examination, and by a soil plating technique, whereby a few grains of soil were placed at intervals over the surface of a silica gel plate suitably enriched. Characteristic, again, were the changes in population which occurred. Peptone caused the appearance of spore-forming rods in great numbers, while carbohydrates, especially mannitol, caused an increase in *Azotobacter*, particularly if no nitrogenous addition was made at the same time. On the basis of these observations, Winogradsky separated the soil micro-organisms into two groups: first, the autochthonous population, those types predominant in fallow soil, uncontaminated by fertilizers or any gross degree of animal droppings, whose life is presumably based on the decomposition of plant remains, and secondly, the zymogenous population, which rises to significance only when some enrichment of the soil with soluble organic matter occurs. As will be seen later, the two types can also be distinguished on the basis of their types of metabolism.

Subsequently Rossi (1928) introduced a further method for the direct microscopy of soil flora. A clean glass microscope slide was pressed up against a freshly cut piece of soil and then removed, together with adherent microbial colonies and soil particles, for staining as in Winogradsky's technique. Cholodny (1930) developed this slide method to give 'Aufwuchsplatten', the slide being left in contact with the soil for some days, and then carefully withdrawn so that the microbial colonies which had meanwhile developed attached to it were disturbed as little as possible. While these techniques have been criticized by Winogradsky for giving too local a picture of the flora to have general validity, they have borne out his own findings with one important addition; actinomycetes can be shown to be very common in the soil, particularly with 'Aufwuchsplatten'. It is probable that the disturbance produced in preparing the gelatin suspension of soil destroys the characteristic morphology of this group.

Even in so complex an environment as soil, therefore, the direct analysis of population has yielded useful results. It has been possible to show that the basic inhabitants of the soil, which can be isolated by suitable techniques, are organisms which have a low metabolic rate, and whose nutritional requirements are generally poorly understood. As soon as the soil is contaminated with soluble organic material, a different microflora superimposes itself, consisting of spore-formers, presumably normally present in the resting stage, and also commonly fluorescent pseudomonads, which must be wind- or water-borne. These enjoy a brief spell of rapid growth, and, with the exhaustion of the substrates, return to the spore stage or die out.

While the autochthonous population of soil has not been very widely investigated, the studies of Lochhead and his collaborators are of great interest in showing that local variations even in fallow soil do occur, and that the nearness of plant roots may affect the soil flora very markedly. These workers (Lochhead & Chase, 1943; Lochhead & Thexton, 1947) have been able to show a very great increase in the number of the soil bacterium *Arthrobacter* within the rhizosphere, the counts rising to almost double the value in root-free soil. Strains of this organism were isolated from the rhizosphere and from free soil, and were classified according to their growth on different media. There was a marked increase in the proportion of strains whose growth was stimulated by amino acids in the rhizosphere, but not of strains requiring growth-factor supplements. The remainder of the increase in numbers was accounted for by strains having no growth requirements over and above those supplied by the basic soil extract medium. Such results must indicate a complex situation; while amino acids may well be present in increased amounts in the neighbourhood of plant roots, as a result of leakage, the same might be expected for growth factors other than amino acids. Indeed, work with mycorrhiza has indicated strongly that this is so (Harley, 1952). The fact that organisms well able to grow without supplements are so much more numerous in the rhizosphere than elsewhere indicates that some as yet unexplained factor, whose elucidation would be of considerable interest, must enter into the picture.

However, the information obtained from such studies is inevitably of a kind to give only broad outlines of the relation between an organism and its environment, and for the detail it is essential to have more knowledge of the metabolic patterns within the morphological groups seen to be present. Although with the development of micro-manipulative techniques it should be possible to isolate directly any chosen cell, the problem of finding a suitable medium in which to place it would prove hard to solve, and such techniques have not, in practice, been used for the study of ecological problems. By far the greatest body of knowledge about soil ecology has come from the use of the elective or enrichment culture. van Niel (1955) devoted some time to the discussion of this technique; it is of such importance, however, that the author may perhaps be forgiven for going over some of the ground again.

The deliberate encouragement of one micro-organism at the expense of others is, of course, an art going back to the first production of alcoholic liquors, and, indeed, the essential interdependence of microbial types is well illustrated by this process, since it is imperative to render the fermenting liquid anaerobic if a secondary growth of acetic acid bacteria is not to destroy the alcohol produced by the yeast. The conscious use of the enrichment culture in scientific research began much later, and one of the first, and certainly most famous, uses of this method was made by Schloesing & Müntz (1877 a, b, 1879) when they allowed ammoniacal liquors to trickle through a column of coke and found that, after a while, nitrate came out at the bottom, and that a living agency was responsible. Winogradsky used the method in his studies of the organisms responsible for these reactions, but it is with the name of Beijerinck that the use of enrichment cultures is primarily associated. In his hands, and those of his school, it was developed to yield a vast body of information about micro-organisms and their ecology.

Darwin's concept of the struggle for existence can be inferred among higher animals and plants, but rarely proved. Among microbes, however, with their immensely shorter generation times, the process can actually be seen to occur, and the enrichment culture technique is, in fact, based entirely on its operation. In principle, a mixed culture of very many different kinds of micro-organisms is exposed to conditions under which one kind, which may or may not have been present originally in significant numbers, is caused to outgrow the others to the extent where its isolation by conventional techniques becomes practicable.

The technique is subject to slightly different applications; in one, the medium used is of the greatest possible simplicity, so that only one, or at most a very small number, of types of organism can grow. The omission of an organic carbon source, for instance, eliminates from significant growth a very large number, and it is only those able to produce all their organic carbon compounds from carbon dioxide that can proliferate. In the absence of oxidizable inorganic material, therefore, but in the light, algae will probably come to the fore; with reduced sulphur or nitrogen compounds, aerobically, colourless sulphur bacteria or nitrifiers will grow. At the other extreme, the medium is rich and complex, and such that many kinds of organisms can develop in it. There then follows a race between the various types, and in due course one outgrows all the others, and rapidly uses up the nutrients of the medium. For instance, aerobic enrichment cultures set up with organic acids as carbon source will very probably yield fluorescent pseudomonads as the predominant form, although it is well known that many other kinds of organism can grow in such a medium. Similarly, anaerobic cultures containing complex nitrogen compounds and glucose nearly always result in a lactic fermentation; while many anaerobic organisms can grow under such conditions, the rapid growth of the *Lactobacilli*, and the concomitant acidification of the medium, prevent the development of other forms.

The elective culture technique can thus be used, first, to differentiate crudely between organisms of differing metabolic pattern, and secondly, by smaller variation in the medium, to separate these groups of organisms into their individual types. Perhaps the highest development of the technique is to be found in its application to the photosynthetic bacteria by van Niel (1931, 1944). By alterations in the concentrations of oxidizable substrate, bicarbonate and hydrogen ions, he was able to develop methods for bringing out any of the various kinds at will, and incidentally to settle finally the controversy that had existed previously as to whether the organisms were autotrophic or photosynthetic.

The use of enrichment culture methods led Beijerinck and his school to explore, and to a very large extent explain, the reactions occurring in soil and water in terms of the metabolisms of individual microbes, and in the fruitful years 1894–1921 organism after organism was isolated and characterized. While Beijerinck was perhaps primarily interested in the diversity of types of micro-organism he could demonstrate, he was none the less aware of the great importance of this tool in studying microbial ecology. Particularly from enrichments set up in which the development of a number of organisms can theoretically occur, it is possible to gain direct information concerning the influence of nutrients on the struggle for existence. His studies on the butyl alcohol and butyric acid fermentations are a case in point (Beijerinck, 1896). A butyric fermentation is by far the commoner, and a reliable enrichment method for the butyl organisms proved hard to develop. The source of starch was critical, and barley flour was better than the others tried. However, even when a butyl fermentation had been successfully started, the causative organism might be overgrown by the butyric acid producer, and Beijerinck spent some time in trying to understand the way in which this was brought about. In this he was not wholly successful, although he established that factors other than nutritional, for instance, temperature, were very important. He stated at the time that he was uncertain whether his difficulties might not have been due to the fact that the same organism was able to produce butyl alcohol or butyric acid under different conditions, a situation which has subsequently been shown to exist at least among some of the *Clostridia* (e.g. Davies & Stephenson, 1941).

While our knowledge of the diversity of microbial types has been obtained in the main by the use of enrichment culture technique, this method has some limitations, when applied to ecological problems, which must be clearly understood. Perhaps the greatest of these lies in the fact that it provokes a struggle; consequently the results of an enrichment experiment tell one nothing about the population originally present except that it contained at least one representative of the organism which eventually becomes predominant. In liquid aerobic enrichment culture with soil as inoculum, pseudomonads are the commonest organisms isolated with a wide range of carbon sources. Yet Winogradsky and others had shown that pseudomonads are rarely seen in soil samples, at least in those from fallow land. The commonest soil organisms, although they can use a wide variety of nutrients, appear to have a low metabolic rate, and are not able to compete with the fast-growing pseudomonads in enrichments, although they are present in vastly greater numbers in the inoculum. The enrichment culture technique, in other words, by its very nature emphasizes the zymogenous population, rather than the autochthonous.

Another difficulty in the use of the method is the fact that a very mixed population is used as the original inoculum; indeed, it is well known that there is no need to use an inoculum in which some degree of natural enrichment has already occurred in order to set up an enrichment culture of any organism. A few grams of garden soil, from any corner of the earth, will contain the desired organism in numbers sufficient to allow a successful enrichment. When, then, such an inoculum is introduced into the medium, a chain of events will probably occur. For example, great care is needed to ensure that cultures of nitrogen-fixing organisms are not contaminated with other organisms, living at the expense of the nitrogen fixed by the first. Likewise, if a glucose medium containing a complex nitrogen source is inoculated aerobically, the first event will probably be the formation of a thin layer of pseudomonads or aerobic spore-formers on the surface. These will effectively make the bulk of solution anaerobic, and suitable for the development of lactic acid bacteria or anaerobic bacilli. Later still, a further change in population is likely, to types using the decomposition products of glucose, mainly alcohols and acids, and the predominant forms at this stage are likely to be pseudomonads, or, if the lactic acid bacteria have made the medium too acid, moulds. It is necessary, therefore, to keep a close microscopical watch on the enrichment culture if the true course of events is to be understood. van Niel (as part of his teaching to students) has emphasized that, with the alteration of only a few words, the well-known Koch postulates concerning the conditions which must be fulfilled before an organism can be considered responsible for causing a disease can be applied to enrichment cultures. The postulates can then be made to read:

(1) The organism must always be present when the relevant chemical process is occurring.

(2) It must be possible to grow the organism in pure culture in the laboratory. (This postulate requires no modification for the present context.)

(3) The chemical reaction should follow when a suitable medium is inoculated with a pure culture of the organism, and it should be possible to reisolate it from this medium at the end of growth. The term chemical process is here used in the wide sense, to include the conditions under which it takes place. Thus if agar decomposition were being considered, the presence or absence of air, the pH, salinity and temperature of the medium are all relevant.

One essential check, after isolating an organism from an enrichment, therefore, is to reinoculate the medium originally used for the enrichment, to make sure that it really can grow under these conditions, and alone.

During the 1940's Lees & Quastel (1946) developed the enrichment culture in a new way in their soil-perfusion apparatus. Schloesing & Müntz's coke column was replaced with a tube of soil, through which the flow of solution could be carefully controlled, so that the soil did not become waterlogged. With the aid of this apparatus they were able to follow the course of enrichment of soil by nitrifying organisms, and to show that, after a time, a state of 'saturation' was reached, in which growth of the organism was presumably balanced by death, so that a constant value for the rate of oxidation of ammonia was reached, which could not be further increased. The microbial population of this column was not entirely composed of nitrifying organisms, and this fact in itself raises some interesting questions.

The pure cultures of nitrifying organisms that have been obtained (Winogradsky, 1949; Meiklejohn, 1950) all have a very low growth rate. Whether this is an essential characteristic of the organism, or whether some change in cultural conditions might be found which would allow more rapid growth, remains to be determined. The soil-perfusion apparatus might lend itself to the investigation of the effect of the soil itself on these organisms if it were modified so as to be run under sterile conditions, and inoculated with a pure culture of *Nitrobacter* or *Nitrosomonas*. There appears to be little direct information about the relationship between soil particles and the microbial flora beyond Winogradsky's finding that the autochthonous population was colonial in habit, and closely associated with the soil colloids. The soil perfusion technique could also be used for the study of many soil reactions in addition to nitrification, and if it could be combined with the preparation of 'Aufwuchsplatten', a very interesting development of Winogradsky's dynamic experiments might be made.

The nutritional interrelationships of micro-organisms cannot, of course, be clearly defined unless the requirements of the individual types are known. Studies with pure cultures have, therefore, a very important place in attempts to solve problems in microbial ecology. The techniques developed for the culture of bacteria under laboratory conditions are, however, such as to give results that can only be applied very cautiously to ecological problems. The media used in the laboratory are generally designed to give a heavy final growth of bacteria, and they therefore contain very high, perhaps nearly toxic, initial concentrations of nutrient. As growth proceeds, there is a continuous change in the medium surrounding the cells, as the nutrient concentration falls and the end-products of metabolism accumulate. At different stages of growth, therefore, the medium may be radically different, and it follows that the term 'optimal medium' can have no clear meaning. Under natural conditions, it is probable that high concentrations of substrates are rarely met with, but at the same time intoxication with metabolic end-products is unlikely to arise as these will be decomposed by some other organism. On solid laboratory media colonies of a size never met with in nature are frequently produced, in which the greater number of cells must necessarily be in a state of acute nutritional deficiency, while in liquid media, though all the cells are in a similar nutritional state, conditions may well deviate considerably from the natural. In addition to the factors mentioned above, many soil organisms have a micro-colonial habit, and special means, such as the incorporation of wetting agents, may be necessary in order to induce dispersed growth. Laboratory culture methods may correspond in some ways to the normal habitat of zymogenous organisms, but not to those of the autochthonous; indeed, it is partly for this reason that knowledge of this latter group remains scanty.

The complexity of changes occurring during growth under conventional conditions makes the results very difficult to interpret. One of the most interesting developments of recent years is, therefore, the use of continuous culture methods, in which it is possible to maintain constant conditions, both as regards size of population, supply of nutrients, and removal of products of metabolism. Apparatus for this purpose has been designed on two principles (Novick, 1955). In both, a culture vessel through which medium flows is used, but in the first the population is kept constant by varying the flow of medium, using a photocell to measure the opacity of the outflow, while in the second the flow is kept constant. The cell density within the vessel becomes constant after a while as some factor becomes limiting. The advantage put forward for the second type of apparatus, the Bactogen of Monod and the Chemostat of Novick, is that the factor which is limiting growth can be identified, and that conditions can be so arranged that any desired factor alone is limiting. It is thus possible to investigate the influence of a single factor on a bacterial population in the log phase of growth. Now that the very considerable technical difficulties of the design and maintenance of such apparatus are being overcome, one may confidently expect advances in knowledge of the conditions governing growth of micro-organisms.

Once the factors controlling the growth and behaviour of individual cultures are clearly understood, the possibility arises of studying the growth of micro-organisms in deliberately mixed cultures. It is rare in nature to meet anything even approaching a pure culture, the nearest being, perhaps, the massive growths of sulphur bacteria which occur in the outflows of sulphur springs, and occasionally in the Baltic sea. In general, micro-organisms exist in association with many metabolically distinct types, and there can be little doubt that they exert considerable influence on each other. Competition for the available supplies of carbon and nitrogen compounds must occur, and also the end-products of the metabolism of one group of organisms may exert a great effect on others. The production of antibiotics forms the subject of a separate contribution, and needs no more than mention in the present context. Substances other than those having a true antibiotic effect may also affect other organisms, however, and it may well be that the acetyl-choline which has long been known to be formed in fermenting vegetable juices, and which Stephenson & Rowatt (1947) showed was formed by several strains of *Lactobacillus plantarum*, may have a pharmacological effect on the Protozoa present. It has been inferred from the presence of acetylcholine and cholinesterase in ciliates (Bayer & Wense, 1936; Seaman & Houlihan, 1951) that the ciliary activity of these organisms is controlled by cholinergic elements.

However, the effect of different types of micro-organisms on each other is not confined to the deleterious, and in many cases the result of the activity of one group is advantageous to another. The ability to attack insoluble substrates such as cellulose and lignin is restricted to a small number of microbial species, but this activity results in the production of soluble compounds which can be used by a much wider range of organisms.

The activity of micro-organisms in producing growth factors may be essential for the existence of others. A number of the growth factors of the B group are found in soil, and the synthesis of B_{12} appears to be a common property of soil organisms (Burton & Lochhead, 1951). This capacity seems to be connected with the dramatic red tide phenomenon of the east and west seaboards of North and Central America. Every few years the sea along these coasts is turned reddish yellow and almost oily by a great multiplication of dinoflagellates, a fact of considerable importance economically, because a toxin in the organism is capable of killing the fish in the area, and causing the sea spray to become so irritant that beaches and even houses in the neigh-bourhood have to be evacuated. Pure culture studies have shown that several strains of dinoflagellates require that B_{12} be added to a mineral medium if growth is to occur, and large-scale experiments have demon-strated that red tide organisms in mixed culture also need B_{12} (Hutner, Provasoli, McLaughlin & Pintner, 1956). The starting ground of red tide outbreaks has been shown to be in the neighbourhood of river estuaries, and the timing to be connected with heavy rains on the nearby land (Slobodkin, 1953). It thus appears that the release of B_{12} which occurs when mud is brought down to the sea following rain may be a very important factor in touching off a red tide.

The interaction between micro-organisms may not be remote in this way, but so intimate as to warrant the use of the term symbiosis. The combined action of different types of micro-organism may result in a substrate undergoing a cyclical change as in the Cyrenaican sulphur lakes investigated by Butlin & Postgate (1953). The shallow shores of these lakes were covered with massive growths of *Chromatium* and *Chlorobium*, while the deeper waters contained very many sulphate-reducing organisms. The photosynthetic activity of the former results in the production both of the oxidized sulphur and organic compounds needed for the growth of the latter. Consequently, the sulphur compounds of the lake are continually being oxidized and reduced, and the incidental deposition of considerable quantities of elemental sulphur in a year has led to commercial interest.

A case of a symbiotic relation between two bacteria in the laboratory has been described by Pollock (1948). He noted that much better growth of *Haemophilus pertussis* occurred in the neighbourhood of a chance contaminant than elsewhere on a plate. Further work showed that the contaminant 'Q', which was found to be a diphtheroid, was similarly aided by growth near to colonies of *H. pertussis*. The explanation was to be found in the behaviour of both organisms towards unsaturated long-chain fatty acids, such as oleic acid. This type of compound was required as a factor for growth by 'Q' and was produced during growth by *H. pertussis*, on which, however, it exerted a toxic effect, which soon brought growth to a stop. Thus mixed culture was mutually beneficial, the one organism gaining a supply of its growth factor, the other having a toxic metabolite removed. It cannot be doubted that such an interaction between pairs or more complex groups of organisms is a common feature of life in mixed populations, and the development of mixed culture techniques will allow a great extension of knowledge of life under more natural conditions.

In all experiments with pure cultures, however, the possibility must be borne in mind that the biological material may not only be lacking in homogeneity as a result of mutation during growth, but that it may differ radically from any organism to be found under natural conditions. It was, indeed, his doubt of the validity of applying directly to natural conditions results obtained with laboratory strains which led Winogradsky to

3

embark on his direct study of soil microbiology. As van Niel (Kluyver & van Niel, 1956) has emphasized, many investigations have now shown that mutation rates of 1 in 10^9 are by no means uncommon. While the finding of Novick & Szilard (1951) that the mutation rate depends on absolute time rather than the number of generations gone through means that too much emphasis should not, perhaps, be placed on this figure, it is none the less clear that there is a good chance that a mutation will occur even during one transfer of a culture. Indeed, a change may have occurred, and been selected, in the very first enrichment culture, and thus even on first isolation the organism may not resemble exactly its wild counterpart; laboratory strains, maintained often through thousands of transfers in some convenient medium, may very well differ from their free-living ancestors. The development of freeze-drying techniques for the preservation of bacterial strains is of the greatest importance from this point of view.

Rumen microbiology. While the soil is quantitatively the most important microbial habitat, its complexity is so great that it is difficult at present to make more than intelligent guesses and sometimes rather strained analogies about its ecology. It would seem valuable, therefore, to discuss some more clearly defined habitat, and to see how the techniques of investigation have been used. The rumen of cattle has been extensively studied, and conditions in the rumen, although at first sight complex, are in fact more susceptible to analysis than those in the soil. In the first place, conditions remain relatively constant, and although it is not strictly true to say that a sheep or a cow is a continuous feeder, the rumen approximates fairly closely to a continuous culture apparatus. Secondly cellulose can be considered the main substrate for attack by micro-organisms, and this substance is defined chemically; the same can hardly be said of many of the substrates degraded in the soil, such as humus or lignin. Again, conditions in the rumen are anaerobic, and thus metabolic and products of greater complexity than carbon dioxide and water are to be expected. The course of degradation of cellulose, and the interrelationships of the organisms responsible, are thus more easily followed than is the case with a complex aerobic system.

The method of direct microscopy has been applied to rumen contents obtained from slaughtered cattle, and to material withdrawn from animals with permanent rumen fistulae. It has been shown that the normal bacterial population is of the order of 10^8–10^9/ml., according to the diet, and that in addition a number of Protozoa are present. Baker and his colleagues have carried out beautifully detailed analyses of the population of herbivores (e.g. Baker & Harriss, 1947), and it has also been shown that changes in composition of this flora occur when the diet is altered. Hungate, Dougherty, Bryant & Cello (1952) have investigated the population changes which occur when acute indigestion is induced in the sheep by feeding grain to an animal previously on a diet of hay. Following the change in diet there is a marked drop in the pH of the rumen, the Protozoa are killed, and a great increase in the proportion of Gram-positive organisms takes place. Among these, the increase in *Streptococcus bovis* is particularly striking, and these authors suggest that the symptoms of acute indigestion arise as a result of the rapid growth of this organism, though whether because of production of acid solely, or of other compounds also, is not yet clear.

In rumen studies, the equivalent of the soil-perfusion level of investigation is perhaps that of the artificial rumen, which has been developed by Marston (1948) and others. A vessel in which a number of factors can be controlled is filled with rumen contents, and, provided the experiment is not continued for too long a period, the microbial population stays closely similar to that in the intact rumen. Variation of conditions can then be effected under circumstances where sampling is easy.

The special properties of the rumen make it possible to use a method of investigation which cannot be applied to many habitats. As the concentration of micro-organisms is so great, it is possible to prepare washed suspensions of the mixed population, and thus to investigate individual rumen reactions under properly controlled conditions. The technique for the preparation of these suspensions, which were first made by Sijpesteijn & Elsden (1952), involves the removal of plant particles and also of the Protozoa, first by straining and then by brief centrifuging; the bulk of the bacteria is then centrifuged down and washed with water containing a reducing agent. The suspension obtained in this manner thus does not contain all the organisms originally present, for beside the Protozoa it is probable that many of the cellulose decomposers, which are commonly found sunk in little pits on the surface of the cellulose fibres, will have been removed. Very delicate organisms, too, may have been inactivated by the washing treatment. None the less, the method can give valuable data about the nature and rate of reactions occurring in the rumen, and has been used, for instance, by Lewis (1951, 1954) in work on the reduction of nitrate and of sulphate in the rumen.

Again, however, the nutritional requirements and pattern of metabolism of the individual micro-organisms of the rumen must be known before their relationships are understood, and very many organisms have been isolated from it (cf. Doetsch & Robinson, 1953). It has been pointed out, however, that the isolation of an organism from the rumen rather than from any other source is not a sufficient ground for assuming that it plays any significant part in rumen metabolism. It is essential to show that, not only can it carry out a reaction known to occur in the rumen, but that it is also present in numbers sufficient to account for the rate at which this reaction goes on (Elsden & Phillipson, 1948). The history of the isolation of the organisms responsible for the breakdown of cellulose in the rumen will illustrate this point. Spore-formers which could decompose cellulose had been isolated from soil on a number of occasions, and it was found possible to isolate similar organisms from the rumen (Hungate, 1944). However, it did not prove possible to obtain such organisms from high dilutions of rumen contents, and direct microscopy had shown that they were at best rare, the bacteria commonly found on the cellulose fibres being cocci or small rods. Hungate therefore concluded that his spore-formers were probably introduced with the food, and were not responsible for the bulk of ruminant cellulose digestion. The true agents for this process were later isolated by Hungate (1947) and by Sijpesteijn (1949), but not until special techniques had been developed. The organisms were found to be very strict anaerobes, to have a high requirement for carbon dioxide, and in addition to need growth factors which were not present in any of the conventional media, but which were found in sterile rumen fluid. The forms isolated were either cocci, or rods, all Gram-negative, and all fermented cellulose fairly rapidly. The chief products of the fermentation were the lower fatty acids and succinic acid, together with hydrogen, carbon dioxide and some ethanol. Propionic acid was not formed, however, although this is known to be one of the acids produced most plentifully in the rumen. Similarly, methane occurs in the rumen but was not produced by these strains, while formic acid and ethanol are not found in rumen fluid. It is apparent, therefore, that secondary reactions, brought about by different organisms, must occur, and considerable progress has been made towards an understanding of the types of organism involved. Those responsible for methane production have not yet been isolated, but the decomposition of formic acid to carbon dioxide and hydrogen is known to be brought about by a number of bacteria, and is a reaction which can be demonstrated with washed suspensions of rumen organisms. It was first considered that propionic acid production might be due to *Propionibacteria*, but although such organisms can sometimes be demonstrated in considerable numbers (Gutierrez, 1953) their low rate of growth renders them an unlikely agent for this reaction. It was therefore of great interest when Johns

(1951) showed that an organism which he identified as a *Veillonella* could be isolated from high dilutions, and was able to decarboxylate succinic acid to give propionic. The discovery of this organism thus solves two problems, since it both accounts for the presence of propionate and the absence of succinate.

While the lower fatty acids predominate in the rumen, those with longer carbon chains and also those with branched chains have also been found (el-Shazly, 1952a). These latter appear to originate from amino acids by a Stickland reaction, at least in animals on a high protein diet (el-Shazly, 1925b), but the straight-chain acids are probably the products of an interesting organism described by Elsden, Gilchrist, Lewis & Volcani (1951). This is a large Gram-negative coccus which is able to increase the length of the carbon chain of fatty acids by 2-carbon steps (Elsden & Lewis, 1953), and has been found in any rumen investigated. This organism is of particular interest in the present context, since it has recently been shown (Bryant & Doetsch, 1955) that a mixture of straight- and branched-chain fatty acids can replace rumen fluid in cultures of *Bacteroides succinogenes*, one of the cellulose decomposers from the rumen. It seems, therefore, that there is here another case of mutual advantage in these two organisms, the one being supplied with its growth factor while the second uses the reaction products of the first as carbon source and hydrogen acceptor.

The broad outlines of the decomposition of cellulose and some of the secondary reactions that occur are therefore known as a result of the application of the various available techniques of investigation. Many problems of the ecology of the rumen remain to be solved, for it is not, of course, strictly true to regard the rumen as nothing but a cellulose-digesting vat. Many other compounds are taken in with the food, and it is known, for instance, that the rumen organisms attack nitrogen compounds and cause considerable wastage of amino acids to the host. Nor is it possible, at present, to distinguish between the indigenous rumen population, and that passing through, as it were, consequent upon its ingestion with the food. In addition, the role of the rumen Protozoa remains anomalous. Many investigations have shown that they can be eliminated from the rumen without any deleterious effect on the host, although detailed analyses of rumen contents, both microbiological and chemical, have not been carried out at the same time. Yet elegant experiments with bacteria-free cultures of *Diplodinia* (Hungate, 1943) showed that these organisms were, apparently, able to ingest and decompose cellulose, and they are certainly present in considerable numbers in the rumen. Despite the unsolved problems the rumen of cattle is one of the ecological niches about which most is known, as regards the population, and the conditions under which it lives.

The techniques available have provided some information about microbial ecology in certain situations. The picture is, however, by no means complete, and one of the greatest gaps lies in the lack of knowledge of the metabolism and growth requirements of the slow-growing microbes. The soil actinomycetes have received considerable study due to their importance as producers of antibiotics, but the emphasis of these studies has necessarily been laid on aspects other than the ecology of these organisms, and the genera *Arthrobacter* and *Agrobacterium* are as yet poorly characterized. The microbial biochemist has, not unnaturally, chosen to work with the metabolically more active organisms wherever possible, and these numerically important organisms have suffered from comparative neglect. The continued existence of these organisms is, indeed, something of a mystery at present. They will usually grow, albeit slowly, in laboratory media suitable for the more vigorously growing organisms. If they are not to be swamped in their natural surroundings, they must either have the capacity to grow at the expense of some substrate which the others cannot use, or possibly be able to use common substrates at lower concentrations. This latter possibility is perhaps favoured by what is known of the degradative capacities of the fast-growing organisms; on contemplating den Dooren de Jong's (1926) list of the compounds which can be used as sole carbon source by *Pseudomonas putida*, it is sometimes hard to understand why this organism has not long since outgrown every other kind of living matter!

The development of continuous culture apparatus holds great promise for the study of microbial ecology in its nutritional aspects and also in others, since it allows many factors governing growth to be investigated. What is most urgently needed now is some method more sensitive than the enrichment culture for the analysis of mixed cultures in their natural habitat. Techniques for this purpose are now being developed at the Rowett Research Institute, for the identification of rumen organisms without recourse to isolation of individual types. MacPherson & Oxford (1952) have described the use of the Neufeld capsular swelling reaction, by means of which encapsulated strains can be made to increase greatly in size by reaction with an homologous antiserum. More recently the method has been extended so as to be applicable to organisms which do not have a capsule, by the preparation of fluorescent antibodies. Samples of rumen contents are allowed to react with antibodies specific against a number of strains of isolated rumen organisms; comparison of the picture seen in ultra-violet and visible light allows organisms of the same antigenicity to be identified in the mixtures (Hobson, Mackay & Mann, 1955). The authors state that they have had very little evidence of cross-reactions, and their initial difficulties due to non-specific adsorption have been largely overcome. It is of considerable interest to note that they have obtained many indications of pleomorphism in their preparations (Hobson, personal communication). This important new technique could also be applied to other microbial habitats. Again spore-formers can be isolated by direct plating of pasteurized inocula; it would be most interesting to see whether the different growth-factor requirements of the species within this group (Knight & Proom, 1950) can be correlated with any difference in distribution in the soil. The study of microbial ecology has been an unfashionable one for the last thirty years, but there seems good reason to hope that the next few years will see a substantial increase of our knowledge in this field.

REFERENCES

BAKER, F. & HARRISS, S. T. (1947). The role of the microflora of herbivora with special reference to ruminants. 2. Microbial digestion in the rumen (and caecum) with special reference to the decomposition of structural cellulose. *Nutr. Abstr. Rev.* **17**, 3.

BAYER, G. & WENSE, T. (1936). Über den Nachweis von Hormonen in einzelligen Tiere. I. Cholin und Acetylcholin in *Paramecium. Pflüg. Arch. ges. Physiol.* **237**, 417.

BEIJERINCK, M. W. (1896). Sur la fermentation et le ferment butylique. *Arch. Néerl. Sci.* **29**, 1.

BRYANT, M. P. & DOETSCH, R. N. (1955). Factors necessary for the growth of *Bacteroides succinogenes* in the volatile fatty acid fraction of rumen fluid. *J. Dairy Sci.* **38**, 340.

BURTON, M. O. & LOCHHEAD, A. G. (1951). Production of vitamin B_{12} active substances by microorganisms. *Canad. J. Bot.* **29**, 352.

BUTLIN, K. R. & POSTGATE, J. R. (1953). The microbiological formation of sulphur in Cyrenaican lakes. *Symp. Inst. Biol. Lond.*

CHOLODNY, N. G. (1930). Über eine neue Methode zur Untersuchung der Boden-mikroflora. *Arch. Mikrobiol.* **1**, 620.

CONN, H. J. (1918). The microscopic study of bacteria and fungi in soil. *Tech. Bull. N.Y. St. agric. Exp. Sta.* no. 64.

DAVIES, P. & STEPHENSON, M. (1941). Studies on the acetone-butyl alcohol fermentation. 1. Nutritional and other factors involved in the preparation of active suspensions of *Clostridium acetobutylicum* (Weizmann). *Biochem. J.* **35**, 1350.

DOETSCH, R. N. & ROBINSON, R. Q. (1953). The bacteriology of the bovine rumen: a review. *J. Dairy Sci.* **36**, 115.

DEN DOOREN DE JONG, L. E. (1926). Bijdrage tot de kennis vanhetmineralisatie-proces. Dissertation, Delft.

ELSDEN, S. R., GILCHRIST, F. M. C., LEWIS, D. & VOLCANI, B. E. (1951). The formation of fatty acids by a Gram-negative coccus. *Biochem. J.* **49**, lxix.

ELSDEN, S. R. & LEWIS, D. (1953). Production of fatty acids by a Gram-negative coccus. *Biochem. J.* **55**, 183.

ELSDEN, S. R. & PHILLIPSON, A. T. (1948). Ruminant physiology. *Annu. Rev. Biochem.* **17**, 705.

EL-SHAZLY, K. (1925a). Degradation of protein in the rumen of the sheep. 1. Some volatile fatty acids, including branched chain isomers, found *in vivo*. *Biochem. J.* **51**, 640.

EL-SHAZLY, K. (1952b). Degradation of protein in the rumen of the sheep. 2. Action of rumen micro-organisms on amino acids. *Biochem. J.* **51**, 647.

GUTIERREZ, J. (1953). Numbers and characteristics of lactate utilizing organisms from the rumen of cattle. *J. Bact.* **53**, 123.

HARLEY, J. L. (1952). Association between micro-organisms and higher plants (mycorrhiza). *Annu. Rev. Microbiol.* **6**, 367.

HOBSON, P. N., MACKAY, E. S. M. & MANN, S. O. (1955). The use of fluorescent antibody in the identification of rumen bacteria *in situ*. *Research, Lond.*, **8**, no 6.

HUNGATE, R. E. (1943). Further experiments on cellulose digestion by the protozoa in the rumen of cattle. *Biol. Bull., Wood's Hole*, **84**, 157.

HUNGATE, R. E. (1944). Studies on cellulose fermentation. 1. The culture and physiology of an anaerobic cellulose digesting bacterium. *J. Bact.* **48**, 499.

HUNGATE, R. E. (1947). Studies in cellulose fermentation. 3. The culture and isolation of cellulose decomposing bacteria from the rumen of cattle. *J. Bact.* **53**, 631.

HUNGATE, R. E., DOUGHERTY, R. W., BRYANT, M. P. & CELLO, R. M. (1952). Microbial and physiological changes associated with acute indigestion in the sheep. *Cornell Vet.* **42**, 423.

HUTNER, S. H., PROVASOLI, L., MCLAUGHLIN, J. J. A. & PINTNER, I. J. (1956). Biochemical geography: some aspects of recent vitamin research. *Geogr. Rev.* **46**, 404.

JOHNS, A. T. (1951). Isolation of a bacterium producing propionic acid from the rumen of sheep. *J. gen. Microbiol.* **5**, 317.

KLUYVER, A. J. & NIEL, C. B. VAN (1956). *The Microbe's Contribution to Biology*. Cambridge, Mass.: Harvard University Press.

KNIGHT, B. C. J. G. & PROOM, H. (1950). A comparative survey of the nutrition and physiology of mesophilic species of the genus *Bacillus*. *J. gen. Microbiol.* **4**, 508.

LEES, H. & QUASTEL, J. H. (1946). Biochemistry of nitrification in soil. 1. Kinetics of, and effect of poisons on, soil nitrification as studied by a soil perfusion technique. *Biochem. J.* **40**, 803.

LEWIS, D. (1951). The metabolism of nitrate and nitrite in the sheep. 2. Hydrogen donators in nitrate reduction with rumen micro-organisms *in vitro*. *Biochem. J.* **49**, 149.

LEWIS, D. (1954). The reduction of sulphate in the rumen of the sheep. *Biochem. J.* **56**, 391.

LOCHHEAD, A. G. & CHASE, F. E. (1943). Qualitative studies of soil micro-organisms. 5. Nutritional requirements of the predominant bacterial flora. *Soil Sci.* **55**, 185.

LOCHHEAD, A. G. & THEXTON, R. H. (1947). Qualitative studies of soil micro-organisms. 7. The 'rhizosphere effect' in relation to the amino-acid nutrition of bacteria. *Canad. J. Res.* C, **25**, 20.

LUNDEGARDH, H. (1924). *Der Kreislauf der Kohlensäure in der Natur*. Jena: G. Fischer.

MACPHERSON, M. & OXFORD, A. E. (1952). The use of the Neufeld capsular swelling reaction in the identification of rumen streptococci *in situ*. *J. gen. Microbiol.* **7**, ii.

MARSTON, H. R. (1948). The fermentation of cellulose *in vitro* by organisms from the rumen of sheep. *Biochem. J.* **42**, 564.

MEIKLEJOHN, J. (1950). The isolation of *Nitrosomonas europaea* in pure culture. *J. gen. Microbiol.* **4**, 185.

NIEL, C. B. VAN (1931). On the morphology and physiology of the purple and green sulphur bacteria. *Arch. Mikrobiol.* **3**, 1.

NIEL, C. B. VAN (1944). The culture, general physiology, morphology and classification of the non-sulfur purple and brown bacteria. *Bact. Rev.* **8**, 1.

NIEL, C. B. VAN (1955). Natural selection in the microbial world. The second Marjory Stephenson Memorial Lecture. *J. gen. Microbiol.* **13**, 201.

NOVICK, A. (1955). Growth of bacteria. *Annu. Rev. Microbiol.* **9**, 99.

NOVICK, A. & SZILARD, L. (1951). Experiments on spontaneous and induced mutation of bacteria growing in the chemostat. *Cold Spr. Harb. Symp. quant. Biol.* **16**, 337.

POLLOCK, M. R. (1948). A case of bacterial symbiosis based on the combined growth stimulating and growth inhibitory properties of long-chain fatty acids. *J. gen. Microbiol.* **2**, xxiii.

ROSSI, G. (1928). Die direkte bakterio-mickroskopische Untersuchung des Ackerbodens. *Festschr. des* 70. *Geburtstag Stoklasa*, Berlin.

SCHLOESING, T. & MÜNTZ, A. (1877 a). Sur la nitrification par les ferments organisés. *C.R. Acad. Sci., Paris*, **84**, 30.

SCHLOESING, T. & MÜNTZ, A. (1877 b). Sur la nitrification par les ferments organisés. *C.R. Acad. Sci., Paris*, **85**, 1018.

SCHLOESING, T. & MÜNTZ, A. (1879). Recherches sur la nitrification. *C.R. Acad. Sci., Paris*, **89**, 891.

SEAMAN, G. R. & HOULIHAN, R. K. (1951). Enzyme systems in *Tetrahymena geleii* S. Acetylcholinesterase activity, its relation to motility of the organism and to coordinated ciliary activity in general. *J. cell. comp. Physiol.* **37**, 309.

SIJPESTEIJN, A. KAARS, (1949). Cellulose decomposing bacteria from the rumen of cattle. *Leeuwenhoek J. Microbiol. Serol.* **15**, 49.

SIJPESTEIJN, A. KAARS, & ELSDEN, S. R. (1952). Metabolism of succinic acid in the rumen of the sheep. *Biochem. J.* **52**, 41.

SLOBODKIN, L. B. (1953). A possible initiation condition for Red Tide on the coast of Florida. *J. Mar. Res.* **12**, 148.

STEPHENSON, M. & ROWATT, E. (1947). The production of acetylcholine by a strain of *Lactobacillus plantarum*. *J. gen. Microbiol.* **1**, 279.

WINOGRADSKY, S. (1949). *Microbiologie du Sol*. Paris: Masson et Cie.

WOODS, D. D. (1955). The integration of research on the nutrition and metabolism of micro-organisms. *J. gen. Microbiol.* **9**, 151.

INFLUENCE OF HYDROGEN-ION CONCEN-
TRATION AND OXIDATION-REDUCTION
CONDITIONS ON BACTERIAL BEHAVIOUR

L. F. HEWITT

Serum Laboratory (Medical Research Council), Carshalton, Surrey

It would not be profitable nor even practicable to attempt to catalogue all the known effects of hydrogen-ion concentration and oxidation-reduction conditions on bacterial behaviour and ecology. Instead, a few examples are discussed in the light of general principles which may stimulate speculation and discussion.

Tissue cells in the higher animals exist in a constant environment, and many of the physiological mechanisms of the body are devoted to maintaining the optimum composition of the blood and other fluids bathing the cells. Nutrients are brought in suitable concentration; waste products are removed; oxygen is supplied in available form and excess carbon dioxide removed; the hydrogen-ion concentration is held at a remarkably constant level. Micro-organisms, on the other hand, not only have no neighbouring cells of different function to aid digestion with their enzyme systems but they are constantly exposed to changing environments which affect their behaviour, their reproduction and indeed their very survival. These hazards are in addition to the fierce competition not only of sister cells but also of other species. We are concerned in this contribution with two somewhat related physico-chemical factors in the environment which have decisive influence on bacteria, the hydrogen-ion concentration and oxidation-reduction conditions of the medium in which they exist. Although dependent to some extent on each other it is convenient to consider the two factors separately.

EFFECTS OF HYDROGEN-ION CONCENTRATION
ON BACTERIA

Except in extreme cases the effect of pH on bacteria is largely indirect. Of course at very low or very high pH levels the acidity or alkalinity may kill bacteria directly, as in the stomach, by denaturing or hydrolysing proteins and other cellular constituents, but this bactericidal effect is of minor biological importance. The main biological significance of pH is at intermediate levels not far removed from the physiological optima, and here the effects are mainly indirect. Unfavourable pH conditions produce at first bacteriostatic and not bactericidal effects, but subsequently when the normal metabolism and multiplication of the bacteria cease, death may ensue through the activity of the cell's own autolytic systems.

For the normal metabolism and reproduction of the bacterial cell to occur the pH level must be suitable for the effective functioning of the cellular enzyme systems. Not only must the important energy-producing and synthetic enzyme systems function, but various minor co-ordination systems must continue so that the chain of reactions is not broken. In many cases the most important system for obtaining the energy for growth and multiplication involves carbohydrate breakdown, but this is a complex of many enzyme processes including phosphorus metabolism; there are in addition nitrogen metabolism and the synthetic processes involving nucleic acids. In some cases alternative metabolic pathways are available, but the breakage of any essential link involves the immobilization of cellular activities. For the complete understanding of the gross effect of pH on bacterial behaviour it is necessary therefore to study the effect of pH on each enzyme system involved in metabolic and synthetic activities. In addition, some of the alternative pathways may not be reversed when the original pH level is restored so that a new competition may result. Some of these irreversible or semi-reversible changes are due to the action of the bacterial enzymes on cellular proteins, polysaccharides and nucleic acids at different pH levels. The destruction of some of these complex molecules may result in a permanent change in the cell and its progeny. For example, nucleic acids control protein, enzyme and polysaccharide synthesis, and destruction of a nucleic acid by a nuclease functioning at a new pH level may result in a failure of synthesis which may be inherited by daughter cells. In addition to all these complications, under natural conditions there coexist different races of bacteria introducing all the complexities of symbiosis and antibiosis.

It is clear that it is premature to attempt the unravelling of the tangled skein of effects at present and it is necessary to confine our attention to the gross results. From this point of view the response of the bacterial cell to change of pH of the environment can be compensatory, adaptive or permanent. In compensatory changes the behaviour of the cell reverts to its former pattern immediately the pH is changed back again. In adaptive changes the enzyme distribution of the cell is altered, and this change persists for a time after the original conditions are restored but ultimately reverts to the original. Permanent changes of various kinds may also follow pH alterations.

The nature of the compensatory mechanisms of bacterial enzyme distribution involved after changes of the pH of the culture medium has been studied by Gale & Epps (1942). Multiplication of *Escherichia coli* was observed in the pH range 4·5–9, but the enzyme content of the cells was not the same in media of different pH values. The cellular enzymes could be divided into two groups as follows:

Group I		Group II
Formic dehydrogenase	Hydrogenase	Serine deaminase
Alcohol dehydrogenase	Succinic dehydrogenase	(Aspartase)
Catalase	Glucozymase	Arginine decarboxylase
Urease	Tryptophanase	Ornithine decarboxylase
Fumarase	Alanine deaminase	Lysine decarboxylase
(Formic hydrogenlyase)	Glutamic deaminase	Histidine decarboxylase

Group I enzymes show a compensatory increase as the pH of the culture medium deviates from the pH of optimal activity of the enzyme. In this way the total enzymic activity of the cell remains approximately constant even when the pH of the culture medium is altered. In the case of group II enzymes, on the other hand, more of the enzymes are formed when the pH of the medium is close to that required for maximal enzyme activity. In some cases even with group II enzymes, however, compensatory increase in enzyme formation occurs at pH values only slightly different from those of optimal activity, but under conditions remote from the optimum the amount of enzyme formed decreases rapidly.

It is concluded that group I enzymes have a protective function in the cell and their presence is essential for bacterial survival. For example, the cells would perish if the amount of catalase present were insufficient to remove toxic peroxide. On the other hand, group II enzymes are formed in quantity only when their presence is necessary for the activities of the cell. Thus amino-acid decarboxylases are produced in response to an acid growth environment to reduce the acidity, and deaminases are formed to reduce the alkalinity in alkaline media. The general conclusion is therefore reached that a change in the pH of the culture medium is followed by changes in the enzymic composition of the bacterial cells, such that essential activities are maintained at a constant level, and an attempt is made to neutralize the external change. It should be noted that these variations do not occur in the absence of growth. Mere suspension of bacteria in a medium of different pH is not sufficient to alter the enzymic constitution.

These conclusions apply to *Escherichia coli* in which multiplication occurs over a wide range of cultural conditions. Some other organisms, particularly the pathogens, are much more exacting in their growth requirements, and this may be due partly to their inability to develop compensatory mechanisms of differential enzyme formation and to their limited enzymic equipment. In the case of haemolytic streptococci and pneumococci, for example, not only do the bacteria lack catalase, as will be discussed later, but their metabolic activities are largely fermentative and they are deficient in oxidizing ability. Hence acid accumulates during carbohydrate breakdown and growth ceases when the pH falls to a value of about 6. The amount of growth can be increased by neutralization of the acids produced. Unless periodic additions of alkali in appropriate amounts are undertaken it is necessary to use a suitable buffer. Most commonly phosphates are used as buffers, but these are not very suitable since not only do they participate directly in enzyme reactions but in addition they are inefficient buffers for stabilizing the pH in the presence of fermentation acids. As an alternative, bicarbonate is a very efficient buffer for many bacteriological purposes (Hewitt, 1932 a, b), since carbonic acid is a very weak acid and carbon dioxide is given off by the culture when the pH falls. The amount of growth and of carbohydrate breakdown by haemolytic *Streptococcus* and *Pneumococcus* cultures may be increased as much as five times by using bicarbonate in place of phosphate buffers. It should be mentioned that growth ceases completely if all traces of phosphate are removed from the culture medium, as would be expected from the theoretical equations of the enzymic reactions involved in carbohydrate metabolism. Incidentally, the presence of traces of carbon dioxide are essential for the growth of many bacteria, and this is possibly due to its ready penetration into cells, where it may be necessary for buffering various enzyme reactions. At this point it should perhaps be emphasized that in our consideration of the effects of pH on the behaviour of bacteria we have been concerned with the pH of the external culture medium, and it is by no means certain that this corresponds to the pH of the interior of the cell. Some ions are less able to penetrate the cell membranes and it is possible that a pH gradient may be established across the cell wall. It is essential, therefore, in considering the effects of pH on bacteria to take into account the nature of the buffer ions present. The presence of some phosphate is necessary for growth but it does not constitute a good buffer; carbonate is a good buffer and provides the carbon dioxide necessary for life, whilst some buffers such as phthalates and borates have definitely toxic effects on the cells.

Other substances besides buffer salts influence the behaviour of bacterial enzymes at different pH values. Epps & Gale (1942) found that the presence of glucose in the medium during the growth of *Escherichia coli* suppressed the formation of various enzymes, and the addition of various fermentation acids to produce the same pH had not this effect. Neutralization of the acids also failed to reverse the effect. On the other hand, the formation of essential protective enzymes of *Micrococcus lysodeikticus*, such as urease, catalase and fumarase, was not suppressed by the presence of glucose in the medium. It should be noted that the effect of glucose was not permanent, since transfer of the organisms to a medium free from glucose results in immediate reversion to the original enzymic constitution. It is interesting to note that the presence of glucose affects the pH optima for the production of the α and θ toxins of *Clostridium welchii* (Gale & van Heyningen, 1942).

The diphtheria bacillus presents an informative example of an organism in which the pH of cultivation affects its biological behaviour. Cultures containing rapidly fermentable sugars develop a quite high acidity and although good growth occurs there is no toxin formation, since toxin formation is usually associated with the alkaline phase of growth. In diphtheria cultures there is generally an initial phase when the pH falls due to the formation of lactic acid, etc., from fermentable sugars. Later the pH rises as the fermentation acids are oxidized to carbon dioxide. In an experiment to show the inhibitory effect of acids on toxin formation three toxigenic diphtheria strains were selected. All three fermented glucose, one fermented starch in addition and one fermented saccharose. Each strain was cultured in four media: (*a*) the basic medium containing minimal amounts of fermentable carbohydrate, (*b*) the basic medium plus glucose, (*c*) the basic medium plus starch and (*d*) the basic medium plus saccharose. Good growth occurred in each case. In the basic medium faintly alkaline reactions were observed and toxin formation occurred. The glucose cultures became acid and no toxin formation was observed. In the starch medium toxin formation occurred except in the culture of the starch-fermenting strain, which became acid. In the saccharose medium the saccharose-fermenting strain alone became acid and failed to produce toxin. Excessive aeration of diphtheria cultures produces high alkalinity and again there is no formation of toxin. Incidentally these experiments provide an example of the interrelation of pH effects and oxidation-reduction conditions in bacterial cultures. The older methods of preparing diphtheria toxin consisted of growing a surface pellicle of organisms in a bottle in which suitable aeration was arranged by choosing an appropriate volume of medium to match the surface area of the culture. Profiting by the experience obtained from penicillin production, far more rapid preparation of more potent toxin is now obtained from submerged cultures subjected to aeration by a stream of air (Linggood, Matthews, Pinfield, Pope & Sharland, 1955).

A further interesting insight into the complexity of bacterial enzyme phenomena can be gained from the work of Pope, Stevens, Caspary & Fenton (1951). Using an agar diffusion technique in which antigens and antibodies are allowed to diffuse and form flocculation zones (Oudin, 1948) they found that ordinary diphtheria toxin was a complex mixture of antigens. Toxic filtrates from diphtheria cultures were found to contain many other antigens besides diphtheria toxin and when injected into animals gave rise to the corresponding antibodies. At least twenty-four antigens were found in diphtheria culture filtrates and a corresponding number of antibodies in commercial specimens of refined diphtheria antitoxin. A curious feature of the observations was that a large number of the antigens were proteolytic enzymes of which the proteolytic activities were neutralized by the appropriate antibodies. Even in the purified toxin of Pappenheimer (1937) fourteen different antigens were detected. It is surprising to find that these proteolytic enzymes have different pH optima. Using crystalline haemoglobin as substrate at least 16 pH peaks were observed, the pH optima varying from 0·75 to 10. The significance of the production of so many proteolytic enzymes of widely different pH optima by a single strain of bacteria is difficult to assess. At any pH level from the most acid to the most alkaline, proteolytic enzymes are active—and this despite the fact that diphtheria bacilli are not generally regarded as strongly proteolytic organisms. It is possible that this is of biological importance in assisting the organism to establish infection in the mucous membranes of the upper respiratory tract, both by enabling the bacteria to gain access to favourable sites and by making available as nutrients proteolytic breakdown products of tissue proteins. It is difficult to accept the value to the organism of the presence of those enzymes which are active only under the most acid or alkaline reactions. The possibility remains that the presence of these proteolytic enzymes may account for the absence of diphtheria toxin from cultures grown at unfavourable pH levels. The toxin may be formed under such conditions but, being a protein, it may be destroyed by the proteolytic enzymes as fast as it is formed. In the body, on the other hand, the proteolytic enzymes may attack body tissues in preference to the toxin and its toxic effects may thus be manifested when it is produced *in vivo*.

As mentioned earlier the response of bacteria exposed to a changed pH of the environment may be the formation of adaptive enzymes which may persist in the strain for a time after the stimulus of changed pH is withdrawn. It is not proposed to deal with adaptive phenomena here, however, since it has been discussed fully at a previous symposium (Symposium, 1953) and elsewhere (Hinshelwood, 1946).

More permanent and irreversible changes in the bacterial cell may be effected by alteration in the pH of the environment. These may arise by several different mechanisms. A genetic change can be produced by selection of those mutants which flourish at a pH remote from the optimum for the original strain. A permanent change of a different kind may be produced by culturing bacteria under conditions favouring the activity of cellular enzymes capable of destroying other cell con-stituents. In some cases the daughter cells continue to be deprived of the destroyed constituent even when the cultural conditions are restored to normal. This aspect is dealt with in more detail in the section on oxidation-reduction conditions.

A further effect of physico-chemical conditions on bacterial behaviour which has received attention only recently but which is, in my opinion, of considerable interest, is their effect on symbiotic infections of bacteria with viruses. These virus infections have profound effects on the pro-perties of bacteria. In many bacterial species nearly every strain examined has been found to be infected symbiotically with bacterial viruses or bacteriophages (Boyd, 1950; Smith, 1948; Rountree, 1949; Williams & Rippon, 1952; Hewitt, 1954a). In many cases more than one kind of infecting virus is present and alterations in the environment produced by pH changes, irradiation or antibiotics have been found to alter the symbiotic balance and one or more of the infecting viruses may be removed (Hewitt, 1954b, c). Since the infecting viruses can produce permanent genetic or other changes in the strains (Lederberg, 1952; Hewitt, 1954b, c) any disturbance of the symbiosis can affect the bio-logical behaviour of the bacteria, but this aspect of the problem is being dealt with in more detail elsewhere.

The intestinal tract at birth is free from bacteria and it has been found possible to rear animals under sterile conditions so that complete sterility is maintained throughout life. Normally, however, bacteria soon appear and the intestinal flora is largely dependent upon diet. In breast-fed infants *Lactobacillus bifidus* predominates but other organisms soon appear when the diet is supplemented (Snyder, 1940). The gastric fluid is so strongly acid that the empty stomach is generally sterile, but the acidity is not sufficient to sterilize all the food passing through the stomach, and lower in the intestinal tract a large variety of organisms is found. The ecology of the intestinal flora is too variable for profitable generalization.

In agriculture the effect of pH on the microbiological flora of soil is of paramount importance in determining soil fertility and crop yield. Sour, acid soils discourage nitrogen-fixing organisms, and even the golf groundsman is provided with a pH testing outfit and aims at adjusting the pH of his greens to produce suitable soil conditions for the sinking of our putts. Acid conditions in silos discourage the growth of putre-factive spoilage organisms and molasses are added to encourage acid-producing carbohydrate-fermenting bacteria. Plants such as rhodo-dendrons cannot grow on alkaline calcareous soils where the necessary mycorrhizae do not flourish. Fungi attacking fruits of low pH must be capable of multiplying under highly acid conditions, otherwise their attack is confined to the carpel walls, etc., which are less acid (Brown & Wood, 1953). In cheese-making the acid-producing organisms not only impart a pleasant flavour, but the acidity developed discourages the growth of putrefactive bacteria. Under natural conditions materials are a dynamic mixture of competing organisms, and alteration of the pH of the environment disturbs the balance which has been established. The flora at any time depends upon a complex of factors dependent upon the enzyme systems of the micro-organisms and their degree of adjustment to the new conditions.

OXIDATION-REDUCTION FACTORS

As already indicated, pH effects and oxidation-reduction conditions are not independent. As in most biological systems alteration of one factor results in a change of each of the others. Thus fermentation reactions can occur in the absence of air and the conversion of carbohydrate to acids results in a fall in pH, but in the presence of air some of the acidic products can be oxidized to carbon dioxide, which may be given off so that the pH rises again. This has been mentioned in the case of diphtheria cultures; initially the culture becomes acid and subsequently, if condi-tions are suitable, the pH rises again and toxin formation occurs.

The oxidation-reduction potential changes in growing cultures are complex and only a few aspects can be discussed here (Hewitt, 1950), but it is necessary to mention some of the results and their interpretation. The oxidation-reduction potential is a convenient method of measuring and recording the oxidation-reduction level in a system. High positive potentials indicate oxidizing conditions and low or negative potentials indicate reducing systems. In a bacterial culture reducing conditions develop and the oxidation-reduction potential falls. This is a necessary consequence of the metabolism of the cells. To obtain the energy necessary for growth, purely anaerobic fermentations are insufficient and oxidative mechanisms are required. For this purpose the cell utilizes free oxygen and suitable oxidized systems, in fact anything reducible. In this way oxidized substances disappear, reducing conditions develop and the oxidation-reduction potential falls. Different bacteria possess different enzyme systems and hence effect different reductions and at different rates. Hence in cultures of some organisms the potential falls quickly and in others more slowly. Naturally again the potential developed depends to some extent on the composition of the medium.

It should be emphasized that the potential measured is that developed in the external medium and it does not necessarily bear any relation to conditions within the cell interior. Another important point to bear in mind is that the oxidation-reduction potential is a measure of reducing or oxidizing level and does not indicate the amount of oxidizing or reducing substances present. In the same way, of course, temperature is not a measure of the amount of heat in a substance; although an electric light filament is at a higher temperature its warming capacity is less than that of the hot-water bottle at a lower temperature. Highly reducing conditions may develop in a bacterial culture, but this condition may be readily disturbed by aeration unless the metabolic activities of the cell are active enough to maintain fresh reduction processes. In the active stage of growth the aerobic bacterial culture is a dynamic system in which a balance, measured by the oxidation-reduction potential, is maintained between the reduction processes of the cell and the oxidizing effect of air. For efficient utilization of nutrient materials an adequate supply of oxygen or oxidized substances is necessary but many bacterial cells are unable to institute growth in highly oxidizing conditions. Various reasons account for this, among them the necessity for sulphydryl groups to activate many enzyme systems. Unless reduced SH groups are present a number of enzymes cannot function, and at high oxidation reduction potentials SH groups are oxidized. In some cases the lag phase before growth of a culture commences may be due to the necessity for the cell to develop locally reducing conditions, either in the cell interior or at the cell wall, so that SH groups are reduced and enzyme systems can be activated. For the rapid multiplication of a bacterial culture, therefore, it is necessary to maintain adequate oxidizing conditions, with local reduced groups in the cell. One of the agents toxic to the cell and making the maintenance of local reducing conditions impossible is peroxide.

Hydrogen peroxide formation accompanies many auto-oxidation reactions and indeed occurs when SH groups are oxidized in air. Removal of the peroxide formed is therefore one of the necessities for the continued life of the cell. Many bacterial cells contain catalase for the destruction of peroxide; in fact the presence of catalase is a necessity for hardy aerobic organisms. Bacteria such as haemolytic streptococci prefer aerobic conditions for active growth but they do not contain catalase, hence in such cultures the oxidation-reduction potential first falls owing to the reduction processes of the cell enzymes; then peroxide formation occurs and the oxidation-reduction potential rises rapidly. In catalase-containing organisms reduction conditions can be maintained for a long time as the peroxide formed is decomposed, liberating oxygen helpful to the cell's metabolism.

The subdivision of bacteria into aerobic and anaerobic organisms is artificial since a constant gradation of oxygen requirements is seen. Although some bacteria will grow only when there is a plentiful oxygen supply and others only when air is totally excluded, most bacteria have requirements falling between these two limits and some are able to multiply under all conditions varying from the fully aerobic on the surface of solid media in air to complete anaerobiosis. McLeod & Gordon (1923) found that obligate anaerobes contained no catalase and suggested that their sensitivity to oxygen was in reality a sensitivity to peroxide which was formed in the presence of air and could not be destroyed by the bacteria. Such hypotheses are difficult to substantiate or disprove. The amount of peroxide necessary to inactivate enzyme systems in the cell may be very small, for it should be remembered that it is not the concentration of peroxide in the culture medium that is important. If the sulphydryl groups in the cell itself are oxidized, enzyme systems will be inactivated and the local concentration of peroxide required to do this is very small. *Haemophilus pertussis* is deficient in catalase and is difficult to cultivate aerobically on the surface of semi-synthetic solid culture media, but it is found that addition of catalase facilitates cultivation (Rowley, personal communication 1956). This suggests that peroxide formation is the inhibiting factor under highly aerobic conditions. Although peroxide formation and the absence of catalase may be important factors in making a bacterium an obligate anaerobe, it is not necessarily the only factor involved. Other enzyme systems besides catalase and peroxidase play a part and unless a bacterium possesses active enzyme systems capable of functioning at a given level of oxidation-reduction potential the cell will not metabolise actively; it cannot multiply and incidentally it cannot reduce the oxidation-reduction potential to a lower level as actively growing cultures do.

In summary, then, bacteria exhibit a whole range of aerophilic and aerophobic properties. Some aerobes can develop only when there is an abundant oxygen supply, anaerobes only when air and oxidizing substances are completely excluded; other bacteria require intermediate aerobic and anaerobic conditions. Some bacteria which are abundantly supplied with whole ranges of different enzyme systems can begin growth under highly aerobic conditions and continue to multiply under a variety of conditions, even down to the level at which hydrogen is liberated in the culture. These varying requirements for aerobiosis or anaerobiosis have considerable ecological significance. In the preparation of silage pits not only acid conditions, as already mentioned, but also tight packing down and the exclusion of air result in desirable anaerobic fermentations and the absence of aerobic organisms causing putrefactive spoilage. On the other hand, absence of aeration, as well as the acidity, in sour soils leads to predominance of anaerobes and the cessation of nitrogen-fixing processes associated with aerobic organisms. The numbers of aerobes falls and their activity ceases under sour anaerobic conditions. In sewage disposal absence of aeration results in incomplete digestion. Air must be available to encourage active bacterial metabolism either in activated sludge tanks into which air is pumped, or in intermittent trickle filters. In both cases oxygen is necessary for bacterial activity.

In the case of individual bacteria the oxidation-reduction conditions of cultivation have important effects on bacterial behaviour. For example, variation amongst the haemolytic streptococci is very complex (Todd & Lancefield, 1928; Lancefield & Todd, 1928; Todd, 1928, 1930a, b, c; Hewitt, 1930). The glossy form is invariably avirulent whilst the matt form may be virulent or attenuated. The matt form contains a specific M substance of protein nature whilst the glossy form is deprived of M. Hence although the matt form can lose M protein and become glossy, the glossy form cannot become matt, unless it proves possible to convey the heritable property of forming the specific substance by means of a nucleic acid as has been effected by Avery, Macleod & McCarthy (1944) for an analogous system in the *Pneumococcus*. The matt form may become glossy when cultured on the surface of solid media exposed to air, and this effect can be traced to peroxide formation. The matt form produces more peroxide and this is bactericidal. Continued subculture on solid media has a selective effect, the matt variants are gradually killed and eventually only glossy variants remain. On solid media there is relatively little diffusion and the peroxide remains in the neighbourhood of the matt colonies which have produced it and these are killed. In liquid medium, although the peroxide diffuses through the medium, and although the matt variants are more sensitive, the selection is slower. The selection can be accelerated by adding peroxide to liquid cultures, when the selective action can take place in the phase of active multiplication before naturally produced peroxide is present in appreciable concentration.

Another effect of oxidation-reduction potentials on the virulence of haemolytic streptococci presents features of some interest. Although virulence can be maintained by animal passage, there is attenuation after continued subculture *in vitro*. Virulence can, however, be maintained if the broth cultures are exposed to aeration, especially in the presence of catalase, which prevents the deleterious effects of peroxide.

The clue to the maintenance of virulence in aerated cultures appears to be found in the work of Elliott (1945). He isolated a proteinase from haemolytic streptococci and found that it attacked the M substance present in virulent organisms but not in the avirulent glossy variants. When this proteinase is active, therefore, the M substance associated with virulence is destroyed. The proteinase, however, requires reduced SH groups for its activation. In ordinary deep broth cultures sulphydryl compounds are in the reduced form, the proteinase is activated and the M substance is destroyed. However, in adequately aerated cultures SH groups are oxidized, the proteinase is not activated and the M substance is preserved. Stamp (1953) has carried the matter further in an investigation of haemolytic streptococcal vaccines. Strains producing much proteinase gave rise to poor vaccines, and in cultures in which low oxidation-reduction potentials developed with consequent activation of the proteinase by reduced SH compounds, again the vaccines were poor.

REFERENCES

AVERY, O. T., MACLEOD, C. M. & McCARTHY, M. (1944). Studies on the chemical nature of the substance inducing transformation of pneumococcal type. *J. exp. Med.* **79**, 137.

BOYD, J. S. K. (1950). The symbiotic bacteriophages of *Salmonella typhimurium*. *J. Path. Bact.* **62**, 501.

BROWN, W. & WOOD, R. K. S. (1953). Ecological adaptations in fungi. *Adaptation in Micro-organisms. Third Symp. Soc. gen. Microbiol.* p. 326.

ELLIOTT, S. D. (1945). A proteolytic enzyme produced by group A streptococci. *J. exp. Med.* **81**, 573.

EPPS, H. M. R. & GALE, E. F. (1942). The influence of the presence of glucose during growth on the enzymic activities of *Escherichia coli*: comparison with that produced by fermentation acids. *Biochem. J.* **36**, 619.

GALE, E. F. & EPPS, H. M. R. (1942). The effect of the pH of the medium during growth on the enzymic activities of bacteria (*Escherichia coli* and *Micrococcus lysodeikticus*) and the biological significance of the changes produced. *Biochem. J.* **36**, 600.

GALE, E. F. & VAN HEYNINGEN, W. E. (1942). The effect of the pH and the presence of glucose during growth on the production of α and θ toxins and hyaluronidase by *Clostridium welchii*. *Biochem. J.* **36**, 624.

HEWITT, L. F. (1930). Oxidation-reduction potentials of cultures of haemolytic streptococci. I. *Biochem. J.* **24**, 512.

HEWITT, L. F. (1932a). Bacterial metabolism. I. Lactic acid production by haemolytic streptococci. *Biochem. J.* **26**, 208.

HEWITT, L. F. (1932b). Bacterial Metabolism. II. Glucose breakdown by pneumococcus variants and the effect of phosphate thereon. *Biochem. J.* **26**, 464.

HEWITT, L. F. (1950). *Oxidation-reduction Potentials in Bacteriology and Biochemistry*, 6th edn. Edinburgh: Livingstone.

HEWITT, L. F. (1954a). Autoadaptation of bacterial viruses and its effect on bacterial variation and evolution. *J. gen. Microbiol.* **11**, 261.

HEWITT, L. F. (1954b). Mechanism of virulence transfer by bacterial viruses. *J. gen. Microbiol.* **11**, 272.

HEWITT, L. F. (1954c). The effect of antibiotics and other chemotherapeutic agents on lysogenicity and virulence transfer by bacterial viruses in *Corynebacterium diphtheriae*. *J. gen. Microbiol.* **11**, 288.

HINSHELWOOD, C. N. (1946). *The Chemical Kinetics of the Bacterial Cell*. Oxford: Clarendon Press.

LANCEFIELD, R. C. & TODD, E. W. (1928). Antigenic differences between matt haemolytic streptococci and their glossy variants. *J. exp. Med.* **48**, 769.

LEDERBERG, J. (1952). Cell genetics and hereditary symbiosis. *Physiol. Rev.* **32**, 403.

LINGGOOD, F. V., MATTHEWS, A. C., PINFIELD, S., POPE, C. G. & SHARLAND, T. R. (1955). Production of diphtheria toxin in submerged cultures. *Nature, Lond.*, **176**, 1128.

McLEOD, J. W. & GORDON, J. (1923). Catalase production and sensitiveness to hydrogen-peroxide amongst bacteria with a scheme of classification based on these properties. *J. Path. Bact.* **26**, 326.

OUDIN, J. (1948). L'analyse immuno-chémique qualitative; méthode par diffusion des antigènes au sein de l'immunserum précipitant gélosé. *Ann. Inst. Pasteur*, **75**, 30.

PAPPENEHEIMR, A. M. (1937). Diphtheria toxin. I. Isolation and characterisation of a toxic protein from *Corynebacterium diphtheriae*. *J. biol. Chem.* **120**, 543.

POPE, C. G., STEVENS, M., CASPARY, E. A. & FENTON, E. L. (1951). Some new observations on diphtheria toxin and antitoxin. *Brit. J. exp. Path.* **32**, 246.

ROUNTREE, P. M. (1949). The phenomenon of lysogenicity in staphylococci. *J. gen. Microbiol.* **3**, 153.

SMITH, H. W. (1948). Investigation on the typing of staphylococci by means of bacteriophage. I. The origin and nature of lysogenic strains. *J. Hyg., Camb.*, **46**, 74.

SNYDER, M. L. (1940). The normal fecal flora of infants between two weeks and one year of age. *J. infect. Dis.* **66**, 1.

STAMP (Lord) (1953). Studies on O/R potential, pH and proteinase production in cultures of *Streptococcus pyogenes*, in relation to immunizing activity. *Brit. J. exp. Path.* **34**, 347.

SYMPOSIUM (1953). *Adaptation in Micro-organisms. Third Symp. Soc. gen. Microbiol.*

TODD, E. W. (1928). Further observations on the virulence of haemolytic streptococci with special reference to the morphology of the colonies. *Brit. J. exp. Path.* **9**, 1.

TODD, E. W. (1930a). Virulence of haemolytic streptococci. I. The influence of oxygen on the production of glossy variants. *Brit. J. exp. Path.* **11**, 368.

TODD, E. W. (1930*b*). Virulence of haemolytic streptococci. II. The influence of oxygen on the maintenance of virulence in broth cultures. *Brit. J. exp. Path.* **11**, 469.

TODD, E. W. (1930*c*). Virulence of haemolytic streptococci. III. The influence of oxygen on the restoration of virulence to matt attenuated cultures. *Brit. J. exp. Path.* **11**, 480.

TODD, E. W. & LANCEFIELD, R. C. (1928). Variants of haemolytic streptococci; their relation to the type specific substance, virulence and toxin. *J. exp. Med.* **48**, 751.

WILLIAMS, R. E. O. & RIPPON, J. E. (1952). Bacteriophage typing of *Staphylococcus aureus*. *J. Hyg., Camb.,* **50**, 320.

THE ROLE OF LIGHT IN THE MICROBIAL WORLD: SOME FACTS AND SPECULATIONS

R. Y. STANIER AND GERMAINE COHEN-BAZIRE

*Department of Bacteriology, The University of
California, Berkeley*

INTRODUCTION

Without light, there would be neither micro-organisms to discuss nor intelligent beings to discuss them. Throughout the earth's history, the radiant energy of the sun has served as the only ultimate energy source for the development and maintenance of life. According to experts on biopoesis (Haldane, 1954; Bernal, 1954), the very emergence of living matter became possible only as a consequence of the prior conversion of solar energy into the bond energy of organic compounds, through photochemical reactions in the atmosphere of the young earth. This store of bond energy, accumulated in the pre-biological stage of terrestrial evolution, would not have supported biological activity for long; and the perpetuation of living matter, that singular by-product of geo-chemical evolution, became assured only when certain living creatures developed the machinery to perform endogenous photochemical reactions which resulted in the conversion of solar radiant energy into chemical bond energy. These reactions, the photosyntheses, although they have no doubt undergone many evolutionary modifications through the course of geological time, are still the mainstay of life on earth.

Photosynthesis is the most important type of photochemical reaction which occurs in biological systems, but by no means the only one. Both phototrophic and chemotrophic organisms often respond to light by directed growth or movement, the processes known as phototropism and phototaxis, respectively. In the microbial world the perception of light which results in tropistic or tactic responses does not necessarily involve the operation of a structurally specialized sensory apparatus, although some micro-organisms do have one. Various flagellate algae possess stigmata, and the fungus *Pilobolus* has developed a photo-sensitive organelle of great precision and elegance. It is mainly in the animal world, however, that the evolution of complex photoreceptors has taken place. By the addition of a lens system, animal photoreceptors have become capable not merely of light perception, but also of image formation.

Only light which is absorbed can be photochemically effective. Hence photosynthesis, phototropism, phototaxis and image formation are all mediated by cellular pigments which undergo photochemical transformations as a consequence of the absorption of light quanta. The primary photochemical transformation is linked to a sequence of 'dark' cellular reactions so as to produce the observed total response. Our knowledge of the inner mechanisms of these light-induced reaction sequences is still woefully inadequate; indeed, the only ones of which we possess a fair comprehension are those which underlie the phenomenon of vertebrate vision. The elucidation of the mechanisms of vertebrate vision, in our opinion one of the most brilliant achievements of biochemistry in the twentieth century, has been largely accomplished by Wald and his collaborators (see Wald, 1951, for a summary). Their work provides a model for all future studies on light reactions in living systems.

For the cellular pigments which are the primary light absorbers in photosynthesis, phototaxis, phototropism and vision, *colour is an essential attribute*. In these cases, colour has adaptive value; the compounds in question are cell components *because they are coloured*. However, living cells also contain many coloured compounds which do not function as light absorbers in light-induced reaction sequences—the heme pigments, for example. In such cases, colour is thrust upon the molecule as an incidental result of a specific molecular configuration which is determined by the *chemical function* of that molecule in the cell. In cellular pigments of this type, colour has no adaptive value, and is an *incidental attribute*.

Photochemical reactions can, of course, take place when light quanta are absorbed by incidentally coloured cell components, but since such photochemical reactions are not linked in any organized fashion to the dark reactions of the cell, the biological consequences are apt to be deleterious ones. For example, the molecular configurations of the proteins and nucleic acids dictate that these substances shall absorb strongly light of wavelengths between 250 and 300 mμ, but such light absorption is catastrophic for the cell. The exploration of the consequences of ultra-violet light absorption provides one of the principal occupations of those biological undertakers, the radiobiologists. Since this subject has been reviewed far too frequently, we shall not discuss it here. Light absorption by cell components in the visible and near infrared regions can also give rise to photochemical changes which might be expected to have deleterious consequences for the cell; but this is a problem that has received almost no study since the earliest days of radiobiology. We shall touch on it in a later section of this essay, in connexion with the discussion of carotenoid function.

THE NATURE OF SOLAR RADIATION

Ecologically speaking, the light emitted by the sun is the only form of light that is important. 'Light' is a psychophysical concept, and is defined as that portion of the electromagnetic spectrum which is capable of activating the photoreceptors of the human eye. The region thus delimited is conventionally supposed to lie between 380 and 770 mμ; but this range is too narrow for the purposes of the microbial ecologist, since some regions of the solar spectrum conventionally considered to be 'dark' have important photochemical effects in micro-organisms. While preparing this essay, we planned at first to redefine light in a biophysical, rather than a psychophysical fashion; namely, as those regions of the solar spectrum which can produce biologically significant photochemical reactions in some living system. We were saved from this heresy by Professor George Wald, who drew our attention to his own studies on the spectral sensitivity curve for human vision. As Griffin, Hubbard & Wald (1947) discovered, the human eye can perceive light of wavelengths as long as 1150 mμ, provided that the stimulus is one of sufficient magnitude. Hence if one clings to the tails of the spectral sensitivity curve, it is still possible to adhere to the psychophysical definition of light, and at the same time use this word to describe all the regions of the solar spectrum that are significant in a microbiological context.

The spectral energy distribution of the solar radiation that reaches the earth's surface is subject to variation, caused principally by the depth of atmosphere traversed (governed by the solar angle and the altitude) and by the quality of the atmosphere (governed by meteorological conditions). Fig. 1 shows the approximate spectral energy distributions for air masses of 0 and 2, taken from the data of Moon (1940). The curve for an air mass of zero gives the energy distribution, calculated by extrapolation, at the surface of the atmosphere; the curve for an air mass of 2 represents a fair average for the spectral energy distribution of sunlight at sea level. From these data, some interesting calculations can be made (Table 1). The ultra-violet region (below 400 mμ) contributes only a small fraction of the total irradiance. The visible and near infra-red regions (400–1100 mμ) together account for about three-quarters of the total, the remaining 20 % being made up by infra-red radiation of wavelengths greater than 1100 mμ. These proportions change very little as a result of passage through the earth's atmosphere.

Not all wavelengths of the solar spectrum give rise to photochemical reactions. The qualitative nature of the effect which an absorbed quantum can produce is governed by its energy content, which changes inversely with wavelength. At wavelengths greater than 1100–1300 mμ, the only effect of absorption is to increase the rotational energy of the absorbing atom or molecule; chemical change cannot occur, the quantum energy being immediately dissipated as heat. The thermal effects of solar radiation are of great ecological importance, but in the

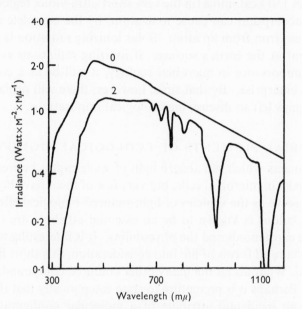

Fig. 1. Spectral energy distribution of solar irradiance for air masses of 0 and 2. Data of Moon (1940).

Table 1. *Gross spectral distribution of solar irradiance for air masses of* 0 *and* 2. *Adapted from data of Moon* (1940)

Air mass ...	0	2
Wavelength (mμ)	Percentage of total irradiance	
290–400	7	3
400–700	41	45
700–1100	28	36
1100–∞	24	16

present Symposium they belong to the domain of Professor Johnson (p. 134). Quantum absorption begins to have photochemical consequences in addition to thermal ones in the near infra-red, where quantum energies exceed 20 kcal./mole, and are sufficient to cause changes in the outer valence electrons of absorbing atoms. Since the solar spectrum at the earth's surface is interrupted slightly above 1100 mμ by one of the absorption bands of atmospheric water, we may say that radiant energy becomes of potential ecological importance as a cause of photochemical reactions at wavelengths shorter than 1100 mμ. The qualitative effects of quantum absorption remain unchanged throughout the near infra-red, visible and near ultra-violet regions; this is the spectral area of pure photochemistry. When the quantum energy approaches 150 kcal./mole (in the very short ultra-violet region, at about 200 mμ), absorption can cause ionization, by the complete ejection of the outer electron from an atom. Solar ionizing radiation is practically non-existent at the earth's surface. If ionizing radiations ever become of major importance in microbial ecology, it will be as a consequence of human enterprise. By that time, however, there will probably be no human beings left to discuss the ecological implications.

MICROBIAL PIGMENTS OF ECOLOGICAL SIGNIFICANCE

Many pigments which can absorb light of wavelengths between 400 and 1100 mμ exist in microbial cells, but very few of them have been demonstrated to serve as the vehicles of light-induced biological effects. Those for which colour is known to be an essential attribute are the chlorophylls, the carotenoids and the phycobilins. It is interesting to note that even if we take all forms of life into consideration, this short list remains unchanged. What about the many other coloured compounds in microbial cells? Perhaps it is premature to state categorically that their colour is always an incidental attribute of a molecular configuration which serves a specific chemical function, but on the whole we are inclined to believe that this is so. The one possible exception may be the flavins, since evidence (still inconclusive, however) is beginning to suggest that at least some phototropic responses may be mediated by these substances (Bünning, 1953). At the present time, however, it seems permissible to restrict the discussion to the chlorophylls, carotenoids and phycobilins. The distribution, structure and colour of these substances are briefly reviewed below.

The chlorophylls

The chlorophylls are uniquely and invariably found in the photosynthetic apparatus of phototrophs. Although they are not alone responsible for the absorption of photosynthetically effective light, much evidence points to the fact that they are the pigments which bring about the conversion of radiant energy into chemical bond energy. At least six different molecular species of chlorophyll exist. In green algae, euglenids and higher plants, a mixture of chlorophylls *a* and *b* occurs;

in the other algal groups, chlorophyll *a* occurs, either alone or in combination with one of the chlorophylls *c*, *d* and *e*. In the photosynthetic bacteria, two other kinds of chlorophyll are found: bacteriochlorophyll in purple bacteria, and chlorobium chlorophyll in green bacteria. The molecular ground plan of the chlorophylls is represented

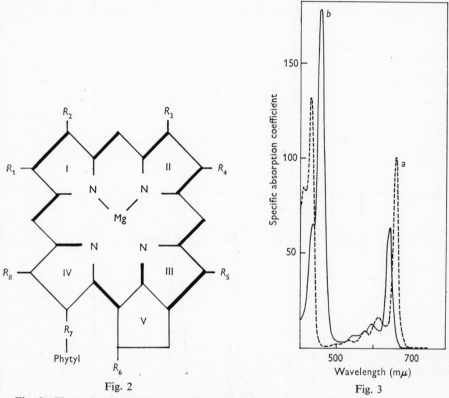

Fig. 2

Fig. 3

Fig. 2. The molecular ground plan of the chlorophylls. Double bonds are indicated as heavy lines. The resonance pattern shown is that characteristic of the chlorophylls which are derivatives of dihydroporphin (e.g. chlorophyll *a*).

Fig. 3. Absorption spectra of chlorophylls *a* and *b*. Data of Smith & Benitez (1954).

diagrammatically in Fig. 2. The central tetrapyrrolic nucleus, chelated with magnesium, bears various aliphatic substituents, designated as R_1, R_2, etc. Attached to pyrrol ring III there is an additional ring, known as the pentanone ring (V). One of the substituents on ring IV is esterified with a long-chain aliphatic alcohol, phytyl alcohol.

Light absorption by the chlorophylls results from resonance in the tetrapyrrolic ring system, and modifications of the molecular ground plan which affect this resonance pattern also profoundly affect the absorption spectrum. In so far as they are known, the chemical differences between the various species of chlorophyll lie in two parts of the molecule, the R groups and the tetrapyrrolic ring system. Modifica-

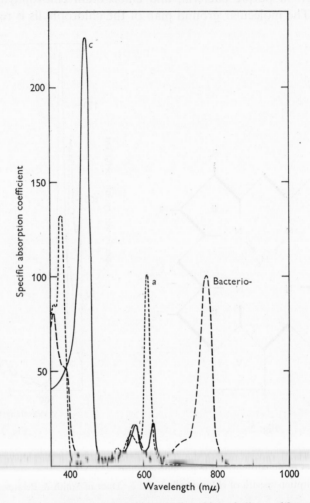

Fig. 4. Absorption spectra of chlorophyll c, chlorophyll a, and bacterio-chlorophyll. Data of Smith & Benitez (1954).

tions of the R groups have a relatively minor effect upon the pattern of light absorption, affecting mainly the relative peak heights. This is shown by the absorption spectra (Fig. 3) of pure chlorophylls a and b, which differ only with respect to one R substituent on ring II. Much more profound are the spectral changes which occur when the oxidation level of the tetrapyrrolic ring system is changed. This is shown by a comparison of the absorption spectra (Fig. 4) of chlorophyll *c*, chlorophyll *a* and bacteriochlorophyll, whose ring systems are derived chemically from porphin, dihydroporphin and tetrahydroporphin, respectively. As the oxidation level of the tetrapyrrolic ring system falls through this series, the relative magnitude of the absorption band at longest wavelength increases enormously, and its position moves farther towards the red. As will be described later, the absorption spectrum of chlorophyll can be greatly modified by its state within the cell, so that the *in vitro* spectra tell only part of the story about photosynthetically effective light absorption. Nevertheless, the spectral character which is conferred by the oxidation level of the tetrapyrrolic nucleus does have ecological significance.

The carotenoids

The carotenoids have a much wider distribution among micro-organisms than have the chlorophylls. They are invariably found in the photosynthetic apparatus of phototrophs, but occur also in the cells of many aerobic chemotrophic fungi and bacteria. In many (probably most) phototrophs, light absorption by carotenoids has an essential function, since the measurement of action spectra has shown that wavelengths absorbed largely or exlusively by the carotenoid pigments can be used for photosynthesis. The evidence will not be discussed here, since it has been summarized in one of the Society's earlier Symposia by Blinks (1954). The elegant studies of Duysens (1952) demonstrated that light absorption by carotenoid pigments in photosynthetic bacteria and various groups of algae results in the appearance of chlorophyll fluorescence; hence it is likely that the carotenoids do not participate directly in the primary photochemical reaction of photosynthesis, but transfer their excitation energy to chlorophyll. Another function of carotenoid pigments in phototrophs will be discussed in a later section of this paper. Among the algal flagellates which possess stigmata, the carotenoids present in these organelles appear to function as photoreceptors for the stimulation of phototactic movements; this is a photochemical reaction not directly coupled with photosynthesis. In blue-green algae and bacteria, on the other hand, phototactic responses may be mediated either by the carotenoids or by the chlorophyll, and the mechanism of phototaxis appears to be far more closely coupled with photosynthesis.

The problem of carotenoid function in chemotrophic micro-organisms is still a largely unsolved one. In a few fungi there are indications that carotenoids mediate in phototropic responses; here, therefore, the colour of these pigments is an essential attribute. But in many fungi, and in the large number of chemotrophic bacteria which contain carotenoid pigments, there is at present no experimental evidence that these pigments have a photochemical function.

Chemically, the carotenoids are aliphatic or alicyclic compounds, which contain characteristically 40 carbon atoms. The molecular structure is a singular one. It consists of a chain of eight isoprene units, linked to form a long chain with methyl groups projecting at regular intervals (Fig. 5). The linkage is such that the two methyl groups nearest the centre of the chain are in positions 1:6, while all other lateral methyl groups are in a 1:5 relationship. To borrow a biological expression, we

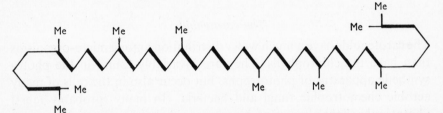

Fig. 5. The molecular ground plan of the carotenoids, as illustrated by a carotenoid hydrocarbon. Double bonds indicated by heavy lines. The basic structure can be modified by hydroxylation, terminal ring closure, and the introduction of ketonic or acidic groups.

may say that the carotenoids are characteristically bilaterally symmetrical, and this bilateral symmetry tends, furthermore, to be maintained through all the various modifications (introduction of hydroxyl groups, terminal ring closure, etc.) which are imposed on the basic molecular pattern in the different classes of carotenoid pigments.

Light absorption by carotenoids is a consequence of the system of conjugated double bonds which runs through the chain. The main relationship between structure and light absorption is a relatively simple one: the larger the number of conjugated double bonds in the chain, the farther the main absorption bands are shifted towards the red end of the spectrum. Thus the relatively saturated C_{40} polyenes, phytoene and phytofluene, are colourless, since they absorb exclusively in the ultraviolet; in the more unsaturated carotenoids, the colour is yellow, orange or red, depending largely on the degree of unsaturation.

The phycobilins

The phycobilins (phycoerythrins and phycocyanins) have an extremely limited biological distribution, existing only in two groups of phototrophs, the red and blue-green algae. They occur together with chlorophyll and carotenoids in the photosynthetic apparatus of these algae, and measurements of action spectra show that they are highly effective light absorbers for photosynthesis (Blinks, 1954). In fact, the investigations of Haxo & Blinks (1950) have revealed the astonishing fact that, in some red algae, light absorbed by the phycobilins is used far more effectively for photosynthesis than light absorbed directly by the chlorophylls, a phenomenon which has not yet been satisfactorily explained. The investigations of Duysens (1952) on fluorescence emission spectra indicate that the excitation energy of the phycobilins is transferred to chlorophyll, just as is the excitation energy of carotenoids. The function of the phycobilins in photosynthesis is therefore probably quite analogous to that of the carotenoid pigments. Chemically, the phycobilins are linear tetrapyrroles which are very firmly conjugated with proteins of the globulin type.

PHOTOSYNTHETIC PIGMENT SYSTEMS
Patterns of light absorption for photosynthesis

It was first shown by Engelmann (1883 a, 1884) that the so-called 'accessory pigments' (carotenoids and phycobilins) of photosynthetic organisms are effective light absorbers for photosynthesis. This conclusion, reached on the basis of very simple experimental methods, has been confirmed with the aid of very elaborate equipment by a number of cell physiologists during the past fifteen years. With a few minor exceptions (see Blinks, 1954, for a discussion), the entire pigment system in the chloroplast or chromatophore of phototrophic organisms appears to be operative in the trapping of light for photosynthesis. In most cases, therefore, the absorption spectrum of the cell is closely correlated with the effective light absorption for photosynthesis. The measurement of absorption spectra on whole cells is complicated by light scattering, but scattering effects can be minimized in a number of ways.* Good absorption spectra for whole cells of a number of phototrophic microorganisms are now available, and some representative data, taken from several sources, are plotted in Fig. 6. In each curve the pigments responsible for the various bands are roughly indicated.

Several interesting facts are made clear by the data juxtaposed in Fig. 6. The first is the marvellous completeness with which the available wavelengths of sunlight have been harnessed by the various groups of

* Perhaps the simplest method to achieve this is to place an opalescent plate (e.g. a pane of opal glass) in the spectrophotometer between the sample holder and the photocell (Shibata, Benson & Calvin, 1954).

phototrophic organisms. From 350 mμ, where the Soret band of bacteriochlorophyll begins to show large absorption, solar radiant energy is successively absorbed by the Soret bands of the plant chlorophylls, by the carotenoids, by the phycobilins, by the α-band of the plant chlorophylls, by the α-band of chlorobium chlorophyll, and, finally

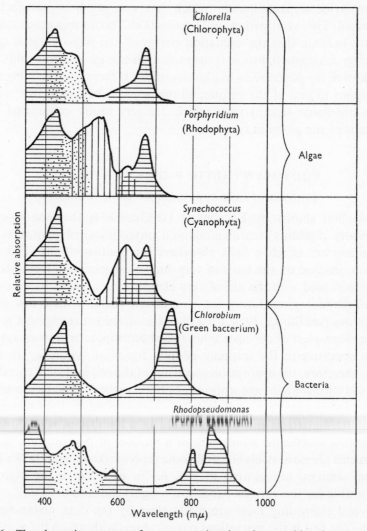

Fig. 6. The absorption spectra of some representative phototrophic micro-organisms, measured on whole cells with the aid of opal glass, except that of *Chlorobium*. Spectra of *Chlorella*, *Synechococcus* and *Porphyridium* taken from Shibata *et al.* (1954); spectrum of *Chlorobium* taken from Larsen (1953), and corrected for light scattering. The contributions by the various classes of photosynthetic pigments are approximately indicated as follows: chlorophylls, horizontal hatching; carotenoids, stippling; phycobilins, vertical hatching.

well in the infra-red, by the α-bands of bacteriochlorophyll. In fact, over the spectral range where photochemical reactions are theoretically possible, the only major segment of solar irradiance that is *not* used for photosynthesis by some living organism is the infra-red region between 950 and 1100 mμ. Since this is close to the borderline of quantum energy required to produce photochemical events, the absence of biological exploitation may well be caused by the fact that the energy content of the light quanta is too low for the performance of the photochemical reaction which underlies photosynthesis.

Complementary light absorption and its implications

A second fact shown by the data in Fig. 6 is the *complementarity* of light absorption by some phototrophs. Complementarity is not particularly evident when one compares the spectra of the different groups of algae, since they all have virtually identical light absorption in the chlorophyll regions. For these organisms, complementarities can occur only in the carotenoid region, as a consequence of qualitative differences in the nature of the carotenoid pigments, and in the phycobilin region, where red and blue-green algae show a strong absorption which does not exist in other groups of algae. However, when one compares the algae as a whole with the two groups of phototrophic bacteria, the complementarities are extremely pronounced. Roughly speaking, light absorption by the algae occupies the middle region of the photosynthetic spectrum, and light absorption by the bacteria fills in the two ends of the spectrum.

The ecological and evolutionary implications of this complementarity are extremely interesting. Bacterial photosynthesis is at the present time of negligible quantitative importance on earth, for the very good reason that the environmental requirements for its occurrence are severely restrictive. Unlike green plant photosynthesis, bacterial photosynthesis is an anaerobic process, and requires the presence of external hydrogen donors (reduced sulphur compounds or organic compounds). In natural environments where the three paramount requirements for bacterial photosynthesis are met (light, low oxygen tension, and suitable hydrogen donors), conditions will also frequently be suitable for the development of algal phototrophs. The algae, however, are not adversely affected by the presence of free oxygen; hence in such ecological niches they tend to occupy the surface areas in contact with the atmosphere, where light intensity is highest. Furthermore, by their photosynthetic activities, they make the regions of high light intensity more aerobic and thus less favourable for the development of the photosynthetic bacteria. In nature, therefore, the photosynthetic bacteria are frequently covered by a thick layer of green or blue-green algae; this phenomenon is particularly conspicuous in grossly polluted, shallow muddy ponds, where one can scrape off the superficial layer of algae to find a layer of purple and green bacteria underneath, immediately overlying the mud. In such environments, the survival of photosynthetic bacteria as a group is absolutely dependent on their ability to use for photosynthesis wavelengths of light that are transmitted by the algae; this is the ecological explanation of the fact that they occupy the two otherwise empty ends of the spectrum of photosynthetic light absorption.

Let us now consider the evolutionary implications of this situation. According to present concepts, all photosyntheses can be regarded as consisting essentially of a photochemical cleavage of water, with the

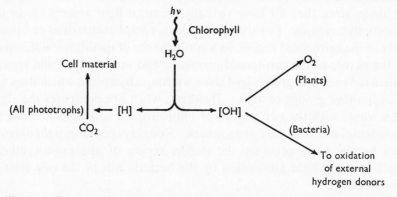

Fig. 7. A diagrammatic representation of the essential reactions of photosynthesis.

formation of an oxidized and reduced free radical. The reducing power thus generated is used to convert CO_2 to organic cell material; the path of carbon fixation is probably the same in all phototrophs (Utoppani, Fuller & Calvin, 1955). In the photosynthetic bacteria, the oxidized fragment from the cleavage of water is disposed of by being used to oxidize an external hydrogen donor; but the green plants have developed a more elegant mechanism for the same disposal job, namely, the conversion of this fragment to molecular oxygen (Fig. 7). Green plants have thus liberated themselves from dependence on the presence of an external hydrogen donor. It has been hypothesized by van Niel (1949) that photosyntheses of the bacterial type emerged first during physiological evolution, and that the trick of oxygen production was a subsequent adaptive modification in the development of photosynthetic systems. According to this hypothesis, therefore, green plant photosynthesis is a relatively late-comer on the evolutionary scene.

An alternative concept of the evolution of photosynthetic systems has been developed by Granick (1951). As we have mentioned earlier, chlorophylls differ in the oxidation level of the tetrapyrrolic ring system; chemically speaking, chlorophyll c is a derivative of porphin, chlorophylls a and b are derivatives of dihydroporphin, and bacteriochlorophyll is a derivative of tetrahydroporphin. The beautiful studies of Granick and his collaborators on mutants of *Chlorella* (summarized by Granick, 1954) have shown that the chain of biosynthesis of chlorophyll

```
                        Bacteriochlorophyll
              ?               ↑  ?   ?
Chlorobium chlorophyll←——Chlorophyll a——→Chlorophyll b
                              ↑  1 step
                        Protochlorophyll (Mg vinyl pheoporphyrin a₅ phytyl esters)
                              ↑  1 step              ?
                        Mg vinyl pheoporphyrin a₅——→ chlorophyll c
                              ↑  4–5 steps
                        Mg protoporphyrin
                              ↑  1 step
        Fe protoporphyrin ←——Protoporphyrin
                              ↑  2 steps
                        Hematoporphyrin 9
                              ↑  n steps
                        Coproporphyrin III
                              ↑  n steps
                        Porphobilinogen
                              ↑  n steps
                        α-Amino-β-ketoadipic acid
                              ↑  n steps
                        Glycine + succinate
```

Fig. 8. The biosynthetic pathway of the chlorophylls, after Granick (1951, 1954).

is an offshoot of the main chain of porphyrin biosynthesis. Furthermore, the reaction in which the tetrapyrrolic nucleus becomes reduced to the level of dihydroporphin is a late step in biosynthesis. It is, consequently, plausible to place bacteriochlorophyll at an even later point than chlorophylls a and b in the biosynthetic chain (Fig. 8), although as yet there is no experimental support for this position. Consideration of biosynthetic mechanisms, therefore, led Granick to conclude that bacteriochlorophyll might well have followed, rather than preceded, the plant chlorophylls in physiological evolution. By a further extension of such reasoning, he suggested that the coloured compounds which are the present-day intermediates in chlorophyll formation might have possessed photochemical function at earlier times in the evolution of photosynthetic systems, the biosynthetic chain gradually lengthening through time as each successive coloured tetrapyrrolic pigment was replaced in turn by a daughter compound which could perform the photochemical act in a more effective fashion. On this view, the complex biosynthetic chain which runs up to the contemporary molecular species of chlorophyll recapitulates the evolutionary history of a long series of adaptive modifications of molecular structure, all concerned with the performance of photochemical reactions. It is a singularly attractive concept that biochemical ontogeny should recapitulate biochemical phylogeny in this manner.

The hypotheses of van Niel and of Granick concerning the evolution of photosynthetic systems are not necessarily in conflict; van Niel was thinking in terms of the *evolution of reaction mechanisms*, Granick in terms of *the evolution of biosynthetic mechanisms*. Their views can be very simply reconciled, by supposing that the reaction mechanism of bacterial photosynthesis is an early evolutionary vestige, while the extra reductive step which occurs in the biosynthesis of bacteriochlorophyll is a very much later evolutionary adaptation. The extra reductive step in chlorophyll synthesis characteristic of the purple bacteria can logically be regarded as one which was forced on them by the crowding of the central portion of the solar spectrum that followed the emergence of green plant photosynthesis.

In this connexion the properties of chlorobium chlorophyll, the molecular species characteristic of the green bacteria, are highly relevant. Although the structure of this substance is still unknown, it has recently been isolated by Goodwin (1955), and his published absorption spectrum provides clear evidence that it is a dihydroporphin, with an absorption pattern very similar to that of chlorophyll *a*, but not quite identical. However, the α-band of chlorobium chlorophyll in the cells of green bacteria lies a full 80 mμ away from the α-band of chlorophylls *a* and *b* in the cells of green algae! This is a difference of position which could not have been anticipated on the basis of the absorption spectra of the pure compounds, and has to be ascribed to the fact that chlorobium chlorophyll is conjugated with other substances in the cell in such a fashion as to change completely its resonance pattern, whereas the plant chlorophylls are not. Thus in the green bacteria, competition with green algae for photosynthetically effective light has been avoided not by any fundamental change in the structure of the chlorophyll molecule itself, but by coupling this molecule with another resonating system (possibly protein) in such a way as to achieve a very large shift in the band positions. Indeed, precisely the same is true of bacteriochlorophyll in the purple bacteria. The fact that the α-band system of bacteriochlorophyll in the cells lies well in the infra-red is not explicable simply in terms of the chemical nature of the bacteriochlorophyll molecule; superimposed on the shift of the α-band caused by the reduced state of the tetrapyrrolic nucleus is an additional shift which must be caused by molecular coupling *in vivo*. Fig. 9 shows the relative magnitude of the shifts, following extraction, in the positions of the α-bands of chlorophyll for a green alga, *Chlorella*, and for a purple bacterium, *Rhodopseudomonas spheroides*. The α-band of chlorophyll in *Chlorella*

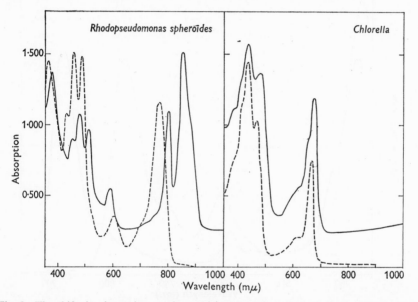

Fig. 9. The shifts in absorption maxima which occur when photosynthetic pigments are extracted from the cell. Solid lines: spectra of whole cells, measured with the aid of opal glass. Dotted lines: spectra of alcoholic extracts.

hardly shifts at all upon extraction, whereas the α-band of chlorophyll in the purple bacterium moves a full 100 mμ to shorter wavelengths. Recently we have been able to obtain an even clearer picture of the *in vivo* modifications of the absorption spectrum of bacteriochlorophyll through studies on the 'blue-green' mutant of *R. spheroides*. This mutant has lost completely the ability to synthesize coloured carotenoids, and hence bacteriochlorophyll is the only major pigment present in the cell. Its spectrum is compared with that of pure bacteriochlorophyll in Fig. 10.

To conclude this part of our essay, we should like to add our own evolutionary speculations to those of van Niel and Granick. It seems probable to us that the general type of photosynthetic reaction

mechanism now characteristic of the photosynthetic bacteria preceded
the photosynthetic reaction mechanism of green plants in evolutionary
time, as suggested first by van Niel. However, these primitive, non-
oxygen-producing phototrophs may well have possessed a pigment
system of the type now found in green plants; i.e. one in which the
chlorophyll was a dihydroporphin, with a resonance pattern not greatly
modified by molecular coupling *in vivo*. As Granick has suggested, this

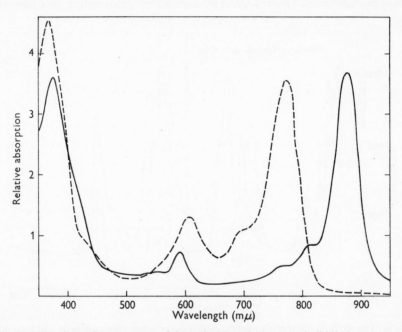

Fig. 10. The absorption spectrum of bacteriochlorophyll *in vivo* (solid line) and *in vitro*
(dotted line). The *in vivo* spectrum (measured with the aid of opal glass) is that of the blue-
green mutant of *Rhodopseudomonas spheroides*. The *in vitro* spectrum is that of pure
bacteriochlorophyll in ether solution (data of Smith & Benitez, 1954).

pigment could have been preceded in time by many other, simpler,
photosensitive porphyrins, each of which had acted as an energy con-
verter for photosynthesis during a certain evolutionary period.

When some members of the photosynthetic community acquired the
mechanism for photosynthetic oxygen production, they thereby obtained
an immediate and decisive ecological advantage over the other photosynthetic forms, which were still dependent upon external hydrogen
donors. In order to survive at all, the latter had to adapt to the use of
previously unexploited regions of the solar spectrum, and this they
managed to do by changing the resonance pattern of their chlorophyll
through molecular coupling. The green bacteria can be regarded as

contemporary models for this evolutionary step. Some of these organisms subsequently acquired the ability to manufacture bacteriochlorophyll, while still retaining the trick of greatly altering its intrinsic resonance pattern by molecular coupling, and were thus able to extend even further the effective spectral range for photosynthesis. The purple bacteria can be regarded as contemporary models for this evolutionary step.

The functions of carotenoids in the photosynthetic apparatus

Carotenoid pigments are a characteristic component of the photosynthetic apparatus in all phototrophs. Their presence can be explained in part by their role as absorbers of photosynthetically effective light, at wavelengths which are poorly absorbed or not absorbed at all by the chlorophylls. This ecologically significant function cannot be postulated in all cases, however; photosynthetic action spectra of blue-green and red algae indicate that in these algal groups the carotenoids of the photosynthetic apparatus are of negligible importance as light absorbers for photosynthesis. It is, therefore, reasonable to ask whether carotenoids could have any other functions in the operation of the photosynthetic apparatus. Two years ago we were so fortunate as to discover a mutant of the photosynthetic bacterium, *Rhodopseudomonas spheroides*, which has allowed us to make an experimental study of this question (Griffiths, Sistrom, Cohen-Bazire & Stanier, 1955). This blue-green mutant has lost in a single mutational step the ability to make the two coloured carotenoids characteristic of the wild type, and their place within the chromatophore has been taken by a colourless polyene, phytoene, whose absorption bands lie well down in the ultra-violet region (Griffiths & Stanier, 1956). Thus, although the blue-green mutant still synthesizes a substance which belongs to the same *chemical class* as the carotenoid pigments, the attribute of *colour* has been lost.

Growth experiments soon showed that the blue-green mutant is able to develop photosynthetically under the conditions which are suitable for the photosynthetic development of non-sulphur purple bacteria. These conditions include: anaerobiosis, light, and the presence of a suitable organic hydrogen donor. At any given light intensity, the blue-green mutant contains less bacteriochlorophyll than does the wild type, and its photosynthetic growth rate is considerably lower (Sistrom, Griffiths & Stanier, 1956a). This relatively low growth rate is probably entirely a reflexion of weak light absorption, brought about by the subnormal chlorophyll content and by the complete absence of carotenoid pigments. At first sight, therefore, the elimination of coloured carotenoids from the photosynthetic apparatus of the blue-green mutant appears not to have deranged the photosynthetic system in any fundamental fashion.

Unlike the purple sulphur and green bacteria, which are obligate anaerobes and consequently obligate phototrophs, the purple non-sulphur bacteria can grow aerobically in the dark, using as energy sources for respiratory metabolism the same organic substances which serve as hydrogen donors for their photosynthetic metabolism. Under conditions of dark aerobic development, the blue-green mutant grows at the same rate as the wild type—a fact which shows that the loss of ability to synthesize coloured carotenoids has had no effect on dark metabolism.

A striking and unexpected physiological consequence of the mutation became evident when a culture of the blue-green mutant, previously growing under anaerobic conditions in the light, was suddenly exposed to air and light. In the wild type and in other classes of pigment mutants which still contain coloured carotenoids, the sudden introduction of air into cultures which are growing photosynthetically causes a virtually complete cessation of chlorophyll and carotenoid synthesis, but has little effect on the growth rate; the population continues to develop, gradually shifting from photosynthetic to respiratory metabolism as the cellular content of the photosynthetic pigments declines by dilution. The behaviour of the blue-green mutant under these circumstances is radically different; growth (as measured by optical density change) immediately ceases, and the chlorophyll content of the population, instead of remaining at a constant level, begins to decline. Viable counts show that the cessation of growth is actually accompanied by a rapid killing of the population; within 2 hr. of exposure to air and light, over 99 % of the original population may be killed. Exposure of a photo-synthetically developing population to air in the absence of light causes no doubt or chlorophyll destruction, and hence the phenomenon is clearly caused by a photosensitization of the cells. Since infra-red light, of wavelengths absorbed exclusively by bacteriochlorophyll, can cause the same effects as white light in the presence of air, it is evident that the intracellular bacteriochlorophyll is the pigment responsible for the photosensitization. In other words, the loss of coloured carotenoids in the blue-green mutant is correlated with the development of photo-sensitivity to the intracellular bacteriochlorophyll. Photosensitization requires the presence of molecular oxygen, and hence cannot be demonstrated under the conditions of strict anaerobiosis necessary for the normal photosynthetic development of purple bacteria.

We are dealing here with a very peculiar and instructive example of the phenomenon known as photodynamic action, namely, the catalysis of photo-oxidations in a biological system by an intracellular pigment. In the systems previously studied, photodynamic effects have usually been induced by the experimental addition of a suitable dye (Blum, 1941). In animals, spontaneous photosensitization can also occur, either as a result of the ingestion of photosensitive pigments, or as a result of deranged porphyrin metabolism (Clare, 1956). The remarkable feature of photodynamic action in the blue-green mutant is its induction by a normal cellular pigment and by one, furthermore, which has an essential metabolic function. As a matter of fact, photosensitized oxidations by chlorophyll in green plants have been observed on many occasions, but in most cases they can be produced only under extreme conditions (blockage of photosynthesis by narcotization or CO_2 depletion, very high light intensities, high partial pressures of oxygen). However, certain land plants and marine algae may exhibit extreme light sensitivity under normal physiological conditions, being rapidly bleached and eventually killed by exposure to direct sunlight (Montfort, 1953; Biebl, 1956).

When one thinks about it, it becomes obvious that living organisms exposed themselves to a serious radiobiological hazard when they began to exploit the possibilities of using porphyrins as catalysts for the conversion of radiant energy into chemical bond energy. In the presence of oxygen, any porphyrin can catalyse photo-oxidations; and consequently, once the biosphere came to contain molecular oxygen (if, indeed, it has not always done so), the acquisition of some mechanism for minimizing the effects of chlorophyll-catalysed photo-oxidations was essential for the preservation of photosynthetic mechanisms. We believe that the behaviour of the blue-green mutant of *Rhodopseudomonas spheroides* provides the first clue to the nature of this protective mechanism, and at the same time explains why the inclusion of carotenoid pigments in the photosynthetic apparatus is of fundamental ecological importance for all phototrophs. The dramatic photosensitivity of this mutant to its own chlorophyll is correlated with the replacement of the normal coloured (and therefore highly unsaturated) carotenoids in the photosynthetic apparatus by a colourless (and therefore far more saturated) C_{40} polyene. It may be postulated that in the wild type of *R. spheroides* the chlorophyll is also capable of catalysing photo-oxidations, but that the associated carotenoid pigments provide a *chemical buffering mechanism* which prevents these photo-oxidations from having biologically deleterious effects. Chemically, the coloured carotenoids are extremely labile substances, and the double bonds provide ready sites for oxidation. If these pigments are so situated in the photosynthetic unit as to provide the most ready substrate for chlorophyll-catalysed photo-oxidations, and if a dark enzymic mechanism exists for their subsequent reduction, there would be a perfect chemical buffering mechanism for the prevention of photo-oxidative damage to the organism.

Let us pursue this hypothesis a little further, and consider what could be expected to happen in phototrophs such as the blue-green mutant, where the coloured carotenoids have been replaced by phytoene. Phytoene has only three conjugated double bonds, and is thus a far less effective substrate for oxidation. Furthermore, it lacks the molecular rigidity characteristic of the coloured carotenoids, and hence the molecular geometry of the chromatophore, which would be of paramount importance in the postulated buffering mechanism, could well be modified by its introduction.* In the presence of air, therefore, the chlorophyll of the mutant photo-oxidizes other cell components. One of these is, obviously, chlorophyll itself. This situation is well known from model systems, when the photocatalytic pigment catalyses its own destruction in the absence of a suitable oxidizable substrate. Recent unpublished experiments by Dr Martin Dworkin have clearly shown that chlorophyll destruction is not the only photo-oxidative process which occurs, since chlorophyll destruction and killing are not always correlated. If the mutant is exposed to light and air at 5° C., the rate of chlorophyll destruction is far less than at 30° C.; but the rate of killing is virtually the same at both temperatures. The death of the cell, therefore, is an almost pure photochemical process, whereas the destruction of chlorophyll is not. We still do not know the cause of cell death. In other biological systems, photosensitization by dyes severely damages the genetic material of the cell (Briggs, 1952; Kaplan, 1956), and hence it seems probable that death results from destruction of DNA.

The fact that the blue-green mutant of *Rhodopseudomonas spheroides* can still lead a relatively normal photosynthetic existence is attributable solely to the anaerobic nature of the bacterial photosyntheses. If our hypothesis concerning carotenoid function in phototrophs is correct,

---

* An indication of disturbances in the molecular geometry of the chromatophore is provided by the peculiarities of chlorophyll synthesis in the blue-green mutant. In addition to containing somewhat less chlorophyll than the wild type, the mutant excretes a complex mixture of phorbides during chlorophyll synthesis. This suggests that there is no intrinsic impairment of chlorophyll synthesis, but that not all the chlorophyll which the cell can synthesize gets incorporated into the chromatophores. The unincorporated surplus is excreted as phorbides (Sistrom *et al.* 1956*b*).

any organism which carries out green plant photosynthesis should suffer a crippling blow as a consequence of undergoing a similar mutation. Mutations which result in the complete loss of coloured carotenoids have been discovered in *Chlorella* (Claes, 1954), in corn (Koski & Smith, 1951) and in sunflowers (Wallace & Schwarting, 1954). Such information as is available about their phenotypic character is in good accord with prediction. Claes (1954) reports that the *Chlorella* mutant can be grown only in the dark, being killed by exposure to light. The behaviour of the sunflower mutant, which has been studied in some detail by Wallace & Schwarting (1954), is even more interesting. As in most angiosperms, the formation of chlorophyll is a light-dependent reaction. Seedlings will turn green, but only in exceedingly dim light; maximal chlorophyll formation is observed at a light intensity of 0·5 foot-candle, and at intensities of 10–1000 foot-candles, which are necessary to evoke maximal chlorophyll formation in normal seedlings, the mutant seedlings are completely bleached. This is clearly the result of a light-catalysed destruction of chlorophyll, following its light-catalysed formation, since mutant seedlings which have become green as a result of exposure to dim light are bleached within a few hours when exposed to bright light, and cannot again manufacture chlorophyll upon re-exposure to dim light. A similar pattern of behaviour was observed in the corn mutant studied by Koski & Smith (1951).

There is, therefore, some reason to suppose that the function of coloured carotenoids as chemical buffers against chlorophyll-catalysed photo-oxidations is universal in phototrophic organisms, and of far greater ecological significance than their function as absorbers of photosynthetically effective light. If this concept is correct, it follows that the colour of carotenoid pigments in phototrophs is only in part essential, and in part an incidental consequence of a specific molecular configuration which confers on these substances the ability to act as substrates for photo-oxidation.

This very speculative discussion of carotenoid function in photosynthesis may be ended appropriately by a few additional evolutionary speculations. All present evidence suggests that it is the chlorophylls, and the chlorophylls alone, which are capable of converting radiant energy into chemical bond energy; in so far as the carotenoids participate directly in the photochemical events of photosynthesis, they do so by transferring their excitation energy to chlorophyll. One can, therefore, envisage a primitive phototroph which contained chlorophyll or a similarly functional porphyrin and no carotenoids; but the converse situation is improbable. Such an organism, for which the blue-green mutant of *Rhodopseudomonas spheroides* provides a contemporary model, could exist photosynthetically as long as its environment remained anaerobic. There would, however, be a considerable selective advantage to extending the range of utilizable solar energy, and hence carotenoids might well have been added to the photosynthetic unit as extra light absorbers for the transfer of energy to the porphyrin. Energy transfer by inductive resonance occurs only over relatively short distances, and hence the carotenoids would have necessarily occupied a position in the cell very close to the porphyrin. Once natural selection had acted to put carotenoids in the photosynthetic unit for this photo-chemical function, an essential *pre-adaptive* step towards the emergence of green plant photosynthesis had also been taken, since a chemical buffering mechanism, essential to any phototroph which produces molecular oxygen, had been simultaneously installed in the photo-synthetic apparatus. According to this evolutionary hypothesis, caro-tenoids found their way into the photosynthetic unit because they were coloured, and later stayed there primarily because they were ideal substrates for photo-oxidation.

Adaptive regulation of pigment synthesis in purple bacteria

It has long been known (see van Niel, 1944) that the photosynthetic pigment system of the non-sulphur purple bacteria is profoundly affected by environmental factors. The most easily observable effects are those produced by oxygen and by illumination; cultures grown anaerobically in the light are deeply pigmented, whereas those grown under strictly aerobic conditions in the dark are virtually colourless. Until recently, however, this matter has not been studied systematically. During the past two years we have begun to investigate the kinetics of pigment synthesis in two purple bacteria, *Rhodopseudomonas spheroides* and *Rhodospirillum rubrum* (Cohen-Bazire, Sistrom & Stanier, 1956). Some of our findings and their implications are discussed below.

The photosynthetic pigment system of purple bacteria consists of bacteriochlorophyll and one or more carotenoids. Bacteriochlorophyll is common to all members of the group, but the nature of the carotenoids is a more or less species-specific character. Although chlorophyll and carotenoids differ greatly in chemical structure (and probably also in biosynthetic origin), their syntheses by the cell appear to be closely coupled, and respond in broadly similar fashion to all environmental factors which influence pigment synthesis.

Under anaerobic conditions photosynthesis is the only type of energy-yielding metabolism which can support the growth of non-sulphur purple bacteria. In cultures which are growing exponentially in anaero-biosis, the differential rate of pigment synthesis* is an inverse function of light intensity. Hence under steady state conditions of growth and pigment synthesis, the dimmer the light, the greater is the pigment content of the cells (Fig. 11). The response of a population under steady-

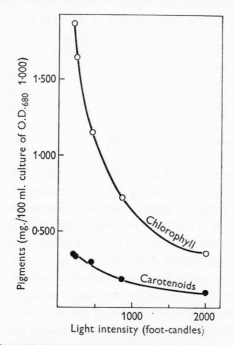

Fig. 11. The effect of light intensity on the pigment content of the cells of *Rhodopseudomonas spheroides*, grown under steady-state conditions in anaerobiosis.

state conditions of growth and pigment synthesis to a sudden change of light intensity is very striking. When the light intensity is abruptly increased, growth continues unimpaired, but the rate of pigment synthesis immediately falls to zero. When the pigment content of the population has diminished, as a consequence of growth, to a level which approaches that characteristic of the changed light intensity, pigment synthesis resumes, and eventually a new steady-state relationship between growth and pigment synthesis is established. Conversely, an abrupt decrease of light intensity causes an almost immediate and very marked increase in the rate of pigment synthesis, so that the pigment

* The rate of pigment synthesis relative to the total rate of synthesis of cell material.

content of the cells rises rapidly towards that characteristic of the changed light intensity. The chlorophyll:carotenoid ratio changes systematically with light intensity, diminishing as the light intensity is increased (Table 2); this effect is produced by slight differences between the rates of synthesis of the chlorophyll and carotenoids during the period of adjustment to changes of light intensity.

Table 2. *Chlorophyll-carotenoid ratios in* Rhodopseudomonas spheroides *grown anaerobically at different light intensities*

Light intensity (foot-candles)	$\dfrac{\text{Chlorophyll}}{\text{Carotenoid}}$ ratio	
	Weight	Molar (approximate)
200	5·35	3·24
230	4·85	2·93
450	3·94	2·38
860	3·84	2·32
2000	3·60	2·18

Even in the presence of light, air completely inhibits chlorophyll synthesis, and almost completely inhibits carotenoid synthesis. Consequently, when a culture which is growing exponentially under photosynthetic conditions is suddenly exposed to air, a regular dilution of the pigment system occurs. After two or three generations of such aerobic growth, the cells lose almost completely the capacity for photosynthetic growth, even when they have been continuously illuminated. When placed once more in anaerobiosis and light, such populations go into lag, the duration and severity of which are governed primarily by the degree to which the photosynthetic pigment system has been attenuated through preceding aerobic growth. Recovery from this lag is brought about by a resynthesis of the photosynthetic pigment system, which at first occurs virtually without any general cellular growth; the differential rate of pigment synthesis under these special conditions approaches infinity.

The powerlessness of light to prevent the inhibition of pigment synthesis by oxygen was somewhat unexpected, since it had been shown previously (van Niel, 1944; Clayton, 1955) that, with resting cells, photosynthesis proceeds more rapidly than respiration when light and air are simultaneously present. Indeed, respiration is almost quantitatively suppressed by light in *Rhodospirillum rubrum*.

Other environmental factors also profoundly influence the differential rate of pigment synthesis: the chemical nature of the organic hydrogen donor, the concentration of carbon dioxide and the temperature. These observations show that the purple bacteria possess a regulatory mechanism which controls the rate of pigment synthesis, and responds with remarkable sensitivity to many different kinds of environmental change. What is the mechanism of this regulation? A comparison of the effects of light and oxygen provided us with the first clue to its nature.

In non-sulphur purple bacteria, the electrons from the organic hydrogen donor are carried through the transport system to one of two alternate final acceptors: oxygen, or the OH radicals derived from the primary photochemical reaction of photosynthesis. The general features of intermediary metabolism in this group are shown diagrammatically in Fig. 12. The steady-state level of oxidation of the whole carrier system is governed by two factors: the flux of electron from the organic donor,

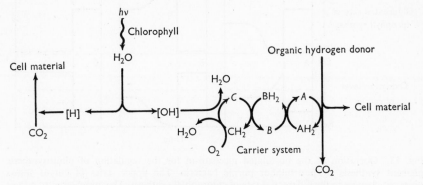

Fig. 12. A diagrammatic representation of the metabolism of non-sulphur purple bacteria.

and the rate at which they are removed by reaction with the two alternate final acceptors. It follows, therefore, that with any given donor, the level of oxidation of the carrier system is controlled solely by the availability of the final acceptors, i.e. by the net rate of generation of OH radicals through the primary photochemical reaction of photosynthesis, and by the presence or absence of oxygen. The effects of light and air on the differential rate of chlorophyll and carotenoid synthesis can be completely and simply explained by the assumption that the regulatory factor is the level of oxidation of some component of the carrier system. When this carrier is highly reduced, pigment synthesis proceeds at a high differential rate; as the carrier becomes more oxidized, the rate of pigment synthesis diminishes, eventually becoming zero at some critical level of oxidation of the carrier.

Let us consider how this hypothesis fits the observations on the effects of light and air. It is evident that under anaerobic conditions the rate of the primary photochemical reaction, which is directly governed by light intensity, will determine the rate at which the carrier system can be re-oxidized, and hence its steady-state oxidation level under steady-state conditions of growth. When light intensity is suddenly increased, the oxidation level of the carrier system must rise abruptly, and if this rise is sufficiently great, pigment synthesis must cease. However, the cells are growing, and hence the cessation of pigment synthesis results in a decrease in the amount of pigment per cell. As a result, the oxidation level of the carrier system immediately begins to fall again, and

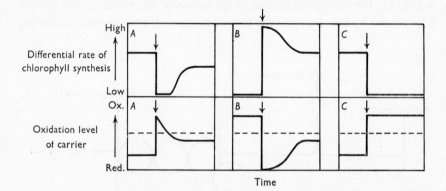

Fig. 13. Operation of the postulated mechanism for the regulation of photosynthetic pigment synthesis by non-sulphur purple bacteria. The upper series of curves shows observed changes in the differential rate of chlorophyll synthesis. The lower series of curves shows changes in the oxidation level of the regulatory carrier, inferred from the known mechanisms of metabolism (Fig. 12). The dotted horizontal line on the lower graph designates the oxidation level of the carrier above which chlorophyll synthesis is totally arrested. A, the effect of a sudden increase of light intensity (arrow) on cells growing anaerobically in the light. B, the effect of imposing anaerobiosis (arrow) on bleached cells, growing aerobically in the light. C, the effect of exposure to air (arrow) on cells growing anaerobically in the light.

eventually reaches the critical level at which pigment synthesis can resume. The resumption of pigment synthesis puts a brake on the decline in the oxidation level of the carrier system, and eventually an equilibrium is re-established at a new steady-state level (Fig. 13). The extremely high differential rate of pigment synthesis observed when bleached cultures are placed under anaerobic conditions in the light fits perfectly. In this situation, the whole carrier system must be thrown into a state of extreme reduction, since the only possibility for re-oxidation is through the photosynthetic generation of OH radicals, and this reaction initially proceeds at a negligible rate, owing to the depletion of the photosynthetic pigment system (Fig. 13).

The inhibition of pigment synthesis by air can be explained on the assumption that when oxygen is available in amounts sufficient to saturate the terminal dark oxidase, the steady-state level of the carrier system is above that at which pigment synthesis can occur; obviously, light is powerless to counteract this situation and can, in fact, only aggravate it. Thus the effect of oxygen is an irreversible one, as long as the oxygen tension remains sufficiently high to saturate the terminal oxidase (Fig. 13). The hypothesis predicts that at very low oxygen tensions, when the terminal dark oxidase is no longer saturated, the oxidation level of the carrier system should fall to a point at which photosynthetic pigment synthesis can be resumed, *even in the dark*. The experimental difficulties have so far prevented a kinetic study of this situation, but qualitative observations show that the prediction is fulfilled; cultures grown in the dark under semi-anaerobic conditions (e.g. liquid cultures where the rate of oxygen diffusion limits growth) can synthesize appreciable amounts of chlorophyll and carotenoids. Although we have considered here only the effects of light and air on pigment synthesis, the effects of temperature, carbon dioxide and the nature of the hydrogen donor also find a ready explanation in terms of the hypothesis outlined above.

The mechanism employed by the purple bacteria to regulate their content of photosynthetic pigments has an obvious adaptive value, particularly in so far as the response to light intensity is concerned. It is clearly advantageous for a photosynthetic organism to increase its pigment content when growing in dim light, since under natural conditions light intensity is probably the environmental factor which most frequently limits the growth rate. Under laboratory conditions, the regulatory mechanism operates non-adaptively in suppressing pigment synthesis in the simultaneous presence of light and air; but this is a combination of environmental factors which occurs only very rarely in nature, where the purple bacteria exist almost exclusively in anaerobic ecological niches. The increase in the content of carotenoids relative to that of chlorophyll which occurs at high light intensities can be considered to possess adaptive value, if our concept of carotenoid function in phototrophs is correct.

The relations between photosynthesis and phototaxis

Space does not permit a thorough analysis of the problem of photo-taxis, but a few aspects of this subject demand brief discussion, on account of their ecological and evolutionary interest.

6-2

Probably all motile phototrophic micro-organisms are capable of directed movement with respect to light. The microbial phototrophs so far studied fall into two entirely distinct groups on the basis of the phototactic mechanisms. The first group consists of the purple bacteria, and possibly also the blue-green algae; the second group consists of the other motile algae.

We shall consider the purple bacteria as representatives of the first group. These organisms respond only to changes of light *intensity*, and are incapable of perceiving the *direction* of a light source. Their phototactic response consists of a sudden complete reversal of the direction of movement ('Schreckbewegung') when the light intensity is abruptly decreased. This may be demonstrated by a very simple experiment: if one is observing a wet mount of motile purple bacteria under the microscope, and the illumination is suddenly and momentarily cut off, every motile cell in the field reverses the direction of its movement. In consequence, a local area of high light intensity acts as a light trap; once the cells have entered it, by purely random movement, they are prevented from leaving again by the 'Schreckbewegungen' which take place every time they approach the darker peripheral regions. Since phototaxis in purple bacteria is essentially effected by a phobic movement when a diminution of light intensity is experienced, they are incapable of a negative phototactic response to very high light intensities.

It was shown long ago by simple spectrophotometric methods (Engelmann, 1883*b*, 1888; Buder, 1919) that the purple bacteria accumulate in wavelengths of light which are absorbed by both chlorophyll and carotenoids. Recent measurements of phototactic action spectra on *Rhodospirillum rubrum* (Manten, 1948; Clayton, 1953*a*) have fully confirmed the activity of both chlorophyll and carotenoids in inducing phototaxis, and have shown furthermore that the intensity of the tactic response is closely proportional to the intensity of light absorption by the cell. There is still some uncertainty about the exact shape of the action spectrum in the region of carotenoid absorption. This is probably the result of variations in the growth conditions, which have been shown (Goodwin & Sissins, 1955) markedly to affect the composition of the carotenoid pigments in *R. rubrum*. Since it is known (Thomas, 1950; Thomas & Goedheer, 1953; Clayton, 1953*a*) that the carotenoids as well as the chlorophyll are photosynthetically effective in *R. rubrum*, it is tempting to conclude that the tactic response of purple bacteria is mediated by a sudden diminution in the rate of photosynthesis. This hypothesis was proposed by Manten (1948), and has been supported, on the basis of much additional experimental evidence, by Clayton (1953 *a*, *b*, *c*, 1955).

In purple bacteria, therefore, there is a very intimate connexion between photosynthesis and phototaxis, the kinetic response being induced through light absorption by the photosynthetic pigment system. Since Engelmann (1882) observed that certain blue-green algae also showed phototactic accumulations in wavelengths of light that are absorbed by their chlorophyll, it seems probable that they possess the same mechanism for responding kinetically to light; to the best of our knowledge, however, this problem has not been re-examined since the time of Engelmann. Curiously enough, the ciliate *Paramecium bursaria*, which contains endosymbiotic green algae, also falls into the same class. Engelmann (1882) observed that under aerobic conditions *P. bursaria* is unresponsive to light; but under conditions of oxygen limitation it accumulates in the spectral regions of maximal light absorption by the chlorophyll of its endosymbionts. This is, of course, a pseudophototactic response; the paramecia are really responding to an internal oxygen gradient, rather than to the customary external one. These very pretty observations explain the physiological basis of the symbiotic relationship. The phototaxis of *P. bursaria* also provides a rather simple model of the mechanism which probably underlies the phototaxis of purple bacteria, where an internal, photosynthetically conditioned, chemical gradient of unknown nature must be postulated.

The second mechanism of phototaxis characterizes the flagellate algae and the diatoms. It has been principally studied in algal flagellates which possess carotenoid-rich eyespots, such as *Euglena* and *Chlamydomonas*. These organisms are wholly unresponsive to light of wavelengths absorbed by their chlorophyll, and all action spectra for phototaxis so far determined resemble in shape the absorption spectra of carotenoids. It seems very probable that in organisms which possess eyespots, only light absorbed by the pigment of the eyespot can initiate the phototactic response. The diatoms, however, show a generally similar type of phototactic behaviour (Nultsch, 1956), and consequently this kind of phototaxis is not *obligatorily* connected with the possession of an eyespot.

The nature of the phototactic response by flagellate algae and diatoms is by no means so simple as that shown by purple bacteria. In the first place, these organisms can perceive and orient themselves with respect to the *direction* of a light source (topotaxis). In the second place, they show a reversal of tactic response as light intensity is increased, moving away from regions of very high light intensity.

The ineffectiveness of light absorbed by chlorophyll for the induction of phototaxis in these organisms shows at once that the kinetic response cannot be mediated by photosynthesis, but is, rather, completely independent of it. At first sight, this separation of the photosynthetic and phototactic reaction systems may seem less advantageous than the coupled reaction system of the purple bacteria. In fact, however, it has made possible a far more efficient response mechanism, as shown by the fact that orientation can occur with respect to the direction of the light. Furthermore, the dissociation of the kinetic response from changes in the rate of over-all metabolism appears to have made it possible to operate the system in such a way as to provide for a reversal of phototaxis at high light intensities. Lastly, the sensitivity of the response has been enormously increased. Manten (1948) estimates that in *Rhodospirillum rubrum* the lower limit of light intensity for phototaxis lies at a level some 10,000 times as great as that for phototaxis by *Eudorina elegans*, a colonial flagellate alga.

The one advantage of the system which operates in purple bacteria is that it permits a response directly proportional to the effectiveness of the light for photosynthesis. Since, as we have previously explained, the photosynthetic bacteria frequently live under a biological light filter, this is a very solid advantage for them. For algal flagellates, however, it would be of minor value, since these organisms are generally exposed to the complete solar spectrum.

In the last analysis, the different mechanisms of response to light which characterize the photosynthetic bacteria and the algae may well be the consequence of the fundamental differences between these two groups with respect to cell structure and organization. The bacteria, which lack the cytoplasmic differentiation characteristic of higher groups (Stanier, 1954; Bradfield, 1956), may have been incapable of evolving a more specialized phototactic mechanism for purely structural reasons. A re-examination of the mechanism of phototaxis in blue-green algae would be of great interest in this connexion, since they are the only other group of living organisms which possess cells on the level of organization of the bacterial cell.

CAROTENOID FUNCTION IN CHEMOTROPHIC MICRO-ORGANISMS

In chemotrophic micro-organisms, the carotenoid pigments are the only cellular pigments which appear to mediate in photochemical reactions. Carotenoid-mediated phototropism is not uncommon in fungi, being particularly characteristic of those species which forcibly eject their spores. In these cases it has an obvious adaptive value, since it permits spores to be shot in a direction where they are likely to encounter minimal obstruction during their trajectory. The most elegant and elaborate phototropic mechanism among fungi is that of *Pilobolus*, which was exhaustively and brilliantly investigated by the great Canadian mycologist, Buller. His account (Buller, 1934) can be read with pleasure by every biologist; unfortunately, space does not permit a recapitulation here of this very beautiful work.

In many carotenoid-containing bacteria and fungi, no function for these pigments has yet been demonstrated. One possible function is suggested by our observations on the blue-green mutant of *Rhodopseudomonas spheroides*. It is conceivable that also in chemotrophic organisms, the carotenoids may serve to protect the cell from the consequences of incidental light absorption by cellular pigments which can catalyse photo-oxidations, such as the iron porphyrins. A number of otherwise unintelligible observations on the carotenoids of fungi and bacteria take on adaptive significance when viewed in this light. In both fungi (summarized by Goodwin, 1952) and mycobacteria (Baker, 1938), carotenogenesis is often greatly stimulated by exposure to light. Fungal spores, which are exposed to intense solar radiation as a consequence of their aerial distribution, frequently have a very high carotenoid content; the same thing is, of course, true of the bacteria (micrococci and sarcinae) most commonly found in the air. Lastly, it may be noted that in chemotrophic bacteria there is a very good negative correlation between the presence of carotenoids in the cell and the anaerobic mode of life; these pigments are rarely found in strict anaerobes, apart from the photo-synthetic bacteria. A direct demonstration that carotenoids can protect chemotrophs from photo-oxidative damage caused by other cellular pigments that absorb visible light remains to be made, however.

REFERENCES

BAKER, J. A. (1938). Light as a factor in the production of pigment by certain bacteria. *J. Bact.* **35**, 625.

BERNAL, J. D. (1954). The origin of life. *New Biol.* **16**, 28.

BIEBL, R. (1956). Lichtresistenz von Meeresalgen. *Protoplasma,* **44**, 63.

BLINKS, L. R. (1954). The role of accessory pigments in photosynthesis. *Autotrophic Micro-organisms. Fourth Symp. Soc. gen. Microbiol.* p. 224.

BLUM, H. F. (1941). *Photodynamic Action and Diseases Caused by Light.* New York: Reinhold.

BRADFIELD, J. R. G. (1956). Organization of bacterial cytoplasm. *Bacterial Anatomy. Sixth Symp. Soc. gen. Microbiol.* p. 296.

BRIGGS, R. (1952). Analysis of the inactivation of the frog-sperm nucleus by toluidine blue. *J. gen. Physiol.* **35**, 761.

BUDER, J. (1919). Zur Biologie des Bakteriopurpurins und der Purpurbakterien. *Jb. wiss. Bot.* **58**, 525.

BULLER, A. H. R. (1934). *Researches on Fungi*, vol. **6**. London: Longmans, Green.

BÜNNING, E. (1953). *Entwicklungs- und Bewegungsphysiologie der Pflanze*, 3rd ed. Berlin: Springer.

CLAES, H. (1954). Analyse der biochemischen Synthesekette für Carotinoide mit Hilfe von *Chlorella*-Mutanten. *Z. Naturf.* **9**b, 461.

CLARE, N. T. (1956). Photodynamic action and its pathological effects. In *Radiation Biology*, vol. **3**. New York: McGraw-Hill.

CLAYTON, R. K. (1953a). Studies in the phototaxis of *Rhodospirillum rubrum*. I. Action spectrum, growth in green light and Weber Law adherence. *Arch. Mikrobiol.* **19**, 107.

CLAYTON, R. K. (1953b). Studies in the phototaxis of *Rhodospirillum rubrum*. II. The relation between phototaxis and photosynthesis. *Arch. Mikrobiol.* **19**, 125.

CLAYTON, R. K. (1953c). Studies in the phototaxis of *Rhodospirillum rubrum*. III. Quantitative relations between stimulus and response. *Arch. Mikrobiol.* **19**, 141.

CLAYTON, R. K. (1955). Tactic responses and metabolic activities in *Rhodospirillum rubrum*. *Arch. Mikrobiol.* **22**, 204.

COHEN-BAZIRE, G., SISTROM, W. R. & STANIER, R. Y. (1956). Kinetic studies of pigment synthesis by non-sulfur purple bacteria. *J. cell. comp. Physiol.* (in the Press).

DUYSENS, L. N. M. (1952). Transfer of excitation energy in photosynthesis. Dissertation, Utrecht, Kemink.

ENGELMANN, T. W. (1882). Ueber Licht- und Farbenperception niederster Organismen. *Pflüg. Arch. ges. Physiol.* **29**, 387.

ENGELMANN, T. W. (1883a). Farbe und Assimilation. *Bot. Ztg*, **41**, 1, 17.

ENGELMANN, T. W. (1883b). *Bacterium photometricum*. Ein Beitrag zur vergleichenden Physiologie des Licht- und Farbensinnes. *Pflüg. Arch. ges. Physiol.* **30**, 95.

ENGELMANN, T. W. (1884). Untersuchungen über die quantitativen Beziehungen zwischen Absorption des Lichtes und Assimilation in Pflanzenzellen. *Bot. Ztg*, **42**, 81, 87.

ENGELMANN, T. W. (1888). Die Purpurbacterien und ihre Beziehungen zum Licht. *Bot. Ztg.* **46**, 661, 677, 693, 709.

GOODWIN, T. W. (1952). *The Comparative Biochemistry of the Carotenoids*. London: Chapman and Hall.

GOODWIN, T. W. (1955). Bacteriochlorophyll and *Chlorobium* chlorophyll. *Biochim. biophys. Acta*, **18**, 309.

GOODWIN, T. W. & SISSINS, M. E. (1955). Changes in carotenoid synthesis in *Rhodospirillum rubrum* during growth. *Biochem. J.* **61**, xiii.

GRANICK, S. (1951). Biosynthesis of chlorophyll and related pigments. *Annu. Rev. Pl. Physiol.* **2**, 115.

GRANICK, S. (1954). Metabolism of heme and chlorophyll. In *Chemical Pathways of Metabolism*. New York: Academic Press.

GRIFFIN, D. R., HUBBARD, R. & WALD, G. (1947). The sensitivity of the human eye to infra-red radiation. *J. opt. Soc. Amer.* **37**, 546.

GRIFFITHS, M., SISTROM, W. R., COHEN-BAZIRE, G. & STANIER, R. Y. (1955). Function of carotenoids in photosynthesis. *Nature, Lond.*, **176**, 1211.

GRIFFITHS, M. & STANIER, R. Y. (1956). Some mutational changes in the photosynthetic pigment system of *Rhodopseudomonas spheroides*. *J. gen. Microbiol.* **14**, 698.

HALDANE, J. B. S. (1954). The origins of life. *New Biol.* **16**, 12.

HAXO, F. & BLINKS, L. R. (1950). Photosynthetic action spectra of marine algae. *J. gen. Physiol.* **33**, 389.

KAPLAN, R. W. (1956). Dose-effect curves of s-mutation and killing in *Serratia marcescens. Arch. Mikrobiol.* **24**, 60.

KOSKI, V. M. & SMITH, T. H. C. (1951). Chlorophyll formation in a mutant, White Seedling—3. *Arch. Biochem. Biophys.* **34**, 189.

LARSEN, H. (1953). On the microbiology and biochemistry of the photosynthetic green sulfur bacteria. *K. norske vidensk. Selsk. Skr.* **1**. Trondheim: Brun.

MANTEN, A. (1948). Phototaxis, phototropism and photosynthesis in purple bacteria and blue-green algae. Dissertation, Utrecht, Schotanus and Jens.

MONTFORT, C. (1953). Photochemische Wirkungen der langwelligen Hälfte des Sonnenspektrums auf Chlorophyllspiegel und Lebenszustand. *Ber. dtsch. bot. Ges.* **66**, 183.

MOON, P. (1940). Proposed standard solar-radiation curves for engineering use. *J. Franklin Inst.* **230**, 583.

VAN NIEL, C. B. (1944). The culture, general physiology, morphology and classification of the non-sulfur purple and brown bacteria. *Bact. Rev.* **8**, 1.

VAN NIEL, C. B. (1949). The comparative biochemistry of photosynthesis. In *Photosynthesis in Plants*. Ames: Iowa State College Press.

NULTSCH, W. (1956). Studien über die Phototaxis der Diatomeen. *Arch. Protistenk.* **101**, 1.

SHIBATA, K., BENSON, A. A. & CALVIN, M. (1954). The absorption spectra of suspensions of living micro-organisms. *Biochim. biophys. Acta*, **15**, 461.

SISTROM, W. R., GRIFFITHS, M. & STANIER, R. Y. (1956a). The biology of a photosynthetic bacterium which lacks colored carotenoids. *J. cell. comp. Physiol.* (in the Press).

SISTROM, W. R., GRIFFITHS, M. & STANIER, R. Y. (1956b). A note on the porphyrins excreted by the blue-green mutant of *Rhodopseudomonas spheroides. J. cell. comp. Physiol.* (in the Press).

SMITH, J. H. C. & BENITEZ, A. (1954). Absorption spectra of chlorophylls. *Yearb. Carneg. Inst.* **53**, 168.

STANIER, R. Y. (1954). Some singular features of bacteria as dynamic systems. In *Cellular Metabolism and Infections*. New York: Academic Press.

STOPPANI, A. O. M., FULLER, R. C. & CALVIN, M. (1955). Carbon dioxide fixation by *Rhodopseudomonas capsulatus. J. Bact.* **69**, 491.

THOMAS, J. B. (1950). On the role of carotenoids in photosynthesis in *Rhodospirillum rubrum. Biochim. biophys. Acta*, **5**, 186.

THOMAS, J. B. & GOEDHEER, J. C. (1953). Relative efficiency of light absorbed by carotenoids in photosynthesis and phototaxis of *Rhodospirillum rubrum. Biochim. biophys. Acta*, **10**, 385.

WALD, G. (1951). The chemistry of rod vision. *Science*, **113**, 287.

WALLACE, R. H. & SCHWARTING, A. E. (1954). A study of chlorophyll in a white mutant strain of *Helianthus annuus. Plant Physiol.* **29**, 431.

MICRO-ORGANISMS RESISTING HIGH CON-
CENTRATIONS OF SUGARS OR SALTS

M. INGRAM

*Low Temperature Station for Research in Biochemistry and
Biophysics, University of Cambridge, and Department
of Scientific and Industrial Research*

GENERAL PRINCIPLES

To introduce the subject of environments of high solute concentration,
it is desirable to give a brief statement of the physical-chemical basis on
which their effects can be measured, because some knowledge of this
must be assumed in discussing such a subject.

The effects of concentration of dissolved substances have commonly
been interpreted in terms of osmotic pressure. Because osmotic pressure
and related properties depend on the molecular concentration of the
solute, due allowance must be made in comparing the effects of different
solutes at a given 'percentage' concentration; for example, it will at
once appear that growth in a saturated sucrose solution is under less
extreme osmotic conditions than in saturated sodium chloride solution,
although the apparent concentration of the former is much the higher.

From the theoretical viewpoint, it is better to express concentration in
terms of molality (moles per 1000 g. of solvent), rather than as molarity
(moles per 1000 c.c. of solution—M) which changes with temperature,
so that fundamental data are usually expressed in molal units. The
difference is not very important biologically with dilute solutions, but
it becomes serious with concentrated solutions. For example, a solution
containing 700 g. (2·04 g.moles) of sucrose per 1000 g. i.e. 6·80 molal,
has a density of 1·344 g./c.c. at 25° C. and is 2·73 molar at that temperature. Thus, to transform molality data into molarity, the densities of
the solutions at the relevant concentrations and temperatures must be
known.

As there have been few determinations of osmotic pressure in concentrated solutions, especially for salts, it is frequently necessary to
calculate them from more accessible data, usually from the vapour
pressures of the solutions by means of the approximate equation

$$P = -\frac{1}{V} RT \ln \frac{p}{p_0}$$

(where P is the osmotic pressure, R the gas constant, T absolute temperature, p_0 and p the vapour pressures of the water and the solution respectively, and V is the partial molal volume of water in the solution). For aqueous solutions, the fraction p/p_0 represents the 'activity' of the water (a_w); Table 1 gives some values of this function for several solutes. The aqueous activity is numerically equal to the relative humidity (not expressed as percentage) of the atmosphere with which the solution is in equilibrium: the so-called 'equilibrium relative humidity'. High osmotic pressures, in an experimental system, are most simply controlled by bringing the system into equilibrium with one of known relative humidity. Solutions suitable for maintaining atmospheres of fixed relative humidity were tabulated by O'Brien (1948). The principles underlying the relations between osmotic pressure and aqueous activity (a_w), and the use of aqueous activity to interpret microbiological phenomena, have recently been reviewed by Scott (1956). These principles provide a coherent basis for comparing the effects of different concentrations of sugar, or of salts, with those of drying, and give quantitative expression to the classical concept of 'physiological dryness' or 'Hydratur' (Walter, 1931).

Table 1. *Molalities of some solutes for various values of aqueous activity* (a_w) *at* 25° C.

Compiled from figures of Scott (1956) and of Christian (unpublished)

a_w	NaCl	KCl	CaCl$_2$	Na$_2$SO$_4$	Glucose	Sucrose	Glycerol
0·98	0·61	0·61	0·42	0·58	1·12	1·03	1·11
0·95	1·48	1·55	0·92	1·50	2·65	2·31	2·76
0·90	2·83	3·08	1·58	2·94	5·10	4·11	5·57
0·85	4·03	4·60	2·12	4·08	—	5·98	8·47
0·80	5·15	—	2·58	—	—	—	11·5
0·75	—	—	3·00	—	—	—	14·8
0·70	—	—	3·40	—	—	—	18·3
0·65	—	—	3·80	—	—	—	22·0

Interpretation in osmotic terms might be taken to imply that the cell boundary behaves as an ideal semi-permeable membrane. This is not true, above all for the halophilic bacteria where, as will be shown, large concentrations of solutes enter the cell and there is a marked selection between different ions.

DISTRIBUTION OF OSMOPHILIC AND HALOPHILIC ORGANISMS

As organisms resisting high concentrations of sugar and salts, one habitually thinks of the osmophilic yeasts and the halophilic bacteria; although, in fact, not all sugar-resistant organisms are yeasts nor all salt-resistant organisms bacteria, and resistance to high solute concentrations is manifested among quite different groups of organisms. The tendency to think in the above terms is due to the point of view from which such organisms have traditionally been investigated, primarily because they cause spoilage in materials commercially preserved by drying, sugaring or salting. Notable examples of such spoilage are the fermentation of dried fruits or concentrated fruit juices, of honey or maple syrup, and of sugar preserves (reviewed by Mrak & Phaff, 1948; Schelhorn, 1951; Mossel & Ingram, 1955), or the 'reddening' or 'rusting' of salted hides, meat, or fish (Stuart, Frey & James, 1933; Lochhead, 1934; Horowitz-Wlassowa, 1931 *a, b*; Schoop, 1934, 1937; Penso, 1947; Dussault & Lachance, 1952; Venkataraman & Sreenivasan, 1954). The sugary substrates are spoiled by yeasts and the salted materials by bacteria, for reasons chiefly other than the nature of the predominant solute, especially because the first group of products is more or less acid, while fish, meat and hides are not; nevertheless, the association of ideas persists. The conditions in these commercial operations are of course unnatural, but the behaviour of such organisms in nature has been comparatively little investigated, except in its possible bearing on the origin of outbreaks of spoilage (Flannery, 1956).

Sugar-tolerant organisms

The classical location for the osmophilic yeasts is in floral nectaries. They have been found in the nectaries of nearly all flowers examined, being apparently much more widely distributed there than non-osmophilic yeasts (Lochhead & Heron, 1929); doubtless because the sugar concentration of nectars often exceeds 40 %, bees having a preference for nectars of high concentration. These yeasts are probably carried to the flowers by the bees. The writer has found osmophilic yeasts on every one of a large number of bees examined, in different parts of Europe. Further, when a particular examination was made of citrus flowers for osmophilic yeasts likely to ferment concentrated citrus juices, it was found that the nectaries are virtually sterile before the flower opens, and that the number of osmophilic yeasts rises rapidly thereafter, as the flowers are visited by bees. The bees must carry such yeasts back to their hives, where the nectar in varying degrees of concentration to honey provides a suitable and lasting home for osmophilic yeasts, which the insects presumably then distribute wherever they range. Provided that high-sugar media are employed, there is no difficulty in isolating osmophilic yeasts from honey in the comb, despite statements that it is sterile

(Sackett, 1919). Lochhead & Heron (1929) found, indeed, that of eleven types of osmophilic yeast isolated from flowers, three were present among four types isolated from hive nectar and, of these three, two were identical with two out of four types isolated from fermented honey.

Osmophilic yeasts occur commonly on the surface of fresh fruits, where they are perhaps planted by chance contact with insects, but the numbers are usually small and variable. On the other hand, there are large numbers in that part of the fruit corresponding to the original position of the floral nectary. The heavy surface infections of dried fruits must seemingly be ascribed to some secondary spread of infection.

More recently, Scarr (1951) has traced the origin of the osmophilic yeasts found in raw sugar back to the original sugar-cane plant. This is grass-like, and the leaves tend to split longitudinally at the sheathing base, allowing the entry of yeasts which proliferate in the internal spaces. Fabian & Hall (1933) described similar yeasts occurring in and fermenting maple syrup, with concentration around 65 % w/w, but gave no indication of the mode of infection. In such cases, too, it seems likely that the yeasts might be spread by nectarophilous insects—bees, wasps, ants or flies, but the detailed investigations of the yeasts carried by *Drosophila* fruit flies have not yet indicated the sugar relations of the species isolated (Phaff, Miller & Shifrine, 1956).

Elsewhere, the occurrence of osmophilic yeasts is sparse, and seems to be related to sugar-rich localities. Lochhead & Farrell (1930) found them only in the soil of apiaries, increasing in frequency with the age of the apiary; I have found them in numbers of the order of 1/g. in the surface soil of citrus plantations. Lochhead & Farrell showed that they must survive freezing in soil. They also occur, but infrequently, in the air of citrus plantations and of citrus processing factories; and Lochhead & Heron (1929) found them in the air of honey-extracting houses.

The yeasts resisting the highest sugar concentrations seem to belong to the subgenus *Zygosaccharomyces*. Kroemer & Krumbholz (1931) divided the osmophilic *Zygosaccharomyces* into two groups: (i) related to *Z. priorianus*, resisting the highest concentrations, of the disaccharides fermenting only maltose weakly (but sucrose if the cells are disintegrated), and producing little volatile acid; (ii) related to *Z. nadsonii*, less sugar-resistant, fermenting not maltose but sucrose and raffinose, producing much volatile acid—type *Z. globiformis*. Schelhorn (1950a) has since reported growth of a strain of *Z. priorianus* down to an a_w of 0·62, and Schachinger & Heiss (1951) present similar data. The *Z. acidifaciens* described by Nickerson (1943) seems to fall in the second group. These species also possess an unusual resistance to acidity (Recca &

Mrak, 1952), and grow optimally about pH 4·5. Slightly less sugar-resistant are strains of *Hansenula anomala* and *Saccharomyces elegans* (Scarr, 1954).

The organisms growing on sugar-rich substrates are not all yeasts. Scarr (1951) reports the presence of Aspergilli of the *glaucus* group in raw cane sugar; and Fellers (1933) mentioned the inversion of maple sugar, containing 5–12 % moisture, by unidentified moulds principally Aspergilli. The resistance of *Aspergillus glaucus* to low aqueous activities was demonstrated by Stille (1948) and that to equivalent high sugar concentrations by Schelhorn (1951). Several other sugar-resistant fungi are mentioned by Kroemer & Krumbholz (1931). Bacteria, however, do not usually multiply in substrates with sugar concentrations above about 50 %; though spores, e.g. of thermophiles, may survive (Whalley & Scarr, 1947).

Salt-tolerant organisms

The halophilic organisms on salted products probably come primarily from the salt itself, as similar bacteria have been isolated from salt by many workers. It is general experience that the crude solar salt which is often used, prepared by the evaporation of naturally occurring salt water in hot dry climates, is heavily infected, wheres mined or refined salts are virtually free from such bacteria (Harrison & Kennedy, 1922; Cobb, 1927; Stuart *et al.* 1933), though there have been different opinions (Müller, 1950).

These observations have led to the demonstration of the organisms in the brine and its surroundings. For instance, Petrowa (1933) compared the flora of the waters of several 'seas' with that of the commercial salts prepared from them, and found sufficient correlation to conclude that the sea brine was the source of the organisms in the salt. Smith & ZoBell (1937) detected an autochthonous salt-tolerant bacterial flora in the water of Great Salt Lake, and Elazari-Volcani (1940) in the Dead Sea. Numerous other workers have isolated very salt-tolerant organisms from the mud of salt waters; Hof (1935) reviewed such work and added to it, emphasizing the wide variety of salt-tolerant types found. This has included various sulphur, nitrifying, denitrifying, urea-, protein-, fat- and cellulose-decomposing bacteria, to which chitinovorous types may be added (J. M. Shewan, personal communication). A similar variety of types was recovered from the water of the Dead Sea (Elazari-Volcani, 1940).

In water, the red halophilic bacteria lose their viability especially rapidly at high temperature and low pH (Castell & Mapplebeck, 1952).

Nevertheless, Stuart (1938) has claimed that halophilic bacteria can be isolated from ordinary sources like water, soil and dung, provided that the materials are enriched in a medium with 25 % NaCl and incubated for very long periods (up to 90 days); and Hof (1935) quotes similar experiences. It seems that such organisms are widely distributed, though probably in small numbers except in saline environments. Statistical information is scanty through lack of suitable procedures for enumeration. Moore (1940, 1941) and Dussault (1954) have described plating techniques claimed to be suitable if the numbers are fairly large; and if otherwise a dilution count procedure has been suggested; in either case, strongly saline dilution fluids and media of special composition are essential.

The salt-tolerant organisms are by no means all bacteria. The green blooms of salt waters are caused by flagellates and algae (Elazari-Volcani, 1940), especially species of *Dunaliella*, some of which tolerate very high concentrations (Lerche, 1937). The 'dun' of salt fish is caused by a budding fungus *Sporendonema epizoum* (Torula epizoa), and other fungi also occur (Klebahn, 1919; Pjetursson & Damm, 1935; Malevich, 1936; Schoop, 1937; Frank & Hess, 1941). Salted meats, and various curing brines, contain yeasts, especially strains of *Debaryomyces membranaefaciens* and *D. guilliermondii* (Hof, 1935; Mrak & Bonar, 1938; Etchells, Bell & Jones, 1953). The ability to tolerate high salt concentrations clearly occurs in a wide diversity of organisms, and hence seems unlikely to be linked to a special type of metabolism.

RELATIONS TO CONCENTRATIONS

Whether in relation to sugars or salts, one can broadly separate three types of reaction, the intolerant, the facultative, and the obligate. In each there may be differences of degree, as illustrated schematically in Fig. 1, and organisms have been found which correspond with most of the possibilities in Fig. 1; some are listed in Table 2. But it will be evident that, at least conceivably, there might be imperceptible gradations between the different types of reaction—for example, IC could approach IIA and B, and IIC could approach IIIA or B; many more organisms will have to be examined before it becomes clear whether these types of behaviour really are distinct.

Though it is easy to object to loose employment of the words osmophilic and halophilic to describe such a diversity of behaviour, there has been disagreement over more detailed terminology. And, underlying the terminological disagreement, there are of course fundamental

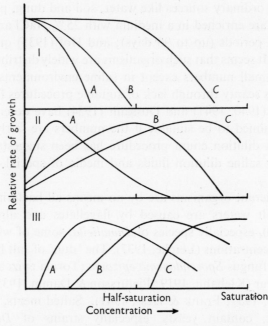

Fig. 1. Idealized patterns of response to different concentrations of sugars or salts:
I, the intolerant; II, the facultative; III, the obligate.

Table 2. *Examples of organisms with different degrees of tolerance to high concentrations of sugar or salt*

Type	Sugar	Salt
I A intolerant, strongly	*Pichia* spp. (1)	{Coliform bacteria (4) {Pseudomonads (4)
B intolerant, moderately	*Sacch. cerevisiae* (2)	Staphylococci (6)
C intolerant, slightly	?	Urobacillus XII (5)
II A facultative, low optimum	normal organisms	{Flavobacterium XVIII {*Bacillus* spp. (4)
B facultative, moderate optimum	*Sacch. stellatus* (3)	Urobacterium XXIV (5)
C facultative, high optimum	*Zygos. polymorphus* (3)	Micrococci (4)
III A obligate, weakly	?	*Vibrio costicolus* (7)
B obligate, moderately	*Zygos. nussbaumeri* (2)	{Colourless halophiles (4) {*Bacterioides halosmophilus* (4)
C obligate, strongly	*Zygos. richteri* (2)	Red halophiles

References: (1) Scarr (1954).
(2) Lochhead & Heron (1929); Scarr (1954).
(3) Kroemer & Krumbholz (1931).
(4) Shewan (1942)

(5) Hof (1935).
(6) Scott (1953).
(7) Christian (1956).

questions: are the behaviour groups in reality distinct and, if so, what is the physiological basis of the distinctions?

In relation to salt-tolerance, for example, Schoop (1934) suggested the following terms: for organisms not growing in high salt concentrations—non-halophilic; organisms growing only in high salt concentrations—obligately halophilic; those growing in high or low concentrations —facultatively halophilic. Rubentschick (1929) used different terms: halophiles—organisms with optimum growth at a comparatively high salt concentration; halotolerant—those growing better at low concentrations than at high; obligate halophiles—those unable to grow in the absence of salt. Horowitz-Wlassowa (1931a) held that the phrase 'obligate halophile' is inherently illogical, and coined the term halobe for this type of organism, retaining halophile for the facultative type. Shewan (1942) followed Schoop, except that salt-intolerant organisms were called halophobic. It will appear, on consideration of Fig. 1, that in distinguishing the different types of behaviour a great deal depends on that at low salt concentrations; for such reasons, Golikowa (1930a) restricted the term halophile to organisms unable to grow in salt-free media, and this point of view has recently been preferred by Christian (1956). In an extreme case such behaviour is highly distinctive; several of the red halophiles require at least 15 % NaCl in their growth medium. There is, apparently, a broad correlation between the two criteria of the halophilic habit; organisms with high optimum salt concentrations tend to have a high requirement, and vice versa; and in both respects the 'facultative' group of halophiles appears intermediate (cf. Fig. 1). It would be interesting to know whether, in nature, the strictly 'obligate' type of halophile is characteristic of habitats with a constantly high salt concentration like some salt lakes, and if the 'facultative' type predominates in brackish waters of fluctuating concentration, as one might expect. Unfortunately, descriptions of the flora of such places have not covered this aspect of the behaviour of the microflora in sufficient detail.

There is similar difficulty over the terminology of sugar-tolerant organisms, the term 'osmophilic' being regarded as misleading for those yeasts (the majority) which grow as well if not better in low sugar concentrations. Nickerson (1943) accepted the existence of the two groups indicated by Kroemer & Krumbholz (1931, see above), and suggested the corresponding adjectives 'osmotophilic' and 'osmotoduric'. Scarr (1954) thought the latter inappropriate, because many facultative strains grow best at concentrations around 30 % (Ingram, 1950) or even higher (Kroemer & Krumbholz, 1931), and so she retained the term osmophilic. The whole basis of the terminology may be questioned, however, because it has yet to be demonstrated conclusively that the phenomena are osmotic with these yeasts. Observations by the writer, indicating that the optimum concentration is near 30% w/w, whether glucose or sucrose is the sugar, raise serious doubts about this; and similar observations were made by Beetlestone (1930). The doubt can only be resolved by more critical experiments in which the effects of different solutes are compared.

Also, it is still not certain that *obligately* osmophilic yeasts exist. Lochhead & Heron (1929) described species developing only with large proportions of honey in the medium, which we have confirmed (Barnett, Ingram & Swain, 1956); but Lochead & Heron (their Table XI) showed a high incubation temperature to be the chief cause of this requirement (cf. Table 3 below). Mrak & Phaff (1948) thought it due to lack of growth factors, provided by honey; but we find that the same strains grow, though less well, on media containing only citric acid and tryptone besides high concentrations of glucose.

Comparisons of different solutes

With yeasts, the only systematic data are those of Kroemer & Krumbholz (1932); they compared the effects of different concentrations of several salts on a wide range of species including osmophilic strains, but glycerol was the only non-electrolyte tried. In general, the osmophilic strains grew vigorously in salt solutions with concentrations of 3 M or more, and in substantially higher concentrations of glycerol; these results are comparable with those obtained in sugar solutions, and plainly suggest that the effect of all these solutes is primarily osmotic. There must, however, be important secondary effects which are specific: for example, in all the data of Kroemer & Krumbholz, it is clear that at equal molarity NaCl was much more inhibitory than the other salts. For this reason it would be interesting to have observations for strains of *Debaryomyces guilliermondii* and *D. membranaefaciens* which are reported to be resistant to both NaCl and sugar.

With bacteria there have, on the other hand, been many investigations in which the reaction to NaCl has been compared with those towards other salts and sometimes non-electrolytes. At the extremes, two types of halophilic behaviour can be distinguished: that in which the requirement for NaCl is specific; and that in which NaCl can be wholly substituted by other solutes.

Specific requirements for NaCl were plainly demonstrated by Schoop (1935) and by Hess (1942). More recently, Robinson & Gibbons (1952) found that the moderate halophile *Micrococcus denitrificans* failed to grow in any of fifteen salts other than NaCl, even NaBr or KCl; and Brown & Gibbons (1955) imply that all their red extreme halophiles had high specific requirements for NaCl. Rippel (1947) stated that, in such cases, the requirement is only Na$^+$ ion and that the Cl$^-$ can be replaced by other anions; but the above data prove that other sodium salts often cannot replace NaCl.

In the majority of cases, however, the effects of NaCl can be duplicated by other (non-toxic) salts or even non-electrolytes, a type of behaviour shown by bacteria 'normal' in their concentration relations. The effect of increasing concentrations of NaCl on 'normal' bacteria is to stimulate their activities up to concentration about 0·1 M (Winslow, Walker & Sutermeister, 1932; Ingram, 1939), hence the customary addition of 1 % NaCl to culture media—and increasingly to depress activity at higher concentrations (Doudoroff, 1940; Ingram, 1940; Foda & Vaughn, 1950; Ware, Childs & Smith, 1955). It seems probable that these effects are primarily osmotic, though Spiegelberg (1944) disagreed, because they can be equated to the influence of other solutes on the basis of the aqueous activity of the medium (Christian & Scott, 1953; Christian, 1955). Some organisms which are more than usually resistant to salt behave similarly, as if the concentration scale were simply enlarged. The Staphylococci are a good and well-known example: their optimum salt concentration is usually about 0·6M; they will grow, increasingly slowly, at concentrations up to about 3M (Nunheimer & Fabian, 1940); and it has been shown that the similar effects of salts other than NaCl are comparable on the basis of a_w (Scott, 1953). There is a wide variety of micrococci in which the reactions to salt are similar, though over somewhat different ranges of concentration (e.g. Fig. 2, p. 107). The reactions of the moderate halophile *Vibrio costicolus*, measured in terms of growth (Flannery, Doetsch & Hansen, 1952) or of glucose oxidation (Flannery *et al.* 1953), were similar, replacement of NaCl by other solutes being possible. This may even hold for organisms tolerating the highest salt concentrations: an anaerobic halophile *Bacteroides halosmophilus* isolated by Baumgartner (1937) grew in NaCl-saturated media, but complete substitution could be effected by the chlorides of other cations; the *amount* of growth at optimum osmotic pressure diminished following the Hofmeister series Na > K > Li > Mg > Ca. The same substitutive behaviour may be exhibited by organisms other than bacteria, e.g. *Sporendonema epizoum* (Vaisey, 1954).

There might be an important connexion between the halophilic character and the extent to which osmotic substitution is possible. This first emerged from the work of Schoop (1935), who compared eleven obligate halophiles of various types with a corresponding number of facultative halophiles; a striking series of tables shows that, without exception, the facultative strains grew in the presence of various salts other than NaCl, while the obligate strains all required NaCl specifically. Hess (1942) too found, with NaCl-tolerant bacteria from salted fish, that replacement of the Na^+ ion by K^+, Li^+, Mg^{2+}, Ca^{2+} or Ba^{2+} inhibited growth of the strict halophiles, but not that of the facultative isolates. These relations suggest that the specificity of requirement for NaCl may be related to the minimum concentration required for growth. So far as they go, the observations reviewed earlier are in agreement: the red organisms of Gibbons and his colleagues are all obligate and specific, while the staphylococci, *Bact. halosmophilus* Baumgartner, and *Sporendonema* are all facultative and substitutive. The few data for yeasts also agree, salt substitution being possible with the facultative osmophiles of Kroemer & Krumbholz (1932); unfortunately, there is still no relevant information about the apparently obligate osmophiles isolated by Lochhead & Heron (1929).

But the distinction between specific and substitutive behaviour is not clear-cut, there being organisms in which more or less substitution is possible. Tables presented by Golikowa (1930b) and by Dumesh (1935) suffice to show, in general terms, that there is a wide range in the degree to which substitution is possible, but much more accurate observations are still needed. Christian (1956), for example, has recently found that though complete substitution appears possible with *Vibrio costicolus* on ordinary media, as Flannery *et al.* (1952) showed, this organism has in fact an irreplaceable NaCl requirement for growth which is well below the NaCl content of normal media. This suggests that all degrees of requirement for NaCl may eventually be demonstrated. It seems also that the above differences in behaviour cannot result from fundamental differences in metabolic character. Frank & Hess (1941) showed that the species *Sporendonema epizoum* contains, besides facultative substitutive strains like that investigated by Vaisey (1954), strains which are typically obligate and specific in their requirement for NaCl.

There is a third behaviour pattern, characteristic of 'normal' organisms; in which the effects of different salts are ascribable to the cations, those of mono-, di- and trivalent cations being equivalent at concentrations roughly in the ratio of 1000:100:1. Relations of this kind were observed, for example, with the viability of *Escherichia coli* (Winslow & Haywood, 1931) and the respiration of *Bacillus cereus* (Ingram, 1939); they are comparable with the effects of the different salts in precipitating electro-negative colloids, or in changing cell permeability. From such experience, one might doubt whether the effects of di- and trivalent cations could be explained on the simple basis of aqueous activity. *Dunaliella viridis* was the first halophilic organism for which cation effects of this sort were suggested, by Baas-Becking (1931). This alga grew at pH 9 at NaCl concentrations between 1 and 4 M and, in this range, tolerated up to 0·1 M-Mg and 0·01 M-Ca either separately, or in combination. The data presented by Brown & Gibbons (1955) for several red halophilic bacteria also indicate a tolerance to Mg concentration about 1/10 as great as that for NaCl, in the presence of high NaCl concentrations. Petter (1932) investigated the effects of Mg and Ca at high NaCl concentrations with *Halobacterium* (*Bacterium*) *halobium*, *Bacterium trapanicum* and *Sarcina morrhuae*. The two former, obligate halophiles, were inhibited by 0·1–0·15 M-Ca, while the facultative *Sarcina* was not. On the basis of rather few results Petter suggested that the best Mg:Ca ratio for these organisms was 1/2, contrasting with values of the order of 10 found for *Dunaliella* by Baas-Becking. Baas-Becking (1931) suggested that the succession of *Dunaliella* by red bacteria in evaporating sea water was related to a rise in the Mg:Ca ratio from about 5 to 20, but this suggestion does not tally with Petter's observations. It is evident that the substitutive type of halophile does not behave in this manner. Dumesh (1935), for instance, records several bacteria which grew in 10 % $MgCl_2$ alone, or with addition of 0·5 % NaCl; these were facultatively halophilic strains. Unfortunately, nobody has yet investigated the effects of cations of high valency on halophiles or osmophiles and, until this is done, the one thing clear is that the specific requirement of some organisms for NaCl stands quite outside these general cation relations.

There are several observations (e.g. Hess, 1942) which show that the tolerance to high concentrations of salt can be raised by the presence of other salts, which may be of importance to the organisms in their natural habitats. Baranik-Pikowsky (1927) found that bacteria from salt lagoons tolerated higher concentrations of lagoon salt than of pure salt. The ecological consequences of this increased tolerance have, however, never been explored.

INFLUENCE OF CONDITIONS ON CONCENTRATION RELATIONS

In comparing the effect of concentration of salt or sugar on organisms in different circumstances, it is important to know how far these relations can be modified by external conditions.

Temperature

For moulds, several workers agree that the greatest tolerance exists at the optimum temperature (Tomkins, 1929; Heintzeler, 1939), with a markedly lower tolerance near the temperature limits (Stille, 1948).

For bacteria, several workers have shown that the maximum salt concentration in which growth occurs is greater at lower temperatures; a remarkable instance was the growth of *Escherichia coli* and typhoid bacteria in 25% NaCl at 5–8°, but not in 10% at 37° (Dumesh, 1935). Christian (1956) found that the NaCl requirement for growth of *Halobacterium halobium* is also less at lower temperatures. These observations suggest that, at temperatures where growth is possible, the salt relations are less exacting when the temperature is low, a suggestion borne out by Table 3; though Labrie & Gibbons (1937) found that the preservative action of salt increased with reduction of temperature from 21 to 10°, which seems to imply a reduced salt tolerance at lower temperature. The observations of Kroemer & Krumbholz (1931) with yeasts likewise show a smaller effect of high sugar concentration at lower temperatures.

Table 3. *The effect of sodium chloride concentration and temperature on the growth of* Halobacterium halobium*

Unpublished data, J. H. B. Christian

Temperature (°C.)	Concentration of NaCl (w/v)					
	10%	15%	20%	20%	30%	Saturated
10	—	—	—	—	—	—
15	—	—	+(17)	+(15)	—	—
20	—	+(11)	+(8)	+(8)	+(9)	+(16)
25	—	+(7)	+(4)	+(4)	+(4)	+(6)
30	—	+(4)	+(2)	+(2)	+(1)	+(2)
37	—	+(20)	+(2)	+(1)	+(1)	+(2)
45	—	—	—	+(1)	+(1)	+(1)

+ = growth; figure in parentheses is number of days' incubation required for visible turbidity.

— = no growth in 28 days.

* In the liquid medium described by Baxter & Gibbons (1954) for *Pseudomonas salinaria*: casamino acids (Difco), 5 g.; yeast extract (Difco), 5 g.; proteose peptone (Difco), 5 g.; Na₃ citrate, 3 g.; KCl, 2 g.; MgSO₄.7H₂O, 20 g.; NaCl, 200 g.; distilled water to 1000 ml. This medium is satisfactory for several different species of strict halophiles.

Hydrogen-ion concentration

The relations to pH resemble those to temperature, tolerance being greatest near the optimum. This sort of behaviour was first noted in the salt reactions of *Escherichia coli* by Sherman & Holm (1922), and confirmed by Joslyn & Cruess (1929). Eddy & Ingram (1956), too, have just recorded a diminished tolerance by their facultative strain of *Bacillus circulans* near the pH limits for growth. Schelhorn (1950*b*) showed that the tolerance of *Aspergillus glaucus* to high sugar concentrations is diminished near the pH limit, and obtained similar results with four osmophilic yeasts (Schelhorn, 1950*a*).

Oxygen

Christian & Scott (1953) found no difference between the water relations of Salmonellae under aerobic or anaerobic conditions. For Staphylococci, Scott (1953) found a slightly reduced tolerance to high osmotic pressures under anaerobic conditions. Stuart & James (1938), and Stuart (1940*a*), claimed that growth of red halophilic sarcinas was better in media of low redox potential; but they changed Eh mainly by changing pH, so that the differences in rH appear trifling. Their claim is contrary to general experience with such organisms that they grow well only in aerated cultures; though Golikowa (1930*b*) recorded better growth of halophiles in broth than on solid media. With the osmophilic yeasts, too, the situation is apparently similar, for in broth cultures of high sugar concentration growth is practically confined to the surface (Lochhead & Heron, 1929; Kroemer & Krumbholz, 1931).

Though some of the moderate halophiles may be facultatively anaerobic, the strong halophiles are nearly all strongly aerobic. There is only one well-authenticated exception, the highly salt-tolerant anaerobe isolated by Baumgartner (1937), though this may be because few have searched for salt-tolerant anaerobes. It is, however, noteworthy that this was not a specific halophile; hence, until exceptions are demonstrated, it must be supposed that the specific requirement for high concentrations of sodium chloride is associated with a strongly aerobic character.

Nutrition

Stuart (1940*b*) observed that an alkaline reaction, and the presence of cysteine and a high concentration of gelatin all favoured growth near the minimal salt concentration (*c.* 3 M) for a red obligately halophilic Sarcina (Table 4). Because lower salt concentrations are desirable for the preparation of media (e.g. to avoid precipitation), these observations led him to recommend for such organisms an agar with 5 % Bactogelatin, 17 % NaCl, a 'trace of' cysteine, and a pH of 7·2. Castell & Mapplebeck (1952) noticed a somewhat similar effect of proteins in stimulating growth of halophiles at high salt concentrations.

The maximum osmotic pressure at which *Salmonella oranienburg* can grow, in a glucose-mineral salt medium, was greatly increased by amino acids, notably proline, and further extended by the addition of eight vitamins; which brought the tolerance up to that attained in complex media (Christian, 1955). These observations, and those of Stuart (1940*b*) just mentioned, suggest that the full potential range of osmotic tolerance is only manifested under conditions of full nutrition. Unhappily, this suggestion cannot yet be properly tested with halophilic organisms, for which suitable synthetic media have still to be discovered. Katznelson & Lochhead (1952) found that some species grew adequately in the absence of added vitamins, purines or pyrimidines, but their basal medium contained ill-defined protein hydrolysates.

Table 4. *Growth* of* Sarcina littoralis *on agar media, in relation to* pH, *gelatin and cysteine content of the medium*

Data of Stuart (1940*b*)

Gelatin concentration (% w/v)		Concentration of NaCl (M)			
	2	3·5	4	4·5	5
1·0	1	1	2	3	3
2·5	2	3	2	3	3
5·0	3	3	3	3	3
7·5	3	4	2	2	2
10	4	4	2	2	1

pH	Cysteine					
6	−	1	1	1	1	1
	+	1	1	1	1	1
7	−	1	2	2	3	3
	+	4	4	4	3	2
8	−	2	2	3	4	4
	+	4	4	4	4	4

* Growth indicated by 1 = definite, 2 = moderate, 3 = heavy, 4 = very heavy.

There is plenty of experience which shows that tolerance to high salt concentrations is greater in rich organic media like foods than it is in simple culture media like peptone water (Clayton, 1932*a*; Tanner & Evans, 1933), but it is not known whether this is an effect on the nutrition of the organism or on something else; Stuart (1940*b*) explained the effect of gelatin (cf. Table 4) as perhaps due to removal of salt by the gelatin.

The reaction of an organism to different solute concentrations can, evidently, be appreciably modified by environmental conditions, for reasons not yet known. But the important point, in the present connexion, is that none of these influences have yet been shown to modify the reactions to solute concentration in a radical manner.

SPECULATIONS ABOUT THE ORIGIN OF OSMOPHILIC AND HALOPHILIC MICRO-ORGANISMS

In most natural environments, the solute concentrations are likely to fluctuate greatly: for example, through the effect of rivers or tides in salt lakes (Rubentschik, 1929; Elazari-Volcani, 1940), or through the drying, and re-wetting by rain, of flowers and fruits. Hence it is natural to wonder whether the production of organisms resistant to low aqueous activities might occur by gradual adaptation during such fluctuations. For example, Clayton (1932b) adopted this view, quoting the conclusion of Korinek, that the optimum salt concentration of the predominant bacteria in a lagoon of variable salinity always corresponded roughly to the salt content of the water.

Table 5. *The salt tolerance of denitrifying bacteria isolated from garden soil by enrichment in media of various salt contents*

Data of Hof (1935)

% NaCl in enrichment medium	% NaCl in test cultures of purified isolates						
	0	3	6	12	18	24	30
0	+	+	+	−	−	−	−
0	+	+	+	−	−	−	−
3	+	+	+	+	+	−	−
3	+	+	+	−	−	−	−
6	+	+	+	+	+	−	−
6	+	+	+	+	+	−	−
12	+	+	+	+	+	−	−
12	+	+	+	+	−	−	−
18	+	+	+	+	+	−	−
18	−	−	+	+	+	−	−
24*	−	−	+	+	+	+	+
30	−	−	+	+	+	+	+

* This isolate used in adaptation experiments.

This adaptation theory was upheld by the Dutch school (e.g. Kluyver & Baars, 1932), and notably expounded by Hof (1935). She tried to isolate salt-tolerant bacteria from water and soil, through enrichment cultures in media with various concentrations of salt, and the salt tolerance of the organisms so isolated was then determined in pure cultures. Her most extensive set of results is presented in Table 5; they show plainly a direct relation between the concentration of salt in the enrichment culture and the salt tolerance of the organisms isolated through it; and similar results were obtained in other experiments. In interpreting such data, Hof began with an assumption, referring especially to obligate halophiles: 'It cannot be accepted that such types, with the potential environment which they possess after isolation, are present in common soil.' Hence, when she found obligate halophiles after enrichment, there was no other conclusion than that they had arisen by adaptation in the enrichment culture. She ignored her own experiments with several *Escherichia coli* strains isolated from water where, despite thorough investigation, no trace of any similar relation could be discovered; but a more serious question is the validity of her basic assumption, for which there was no experimental evidence. The fact that other workers, especially Stuart (1938), claim to have isolated halophilic bacteria from ordinary environments, would not be taken as evidence here, because they of course also isolated them via high salt media; indeed, if one accepts the view that adaptation can occur at once in such media, there seems to be no way of deciding that halophilic bacteria exist naturally anywhere. However, the assumption that salt-requiring bacteria cannot exist in soil seems open to question on general grounds, because high salt concentrations must exist in the upper layers of soil, in equilibrium with 'dry' air. If one does not accept Hof's basic assumption, a much more reasonable explanation of the type of result obtained by her and by Korinek is that the salt concentration simply selects those organisms to which it happens to be suited; neither worker investigated the strong possibility that the organisms recovered at different salt concentrations might be completely and permanently different. It will be clear that this type of reasoning is wholly unsatisfactory.

Circumstantial evidence of adaptation appears when strains of ostensibly the same organisms are found with significantly different concentration relations, and this occurs fairly frequently. For example, Verhoeven (1952) isolated unusually salt-tolerant strains of *Bacillus licheniformis*, and Yamada & Shiio (1953), and Eddy & Ingram (1956) have had similar experience with *B. pumilus* and *B. circulans* respectively; Burcik (1950) noted differences between different strains of *B. mycoides* and of *Pseudomonas pyocyanea*; Hof (1935) quotes a salt tolerance for *Micrococcus denitrificans* much lower than that of the apparently similar *M. halodenitrificans* of Robinson & Gibbons (1952); analogous observations by the writer are in Fig. 2. With yeasts also, Burcik (1950) found that his strain of *Saccharomyces rouxii* failed to grow at an a_w below 0·90, though Lodder & van Rij (1952) included in this species highly osmophilic yeasts which grow at much lower values, and Scarr (1954) isolated two strains of *Zygosaccharomyces bisporus* with quite different tolerances towards sugar. There can be no doubt that strains with different concentration relations may exist within the same species.

The difficulty here is to establish that the strains differing in concentration relations are otherwise identical. The species *Saccharomyces rouxii* Lodder & van Rij certainly includes a wide variety of different types (Barnett & Ingram, 1955). The identification of a species in the genus *Bacillus* is notoriously difficult; and the same is true of the micrococci. The difficulty is even greater with the halophilic bacteria. Velu & Balozet (1929) claimed that the causal agent in the reddening of salted goods is a halophilic variant of *Serratia marcescens*, but Petrowa (1935), examining one of Velu's cultures, decided that it was a variant of *Micrococcus roseus*; an eloquent testimony to the difficulty of such comparisons. Various reasons for this will appear below. It means that the only really convincing evidence must come from the experimental modification of the concentration relations of a single culture.

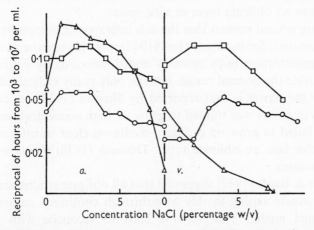

Fig. 2. The different relations between growth and NaCl concentration, in different strains of *Micrococcus* isolated from hams: (*a.*) *M. aurantiacus*; (*v.*) *M. varians*. (Cultured in peptone water, pH 7, at 25°.)

Work with pure cultures has shown that there are many organisms whose tolerance to salt or sugar seems to be fixed. For example, Hof (1935) and Doudoroff (1940) failed to alter the salt tolerance of *Escherichia coli* significantly; Christian (1955) had the same experience with *Salmonella oranienberg*; Burcik (1950) reports an analogous situation for *Serratia marcescens*. For yeasts, Burcik (1950) found a high degree of constancy in the water requirements of several species; and, in particular, prolonged efforts to change those of *Trichosporon pullulans*, by repeated subculture on different media, were unsuccessful. Although Whalley & Scarr (1947) did increase the sugar tolerance of a commercial strain of *Saccharomyces cerevisiae* by training, the limit attained was no higher than that reported by other workers. The fact that it is possible to make acceptable statements that particular species will not tolerate more than a particular concentration (cf. Clayton, 1932a; Hof, 1935) shows that adaptation to higher concentrations must at least not be common. Nevertheless, it is clear that the concentration reactions of some organisms can be changed experimentally. Scarr (1954) and the writer have found that cultivation of facultatively osmopilic yeasts on low sugar media reduces their tolerance to high concentrations, which can be restored—though more slowly—by training back to higher concentrations. The writer's experience with salt-tolerant Micrococci has been similar. In such experiments, some modification by training might reasonably be expected in the relations of a facultative type of organism which already grows over a wide range of osmotic situations; and accordingly the decisive test is the conversion of a typically intolerant into an obligate type, or vice versa.

There are several reports that the salt tolerance of halophilic bacteria can be increased; for instance, Hess (1942) was able to expand the limits of salt concentration both upwards and downwards by cultivation in media outside the normal range, but the only really radical adaptation known to the writer is that reported by Shewan (1938). A culture of *Micrococcus roseus* was trained to grow on high concentrations of salt, and then failed to grow on ordinary media—a clear transformation of a facultative into an obligate type. Dumesh (1935) mentions similar transformations.

Kluyver & Baars (1932) suggested that all obligate strains are physiological artefacts arising in this way through continued cultivation on concentrated media. This view is hard to reconcile with repeated experience, both with sugary (e.g. Lochhead & Heron, 1929) and with saline (e.g. Stuart, 1938) materials, that the obligate types are not recovered on ordinary media even at primary isolation, when they appear at once if concentrated media are used, often in vast numbers.

If all obligate strains were physiological artefacts, one might expect that it would be possible to readapt them to low concentrations without much difficulty. Only limited success has been achieved in this direction, by the use of old cultures; Christian (1956) finds the salt requirements of young cultures of halophiles to be quite stable. Thus Hess (1942) reduced the salt requirements of several obligate halophiles slightly by subculturing from 30-day cultures into salt concentrations below the normal. Schoop (1935) also was able to reduce the requirements of obligate halophiles only slightly. Hof (1935) trained one of her isolates (marked in Table 5), which at first grew at 6 % but not at 3 % NaCl, to grow at 0·75 % NaCl, though growth remained much better at the higher concentrations. More striking is the statement of Stuart & James (1938) that all the so-called obligate halophiles they examined would develop even in media with little or no salt, if cultures aged 30 days or more were used as inocula. But the results they presented, for *Sarcina littoralis*, are peculiar in that there was poor growth with a changed morphology on intermediate salt concentrations (10–15 %); and also in that one series of cultures with 7·5% salt produced pigmented growth while all the other low salt cultures were non-pigmented. Hence it seems possible that Stuart & James were working with mixed cultures; although they noted this difficulty, they apparently relied for proof of identity on the fact that their cultures at both high and low salt concentrations had similar morphology. It is noteworthy that Brown & Gibbons (1955) classed *S. littoralis* with *Pseudomonas salinaria*, as having a high salt requirement. This observation, and similar ones mentioned earlier, indicate that readaptation does not take place readily, which argues against the proposition that such organisms are cultural artefacts.

In much of this work there is a possibility that the apparent adaptation may actually have been the selection of a different organism. Several authors have emphasized the difficulty of obtaining single cells of halophilic bacteria, because they clump together and are embedded in mucus (Stuart *et al.* 1933; Shewan, 1938), or because of symbiotic dependency of two or more species and the failure of isolated cells to grow (Petrowa, 1933). As a result, much work has been done with admittedly impure cultures. Moreover, the morphological alterations with change of salt concentration are sometimes so great that they can give little confirmation of the purity of the culture. Petrowa (1933), for instance, recorded *Bacillus vulgatus* and *B. mesentericus* as growing on media saturated with salt; but, because the bacteria were morphologically very different and did not form spores at high salt concentrations, one doubts whether the cultures were pure, especially as Petrowa observed a tendency of the halophiles to grow in association with the spore-formers. Horowitz-Wlassowa (1931*b*) also observed this symbiosis, and attributed it to stimulation by the products of protein decomposition. Golikowa (1930*b*) mentions the formation of plectridium type spores by bacteria tolerating salt-saturated media.

Because of such uncertainties, adaptation experiments would only be thoroughly convincing if they were carried out from a single cell culture; or, failing this, if the adapted strain were trained back again to its original state as proof of its identity. Neither of these has ever been done, to the writer's knowledge. Though the hypothesis that obligate strains arise by such adaptations seems reasonable and natural, and is universally held, there appears to be surprisingly little unequivocal evidence to support it.

PECULIAR PROPERTIES OF OSMOPHILIC AND HALO-PHILIC MICRO-ORGANISMS

The difficulties inherent in the foregoing discussion can only be properly appreciated from knowledge of the peculiar reactions of the organisms to changes in their osmotic environment, which will now be briefly described (see also Flannery, 1956).

Pleomorphism

Many workers, especially the earlier ones, recorded pronounced alterations in the shape of the cells in solutions of various concentrations, especially for halophilic bacteria (e.g. Klebahn, 1919; Harrison & Kennedy, 1922; Petrowa, 1935; Stuart, 1935).

It is necessary here to distinguish between the immediate result of a change in concentration, and the effect of growing the cells at the new concentration. The immediate effects of concentration change are chiefly osmotic. Transfer to a higher concentration causes a corresponding diminution in the size of the cells (Mitchell & Moyle, 1955), plasmolysis (though the protoplast may not separate from the wall in Gram-positive bacteria and some yeasts) and, in the extreme, deformation. Transfer to lower concentrations causes swelling. If the concentration change is substantial, the wall of the cell may burst and cytoplasm be extruded (plasmoptysis); this appearance in halophilic bacteria was well described by Klebahn (1919) and Dierchen (1938). Such cells are no longer viable. With a large enough fall in concentration the cytoplasm bursts and the suspending medium becomes viscous. The changes can be followed conveniently by measurement of optical density (Mitchell & Moyle, 1955); at the lysis point there is an abrupt and marked fall in optical density (cf. Fig. 3, p. 118). In these respects there seems to be a significant difference between rods and cocci, the latter being much more resistant to osmotic changes, conceivably because of greater strength in their cell wall. Whatever the reason, the changes in optical density with salt concentration are smaller and less abrupt with cocci (Christian, 1956), which Mager, Kuczynski, Schatzberg & Avi-dor (1956) relate to the Gram reaction. These osmotic adjustments are rapid, being made in a matter of minutes. If they fall short of permanent damage to the cell, there follows a period of readjustment, lasting at least several hours, when the plasmolytic picture gradually disappears.

But even if the organism becomes able to divide in its new environment, it may assume a different form, and these alterations of form follow no readily discernible pattern. For example, the cells of osmophilic yeasts are said to be smaller at high sugar concentrations (Scarr, 1951), while the reverse has been reported for salt-tolerant yeasts (Kroemer & Krumbholz, 1932); and Harrison & Kennedy (1922) observed in their *Pseudomonas salinaria* a transition from coccoid to long rod-shaped cells with increasing salt concentration, while Stuart (1935) suggested that on the contrary a high salt concentration suppresses the rod-shaped phase in *Myxococcus rubescens*. It is notable that recent investigators report these high degrees of pleomorphism less frequently. Shewan (1938) found for example that his salt-adapted strain of *Micrococcus roseus* did not exhibit any of the bizarre forms attributed by Petrowa (1935) to that species. Stuart & James (1938) state that the chief effect of salt concentration is simply to change the size of the cells; similar observations have just been mentioned. Probably much of the pleomorphism reported by the earlier workers arose from impure cultures.

Besides changes in the osmotic status of the medium, changes in the nature of the nutrients too may cause profound morphological alterations. For instance, Stuart's *Myxococcus* grew as a rod on peptone or dextrose, but as a coccus on gelatine or cellulose (observations since confirmed in unpublished work by J. M. Shewan). It has also been shown (Brown & Gibbons, 1955) that the halophilic rods can be transformed, sometimes permanently, into cocci by growth on Mg-deficient media (though the halophilic cocci are not affected), and the Mg^{2+} requirement for normal growth is unusually high ($c. 0.1 M$). Comparison of the microphotographs of *Pseudomonas salinaria* presented by Brown & Gibbons (1955) with those of Dussault (1955), suggests that the pleomorphic forms observed by the latter might have been caused by exhaustion of Mg in the growth medium.

Because these organisms usually have to be grown on special media in which, apparently, the conditions might give rise to morphological peculiarities, it is difficult to place much reliance on morphology as a criterion in the identification of these organisms, which is one reason for the confusion over the identity of so many of them. Anderson (1954) emphasizes another likely source of error—the large alterations in morphology which often take place during staining for microscopic examination.

Staining

The orthodox heat fixation and bacteriological stains give wholly unsatisfactory preparations, frequently containing few cells not obviously damaged (Penso, 1947). For halophiles, fixation in acetic acid is recommended by Browne (1922), Kurochkin & Emilianchik (1935) and by Dussault (1955); and staining by Giemsa's procedure (Harrison & Kennedy, 1922; J. M. Shewan, personal communication). In morphological investigation, dark field or phase-contrast microscopy avoids these difficulties (Anderson, 1954).

The same difficulty applies to the Gram stain, which is so important a diagnostic character. Unmodified, it gives poor preparations; but modification, as is well known, is likely to give erroneous results, especially with organisms of doubtful reaction. That the halophiles are of this nature may be illustrated by the observation of Petrowa (1935) that a salt-tolerant coccus, isolated from various samples of salt and from pickle brines and regarded as the most important species, was Gram-positive when grown on ordinary media, but Gram-negative on saline media. Robinson & Gibbons (1952) included their halophilic denitrifying *Micrococcus* in the Gram-positive genus *Micrococcus*, although they found it Gram-negative.

Similarly, orthodox procedures for staining flagella, more or less unsatisfactory at best, are especially so with halophilic bacteria. Electron micrography might give better information (cf. Houwink, 1956).

Pigments

It is remarkable that so many of the more strict halophiles are pink or red, suggesting some connexion between the two properties; and salt-tolerant *Bacillus* strains have also been remarked as peculiar in being yellow or orange in colour (Horowitz-Wlassowa, 1931 a). Most observers agree that the pigmentation becomes more intense the higher the concentration of salt in the medium and the higher the temperature of incubation; though Golikowa (1930a) makes an opposite statement. Klebahn (1919) and Horowitz-Wlassowa (1931 b) noted that oxygen is necessary for the production of pigment (it is not clear how far this was due to its necessity for growth). Dussault & Lachance (1952) found that pigment production is stimulated by the presence of glycerol in the growth medium.

Petter (1932) has shown that the red pigments are carotenoids. This prompts comparison with the Rhodotorulae, which also have carotenoid pigments and, like the red halophilic bacteria, a strongly aerobic metabolism. The metabolic function of the pigments is not yet known.

Stuart & James (1938) reported that non-pigmented cells of *Sarcina littoralis*, grown in low salt media, had a reductive metabolism contrasting with the oxidative metabolism of pigmented cells grown on high salt media, and hence suggested that the pigment may play some role in oxidation. Here, again, arises the doubt as to whether they were working with a single organism (cf. above). Another suggestion is that the pigments are connected with the extraordinary resistance of the red halophiles to sunlight; a property, remarked by several workers (e.g. Horowitz-Wlassowa, 1931*b*), which is likely to have a strong influence on their survival, for example, in solar salt.

Metabolism

The rates of metabolic processes of course change with changes in salt and sugar concentration. The changes in respiration, for example, usually parallel those for growth (Rubinstein, 1932; Flannery *et al.* 1953; Yamada & Shiio, 1953). It is not safe to assume that the same is true of other aspects of their metabolism, though many workers quote biochemical activities without any indication of the influence of salt or sugar concentration on them, and sometimes do not even state the concentration at which they were determined.

It seems important to know whether the metabolic characters can be drastically altered, especially those which are used as taxonomic criteria. The only systematic observations known to the writer were made by Dumesh (1935), and they are disturbing. He worked with several halophiles capable of growing on low salt media, though the optimum concentration for their growth was about 15 %. On salt-free media, fermentation reactions were all negative; with 5 % salt there were several strong fermentation reactions; at 7 % salt these had become weak or negative, while some reactions negative at 5 % had become positive. There was unfortunately no information as to how much growth took place, though it seems certain that two of the organisms would not have grown on the salt-free media, nor what the reactions were at higher concentrations. At their face value the results suggest that the metabolism of the organisms was different at different concentrations. It should be added that no sign of similar alterations has yet been reported with the osmophilic yeasts which seem suitable to exhibit them. Equally startling changes were recorded by Dumesh in the biochemical and serological reactions of typhoid bacteria adapted to high salt concentrations at low temperatures (5–8°). If his observations are to be credited, the whole character of an organism may alter on adaptation to a substantially different solute concentration in the medium. If this is so, how is one to compare strains from high and low concentrations; and which set of reactions is to be regarded as taxonomically valid? More observations are greatly to be desired here.

Much of the difficulty in classifying these organisms arises because they give predominantly negative fermentation reactions in taxonomic tests; this applies even to the yeasts (Barnett & Ingram, 1955). With the halophilic bacteria so far investigated, there seems indeed to be comparatively little carbohydrate metabolism: Katznelson & Robinson (1955) report that they fail to oxidize many common carbon substrates, and the carbohydrate content of their cells is small (Smithies, Gibbons & Bayley, 1955). On the other hand, several halophilic bacteria oxidize various amino acids rapidly (Katznelson & Robinson, 1955). Robinson & Katznelson (1953) found that, while intact cells of *Pseudomonas salinaria* oxidized aspartate and glutamate, cell-free preparations prepared by plasmoptysis contained an aspartate-glutamate transaminase whose activity was increased by pyridoxal phosphate. The osmophilic yeasts are obviously quite different, their principal metabolic activity being the conversion of sugars to alcohol and acids, confirming the view that resistance to high solute concentrations is not linked to some particular type of metabolism.

Growth

A difficulty with highly halophilic bacteria is that they grow only slowly, even on special media with efficient aeration, and no suitable synthetic medium has yet been evolved. The difficulty is probably connected with amino-acid metabolism. Katznelson & Lochhead (1952) showed that some halophiles can grow on relatively simple media if they contain protein hydrolysates, although complex media containing milk or fish extract are usually recommended (Dussault & Lachance, 1952). Halophilic bacteria have been found in several investigations to prefer slightly alkaline conditions for growth (Lefevre & Round, 1919; Stather & Liebscher, 1929; Stuart, 1940 a). Brown & Gibbons (1955) found that the requirement of red extreme halophiles for Fe does not differ from that of normal organisms, and that the requirement for K was only slightly greater; but that 0·1 M-Mg was necessary for maximum growth, a deficiency causing marked changes in morphology. This high Mg requirement was not observed by Katznelson & Lochhead (1952) for non-pigmented halophiles.

Little that appears unusual has so far been reported about the metabolism of the sugar-tolerant organisms. Lochhead & Heron (1929) indicated that adequate nitrogen sources are critical in the development of osmophilic yeasts, but this is equally true of non-osmophilic yeasts (Challinor, 1955). Examination of vitamin requirements by Lochhead & Landerkin (1942), to elucidate the nature of a bioactivator in honey, likewise revealed nothing obviously peculiar.

It has appeared remarkable, from the ecological point of view, that many of the yeasts from sucrose-rich substrates should be unable to ferment sucrose (Mossel & Ingram, 1955); but Scarr (1951) demonstrated that, if a small proportion of the sucrose is inverted, the degradation of the monosaccharides produces so much acid that the inversion proceeds until most of the sucrose is ultimately fermented. Scarr claimed that these yeasts contain no invertase; Kroemer & Krumbholz (1931) stated that sucrose could be fermented by cells disintegrated by grinding.

Chemical composition

Smithies et al. (1955) analysed the cells and cell walls of four halophilic species of bacteria. They found higher nitrogen contents with much lower carbohydrate contents than for normal bacteria, and most of the carbohydrate was external nucleic acid pentose. The cell walls were lipoprotein, and those of two species were unusually fragile as judged by the times needed for sonic disintegration: *Pseudomonas salinaria* 10 min., *Vibrio costicolus* 20 min., compared with *Escherichia coli* 40 min. (Baxter & Gibbons, 1954).

Later, Smithies & Gibbons (1955) reported the existence of a slime layer on the cells of *Vibrio costicolus* and *Micrococcus halodenitrificans*, which could be removed by deoxyribonuclease. Apparently the same material raises the viscosity of the suspending medium. This slime was peculiar to the halophiles; but its removal did not affect respiration, viability or growth, so it seems to have no direct bearing on the halophilic character. The cells from which the slime had not been removed were, however, much more resistant to desiccation, which could be of survival value in the natural environment.

It is interesting that the cells of some osmophilic yeasts also develop an ill-defined slime layer, especially in concentrated sugar solutions (Ingram, 1950), but nothing is known of its nature.

Temperature relations

Halophilic bacteria are often incubated at 25° (e.g. Robinson & Gibbons, 1952). But the optimum temperature is considerably higher in solutions of high salt concentration (Hess, 1942, and Table 3). This may be a general phenomenon, because the same happens with osmophilic yeasts (Kroemer & Krumbholz, 1931; Ingram, 1950; Scarr, 1951); though they too are usually incubated at 25°, growth is faster at higher temperatures on high-sugar media. If one regards the diminution of activity at supra-optimal temperatures as due to partial heat inactivation of the relevant enzymes, this effect can be explained as likely to follow from diminished inactivation at the lower aqueous activities obtaining in concentrated solutions. Harrison & Kennedy (1922) quoted the optimum temperature for growth of *Pseudomonas salinaria*, of necessity on a medium of high salt concentration, as 42°. The minimum temperature for growth was about 10°, though other workers have reported growth down to 5° for other red halophiles (e.g. Horowitz-Wlassowa, 1931 *b*). Not all halophilic organisms have such high optimum temperatures, however; for *Sporendonema epizoum* the optimum is 25° (Klebahn, 1919) for both obligate and facultative strains (Frank & Hess, 1941).

This brief account should suffice to show the difficulties of comparing, say, a halophilic isolate with a 'normal' type culture. The morphology of the organism, its staining reactions, its relation to oxygen, its fermentation reactions, and its temperature optimum may all conceivably have been changed by the saline environment; and, if it is an obligate organism which cannot be grown in ordinary media, strict comparison with normal strains becomes impossible. Fortunately, there seems to be much less difficulty with osmophilic organisms, most of which grow on ordinary media, and exhibit greater constancy of character.

THE PHYSIOLOGICAL BASIS OF RESISTANCE TO HIGH SOLUTE CONCENTRATIONS

Because many of the enzyme systems of classical biochemistry are inhibited by strong solutions of salts or sugars, it is natural to wonder how organisms are able to survive and grow in such solutions. Broadly, there are two alternatives: (*a*) that the solutes do not penetrate the cell in high concentration; or (*b*) that they do, but that the enzyme systems of the cell are so constituted as to resist the intracellular concentrations. The first was the view originally held and, as the traditional approach has been osmotic, this aspect may conveniently be considered first.

Osmotic pressure

If the internal concentrations were low, a cell growing in sugar solutions of a_w about 0.65, as reported by Schelhorn (1950*a*), would have to withstand an osmotic pressure of the order of some 200 atmospheres, and that for bacteria growing in saturated NaCl solution (a_w c. 0·75) would be of a similar order. This, for a spherical organism of radius 1μ, corresponds to a wall tension of about 10^4 dynes/cm., which, in a wall c. 10 mμ thick (Salton, 1955), implies a tensile strength of the order of 10^{10} dynes/sq.cm. Such a strength is not unreasonable, being roughly 100 times less than that of cellulose (Preston, 1952). But the cell walls of the extreme halophiles are unusually fragile (Smithies et al. 1955), and thus seem ill-adapted to sustain the especially high tensions postulated on this view. R. Muller is quoted by Müller (1950) as having suggested that these large osmotic pressures are not, in fact, withstood by the cells, because they are permeable and allow the solutes to enter them.

Plasmoptysis

The swelling of cells on transfer to dilute solutions or water is regarded as due to the osmotic pressure, set up because the intracellular solute concentration then exceeds the external; and the diminution of external concentration needed to bring about such changes is related to the intracellular solute concentration. With organisms grown on substrates of high solute concentration, these changes occur following only a moderate degree of dilution (e.g. Robinson & Katznelson, 1953), suggesting that the intracellular concentrations are substantial. Christian (1956) has investigated this phenomenon quantitatively, and typical results are Figs. 3 and 4. Two striking points emerge: (a) lysis occurs at an external Na^+ concentration which is a constant fraction of the concentration in the growth medium, for a given organism (roughly 0·3 for *Vibrio costicolus* and 0·5 for *Halobacterium halobium*); (b) lysis occurs immediately if the external Na^+ is replaced by an even slightly lower concentration of K^+. The former observation is taken to mean: first, that the internal concentrations must appreciably exceed 0·3 and 0·5 of the external concentrations for the two species respectively; and secondly, that the intracellular concentration rises in rough proportion to the external concentration in the growth medium. The clear implication is that the salt concentration inside the cells is not low.

The density of the cells

Various workers have centrifuged halophilic bacteria from liquid media with high salt concentrations. Although the sedimentation may be relatively slow, it does take place. The only case in which difficulty has been reported is that of *Halobacterium halobium*; the cells contain gas vacuoles, and can only be centrifuged down if the vacuoles are eliminated, e.g. by pressure (Houwink, 1956). This sedimentation in near-saturated solutions means that the cells must have a remarkably high specific gravity, of the order of 1·2, a fact realized by Baas-Becking (1928) who concluded that the cells of halophilic bacteria could not be highly hydrated.

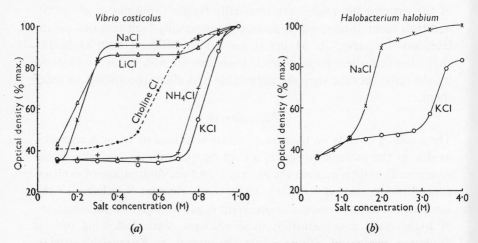

Fig. 3. The lysis of the cells of 'facultative' (a) and obligately (b) halophilic bacteria, on removal from the salt concentration at which they were grown and resuspension in solutions of lower concentration: a, *Vibrio costicolus*; b, *Halobacterium halobium*. The lysing concentration is that at which there is an abrupt fall in optical density (J. H. B. Christian, unpublished data).

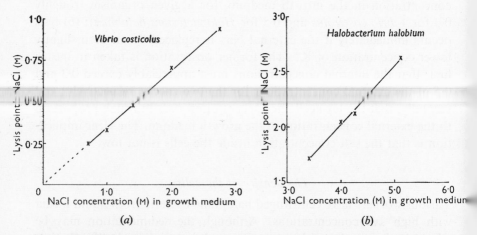

Fig. 4. The relations between the salt concentration at which lysis occurs on dilution and that of the medium on which the cells were grown, for a 'facultative' and an obligate halophile: (a), *Vibrio costicolus*; (b) *Halobacterium halobium*. The lysing concentrations were measured from curves like those in Fig. 3 (J. H. B. Christian, unpublished data).

With osmophilic yeasts grown in very concentrated sugar solutions, the cells at first rise to the surface on centrifuging, but this movement is reversed if the solutions are diluted slightly. The observations in Fig. 5 suggest that cells grown in 65 % sucrose would have been in equilibrium at about 40 % sucrose, corresponding roughly to a specific gravity again about 1·2. As the cells themselves might obviously have imbibed some water in the rather long time (30 min.) needed to centrifuge them after dilution of the medium, the original values may well have been higher.

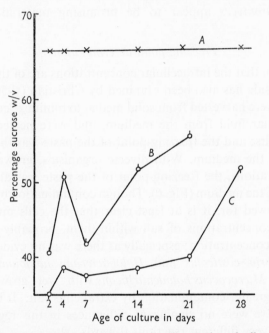

Fig. 5. The degree of dilution necessary to permit sedimentation of cells of an osmophilic yeast grown in high concentrations of sucrose: *A*, concentration of medium; *B*, dilution at which sedimentation did not occur on centrifuging; *C*, dilution at which sedimentation did take place (M. P. Scarr, unpublished data).

The specific gravities of pure protein and of fat are about 1·1 and 0·9 respectively, and solution or emulsion of these materials brings the values nearer 1·0. The only major constituent of cells which is appreciably more dense is solid carbohydrate with a specific gravity of about 1·5—hydration reduces this. Hence a cell might have an overall specific gravity of 1·2 if about 40 % of its total volume were occupied by solid (unhydrated) carbohydrate, e.g. reserve glycogen. Microscopic examination of osmophilic yeast cells does not reveal so high a proportion; and the situation with halophilic bacteria is even more clear, for Smithies *et al.* (1955) have shown that their cells have an unusually low carbo-hydrate content. The only other materials present in concentrations likely to influence the situation seriously are the solutes dissolved in the external medium; hence the conclusion is that they are probably responsible for the high density of the cells, which means that the cells contain concentrations at least approaching those outside them.

The interference microscope now offers the prospect of determining the solids content of the cells by an independent direct method (Davies, Wilkins, Chayen & La Cour, 1954); osmophilic strains of the large-celled *Schizosaccharomyces* appear to be promising material for such a technique.

Freezing-point determinations

Confirmation that the intracellular concentrations are of the same order as those outside has also been obtained by Christian (1956) in another way. Cells were harvested from solid media, to minimize contamination by intercellular fluid from the medium, and were heated to free the contained salts; and the freezing-point of the paste was then compared with that of the medium. With diverse organisms, grown at different salt concentrations, the freezing-point of the paste was always slightly below that of the medium (Fig. 6). Though contamination by the medium was not allowed for, it is at least clear that the cells must have had substantial concentrations of salt within them, probably approaching the external concentration; especially as there was no evident difference between *Vibrio costicolus* and *Halobacterium halobium* with 'dry' growth, and *Micrococcus halodenitrificans* with 'wet' growth and hence presumably greater contamination by extraneous salt. It is interesting, too, that there were no significant differences in this regard between species with very different reactions towards salt.

Chemical analysis of cells

In principle, direct analysis is the least equivocal way to decide the intracellular solute concentration. In practice considerable inaccuracies arise, through uncertainty in estimating the proportion of suspending fluid remaining outside the cells, which might have different barriers for different solutes. This problem is particularly acute here because of the high solute concentration in the intercellular fluid, and because its proportion is large as the cells do not pack well on centrifuging.

Though no such analysis has yet been undertaken for yeasts in strong sugar solutions, the internal concentration of cells of *Saccharomyces cerevisiae* and of *Bacillus cereus* in salt solutions was indicated 20 years ago as being of the same order as that externally up to a range of 1–2 M (Ingram, 1938). This conclusion was later supported by Gibbons & Baxter (1953). They found the internal salt concentration of cells of *Micrococcus halodenitrificans* to increase, from 1·5 % in cells grown in

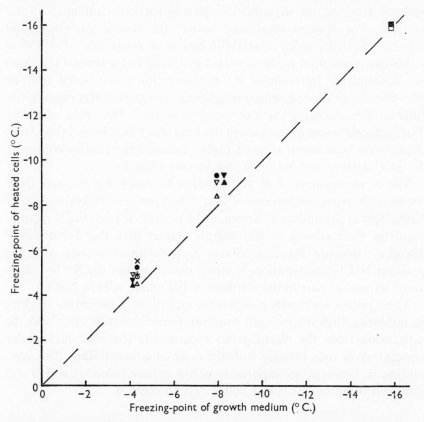

Fig. 6. The freezing-points of cell pastes of salt-intolerant, facultative and obligately halophilic bacteria, compared with those of the saline media on which the cells were grown (J. H. B. Christian, unpublished data). Grown on media with added NaCl only: ▼, *Vibrio costicolus*; ▲, *Micrococcus halodenitrificans*. Grown on media with equimolar additions of NaCl and KCl: +, *Escherichia coli*; ○, *Micrococcus lysodeikticus*; ×, *Staphylococcus aureus*; ▽, *Vibrio costicolus*; △, *Micrococcus halodenitrificans*; ●, *Bacillus circulans*; ■, *Sarcina littoralis*; □, *Halobacterium halobium*.

2–4 % NaCl, to about 5 % in cells grown in 8 % salt and to remain at this level in higher concentrations up to 22 %; with *Sarcina littoralis*, the internal salt concentration increased linearly from 10 to 19 % with increase of the external concentration from 18 to 27 %. These figures were based solely on estimation of chloride. Yamada & Shiio (1953) also presented analyses suggesting that, with a salt concentration of

10·8 % in the medium, the intracellular concentration was 8·9 % in the cells of a halotolerant *Bacillus pumilus*; but they demonstrated a large excess of Na^+ over Cl^-, conceivably the result of Donnan phenomena. The earlier work of the writer (Ingram, 1938) had also indicated that the cation might be in considerable excess; hence Christian (1956) has recently repeated the investigation, paying particular attention to the cations. For reasons mentioned above, the results are not highly accurate, but they serve to establish orders of magnitude. For *Vibrio costicolus* grown in a medium with 1·0M-NaCl but a normal (i.e. low) K^+ content, the intracellular K^+ concentration was *c*. 0·3M and the Na^+ concentration of a similar magnitude; in separate experiments, the internal K^+ concentration was found to increase three-fold when the NaCl concentration in the growth medium was raised from 1·0 to 3·0M. There were indications of even higher intracellular concentrations of K^+ in *Halobacterium halobium* and *Sarcina littoralis*.

The concentrations of K accumulated by halophilic bacteria from media with usual proportions of that cation are remarkable, especially in the light of the finding of Brown & Gibbons (1955) that the K requirement for their growth is only slightly greater than that for ordinary bacteria. Because the intracellular K concentration rises with the external NaCl concentration, it seems probable that the K^+ ion plays some important part in the relations of halophilic cells to NaCl.

These results are clearly comparable with those of the earlier workers in indicating high internal salt concentrations; and they agree with the conclusion from the plasmoptysis experiments that the intracellular concentration rises broadly with the external concentration. This conclusion is, however, so important, as will appear below, that it is still desirable to obtain more and better data to verify it.

Studies on Isolated enzymes

Because of the difficulties of direct measurement of intracellular solute concentrations, attempts have been made to infer them from the behaviour of enzymes extracted from the cell. The assumptions in this approach have been (*a*) that the concentration optimum of the enzyme is the same when extracted as it was in the cell and (*b*) that in the cell the enzyme will be working under optimum conditions; so that the concentration optimum of the extracted enzyme measures the intracellular solute concentration. This reasoning was implicit, for example, in the interpretation by Robinson, Gibbons & Thatcher (1952) of the effects of inhibitors on the salt relations of nitritase activity in *Micrococcus halodenitrificans.* Untreated cells had optimum activity in 2–3 % NaCl, while cells treated with tetramethyl-*p*-phenylenediamine showed greatest activity with < 0·5 % NaCl. Their interpretation was, apparently, that the intracellular concentration in untreated cells in 3 % salt was < 0·5 %, for they concluded that the inhibitor destroyed a mechanism maintaining the concentration difference. It is an unwarranted assumption to suppose that enzymes work under optimum conditions in the natural state, as the recent experience of Kaplan (1955) emphasizes. It may also be wrong to take the concentration relations of an extracted enzyme as representing those obtaining within the cell; Ingram (1938) found that the behaviour towards salt of an extracted enzyme varied with its treatment. Robinson (1952), Robinson & Katznelson (1953) and Baxter & Gibbons (1954) have observed that enzymes from the obligate halophiles *Micrococcus halodenitrificans* and *Pseudomonas salinaria* are inactivated by exposure to low salt concentrations; whence it might be expected that extraction, for example, by autolysis in solutions of low concentration, as practised by Egami, Yamadi & Shiio (1953), would completely fail to reveal similar enzymes. It has been suggested (Ingram, 1947) that the reactions of enzymes to high salt concentrations depend on the stability, in particular the solubility, of the enzyme proteins, and any treatment which prejudices this is likely to be misleading. We need much more information about the effect of different treatments in preparation before we can rely on the behaviour of cell-free enzymes as an index of their reactions to solute concentration *in vivo*, and the observations described below are to be regarded with this reservation.

From experiments with the nitritase of *Micrococcus halodenitrificans*, Robinson *et al.* (1952) concluded that the intracellular salt concentration must be low. The optimum salt concentration for this enzyme in intact cells was 2·2 %, whereas that of a preparation obtained by grinding the cells in 3·3 % NaCl was only 0·9 %. The concentration in which the cells had been grown, 3·3 %, was, however, in itself quite low. Shortly after, similar results were presented by Egami *et al.* (1953). From cells of their halotolerant strain of *Bacillus pumilus*, grown in 10 % NaCl, they identified various enzymes after autolysis of the cells in low salt buffers, and found that none of the enzymes showed any unusual reaction towards salt. Both these investigations seem open to doubt for reasons just explained; the first, in the interpretation of the significance of the concentration optimum; the second, because the preparation of the enzymes was done at low salt concentrations. In any case, the general conclusion that the intracellular concentrations are low is incompatible with the direct analytical results obtained later by the same investigators.

Recently, more 'halophilic' enzymes have been recovered and they have been found to be different in this respect, and virtually only in this respect, from analogous enzymes from salt-intolerant organisms. Baxter & Gibbons (1954) prepared cell-free glycerol dehydrogenases from *Pseudomonas salinaria* (in 20 % NaCl), *Vibrio costicolus* (in 4 % NaCl) and *Escherichia coli* (no salt): whereas the salt optima for the two latter were 0·5 and 0·25 M-NaCl respectively, that for the *Pseudomonas* was about 2 M with NaCl and > 3·5 M with KCl (Fig. 7). Analogous results obtained about the same time were reviewed briefly by Egami (1955).

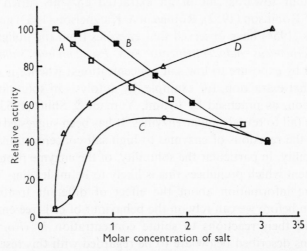

Fig. 7. Relations between salt concentration and the activity of cell-free glycerol dehydrogenases prepared from salt-intolerant, facultative and obligately halophilic bacteria: *A, Escherichia coli*, NaCl; *B, Vibrio costicolus*, NaCl; *C, Pseudomonas salinaria*, NaCl; *D, Pseudomonas salinaria*, KCl (data of Baxter & Gibbons, 1954).

The alkaline phosphomonoesterase (Fig. 8) and the glucose dehydrogenase (Fig. 9) of his obligately halophilic *Pseudomonas* were found to have salt optima in the range 2–4 M, while the glucose dehydrogenase of *P. fluorescens* was practically inhibited at 1 M; in these cases, reactions to NaCl, KCl and Na_2SO_4 were similar at equal concentrations of cation.

In passing, we may note that the above observations shed light on several peculiarities of the halophilic bacteria. The instability of the enzyme from *Pseudomonas salinaria* at low salt concentrations was compared by Baxter & Gibbons (1954) to the salt requirement of this species for growth. The resistance of these enzymes to high concentrations of KCl is understandable if, as suggested by Christian's work, the cells contain unexpectedly high concentrations of that salt. The high

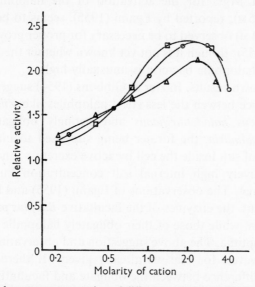

Fig. 8. Relations between concentration of different cations and the activity of a cell-free alkaline phosphomonoesterase from a halophilic *Pseudomonas*: o, NaCl; □, KCl; ∧, Na₂SO₄ (data of Egami, 1955).

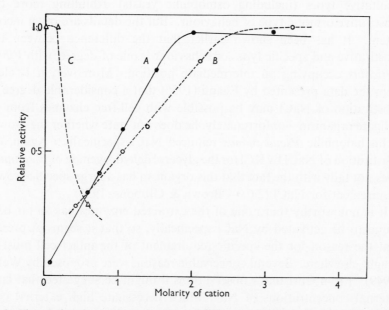

Fig. 9. The relations between concentration of different salts and the activity of a cell-free glucose dehydrogenase from a halophilic *Pseudomonas*, compared with those for a similar enzyme from *P. fluorescens*: *A*, Halophilic *Pseudomonas*, NaCl, NaBr or KCl; *B*, Halophilic *Pseudomonas*, Na₂SO₄; *C*, *P. fluorescens*, NaCl (data of Egami, 1955).

requirement of Mg^{2+} for the activation of the halophilic phospho-esterase (c. 0·05M), reported by Egami (1955), seems to be comparable with that (c. 0·1M) observed to be necessary for proper growth by Brown & Gibbons (1955): though it is not yet known whether the Mg^{2+} content of the cells of halophilic bacteria is unusually high.

From their own results, Baxter & Gibbons (1954) suggested a fundamental difference betwen the less strict halophiles like *Vibrio costicolus* and *Micrococcus halodenitrificans* and strongly obligate types like *Pseudomonas salinaria*, the former being supposed to maintain a low concentration of salt inside the cell by active excretion, and the latter to accept a relatively high internal salt concentration but to develop resistant enzymes. The observations of Egami (1955) and his colleagues are in agreement, the enzymes of the facultative *Bacillus pumilus* having low salt optima, while those of their obligately halophilic *Pseudomonas* had high salt optima. The above suggestion and observations seem open to doubt, however, for reasons already given. If there were such a fundamental difference between the obligate and facultative halophiles, one might expect it to be related to the extent to which the requirement for NaCl is specific or can be substituted. Here there is broad agreement, the obligate types having a large specific requirement for NaCl, and the facultative types (including osmophilic yeasts) exhibiting more the substitutive osmotic type of behaviour. But the details are often inconsistent. It has been shown earlier that the difference between the substitutive and specific types of behaviour is one of degree, with *Vibrio costicolus* occupying an intermediate position. Moreover, it is clear from the data presented by Egami (1955) that a considerable degree of substitution of NaCl may be possible with cell-free enzymes from an obligate organism—unfortunately, he does not state whether the growth of his halophilic *Pseudomonas* required NaCl specifically. Again, the substitution of NaCl by KCl for the glycerol dehydrogenase of *P. salinaria* does not tally with the fact that this organism has a large specific growth requirement for NaCl (2·0M—Brown & Gibbons, 1955).

It is noteworthy that none of the extracted enzymes has so far been found to be activated by NaCl specifically, so that it seems at present that the reason for the specific requirement of the intact cell must be sought elsewhere. Several conceivable reasons were proposed by Weber (1949). From Christian's observations it might be suggested that large internal concentrations of Na^+, which necessitate high external concentrations because this ion readily passes the cell boundary, are needed to balance the large internal concentrations of K^+ and, conceivably, of Mg^{2+}. The observations of Dumesh (1935), that the minimum requirement for NaCl rises with the concentration of KCl in the medium, and of Baas-Becking (1931) that the optimum Mg:Ca ratio rises with the external NaCl concentration, lend support to this idea. While it is not known why such an ionic balance should be necessary, it would at least be interesting to see whether the requirement for Na^+ could be reduced by curtailing the amounts of the antagonistic ions available to be absorbed into the cell.

CONCLUSIONS

It will be clear that considerable advances have been made in the past few years in the understanding of how organisms resist high solute concentrations in their environment. The recent observations all lead to the conclusion that the internal solute concentration of their cells is roughly comparable with that of the medium in which they grow. Moreover, there is no evidence of any significant difference in this respect between organisms with different types of reaction—intolerant, facultative or obligate. The halophilic bacteria appear to survive their situation because they have enzymes adapted to high intracellular salt concentrations; and, when salt-intolerant enzymes are extracted from a halophilic cell with a high intracellular concentration, it now seems likely that the extraction technique was misleading, or that the full functioning of the particular enzyme is unnecessary to the cell, or that there is a high degree of heterogeneity in the distribution of the salt inside the cell. Because so many different kinds of bacteria are able to tolerate high salt concentrations, it is unlikely that salt tolerance will prove to be a characteristic of particular types of enzyme. The most promising line of investigation would at present seem to be the isolation of more enzymes from a wider range of halophilic and osmophilic organisms, and efforts to discover what factors determine their reactions to concentration and to specific salts. The reason for the high specific requirement of some species for NaCl is still unexplained, though it may have some relation to the remarkably high concentrations of K^+ probably accumulated by their cells. Little can be said about the osmophilic yeasts, because no corresponding investigations have yet been made with them, although they should in some ways present a simpler situation.

It must be remembered, of course, that most of the foregoing discussion has been based on investigations with a rather small number of organisms, especially the red halophiles; and, as the range of observation is extended, new facts may well come to light which will invalidate suggestions hitherto made. Observations on the osmophilic yeasts, and on the non-pigmented obligate halophiles which have been neglected in favour of their more colourful counterparts, would be particularly instructive at the present time.

This paper was prepared as part of the programme of the Food Investigation Organization of the Department of Scientific and Industrial Research. The author is indebted to Mr J. H. B. Christian, Dr M. Pamela Scarr, Mr W. J. Scott and Dr J. M. Shewan for helpful discussions and the use of unpublished observations.

REFERENCES

ANDERSON, H. (1954). The reddening of salted hides and fish. *Appl. Microbiol.* **2**, 64.

BAAS-BECKING, L. G. M. (1928). An organism living in concentrated brine. *Tijdschr. ned. dierk. Ver.* III, **1**, 1.

BAAS-BECKING, L. G. M. (1931). Salt effects on swarmers of *Dunaliella vividis* Teod. *J. gen. Physiol.* **14**, 765.

BARANIK-PIKOWSKY, M. A. (1927). Über den Einfluss hoher Salzkonzentrationen auf die Limanbakterien. *Zbl. Bakt.* Abt. II, **70**, 373.

BARNETT, J. A. & INGRAM, M. (1955). Technique in the study of yeast assimilation reactions. *J. appl. Bact.* **18**, 131.

BARNETT, J. A., INGRAM, M. & SWAIN, T. (1956). The use of β-glucosides in classifying yeasts. *J. gen. Microbiol.* **15**, 529.

BAUMGARTNER, J. G. (1937). The salt limits and thermal stability of a new species of anaerobic halophile. *Food Res.* **2**, 321.

BAXTER, R. M. & GIBBONS, N. E. (1954). The glycerol dehydrogenases of *Pseudomonas salinaria*, *Vibrio costicolus*, and *Escherichia coli* in relation to bacterial halophilism. *Canad. J. Biochem. Physiol.* **32**, 206.

BEETLESTONE, N. C. (1930). Osmosis and fermentation. *J. Inst. Brew.* **36**, 483.

BROWN, H. J. & GIBBONS, N. E. (1955). The effect of magnesium, potassium and iron on the growth and morphology of red halophilic bacteria. *Canad. J. Microbiol.* **1**, 486.

BROWNE, W. W. (1922). The staining of halophilic bacteria. *Abstr. Bact.* **6**, 53.

BURCIK, E. (1950). Über die Beziehungen zwischen Hydratur und Wachstum bei Bakterien und Hefen. *Arch. Mikrobiol.* **15**, 203.

CASTELL, C. H. & MAPPLEBECK, E. G. (1952). The survival of red halophiles in water and in brines. *J. Fish. Res. Bd Can.* **9**, 377.

CHALLINOR, S. W. (1955). Cider yeasts and the fermentation of apple juice. *J. appl. Bact.* **18**, 212.

CHRISTIAN, J. H. B. (1955). The influence of nutrition on the water relations of *Salmonella oranienburg*. *Aust. J. biol. Sci.* **8**, 75.

CHRISTIAN, J. H. B. (1956). The physiological basis of salt tolerance in halophilic bacteria. Dissertation, Cambridge.

CHRISTIAN, J. H. B. & SCOTT, W. J. (1953). Water relations of Salmonellae. *Aust. J. biol. Sci.* **6**, 565.

CLAYTON, W. (1932*a*). The bacterial flora of common salt. III. Salt tolerance. *Food Manuf.* **7**, 76.

CLAYTON, W. (1932*b*). The bacteriology of common salt. IV. The reddening of salted fish. *Food Manuf.* **7**, 109.

COBB, J. N. (1927). Pacific cod fisheries. *Docum. U.S. Bur. Fish.* no. 1014, p. 457.

DAVIES, H. G., WILKINS, H. M. F., CHAYEN, J. & LA COUR, L. F. (1954). The use of the interference microscope to determine dry mass in living cells and as a quantitative cytochemical technique. *Quart. J. micr. Sci.* **95**, 271.

DIERCHEN, W. (1938). Über die Einwirkung von Neutralsalzen auf die Zellgrenz-schicht von Bakterien. *Zbl. Bakt.* Abt. II, **98**, 110.

DOUDOROFF, M. (1940). Experiments on the adaptation of *Escherichia coli* to sodium chloride. *J. gen. Physiol.* **23**, 585.

DUMESH, M. G. (1935). Halophilism and salt tolerance of bacteria. (In Russian.) *Microbiology, Moscow*, **4**, 45.

DUSSAULT, H. P. (1954). Adaptation of the 'Drop-plate' method for the enumeration of red halophilic bacteria. *J. Fish. Res. Bd Can.* **11**, 261.

DUSSAULT, H. P. (1955). An improved technique for staining red halophilic bacteria. *J. Bact.* **70**, 484.

DUSSAULT, H. P. & LACHANCE, R. A. (1952). Improved medium for red halophilic bacteria from salt fish. *J. Fish. Res. Bd Can.* **9**, 157.

EDDY, B. P. & INGRAM, M. (1956). A salt-tolerant denitrifying *Bacillus* which blows canned bacon. *J. appl. Bact.* **19**, 62.

EGAMI, F. (1955). Recherches biochimiques sur les bactéries halotolérantes et halophiles. *Bull. Soc. Chim. biol.*, Paris, **37**, 207.

EGAMI, F., YAMADA, T. & SHIIO, I. (1953). Sur une méthode simple pour l'extraction des enzymes bactériens. *C.R. Soc. Biol.*, Paris, **147**, 1531.

ELAZARI-VOLCANI, B. (1940). Studies on the microflora of the Dead Sea. Dissertation, Jerusalem.

ETCHELLS, J. L., BELL, T. A. & JONES, I. D. (1953). Morphology and pigmentation of certain yeasts from brines and the cucumber plant. *Farlowia*, **4**, 265.

FABIAN, F. W. & HALL, H. H. (1933). Yeasts found in fermented maple syrup. *Zbl. Bakt.* Abt. II, **89**, 31.

FELLERS, C. R. (1933). Spoilage of maple products by molds. *J. Bact.* **25**, 67.

FLANNERY, W. L. (1956). Current status of knowledge of halophilic bacteria. *Bact. Rev.* **20**, 49.

FLANNERY, W. L., DOETSCH, R. N. & HANSEN, P. A. (1952). Salt desideratum of *Vibrio costicolus*, an obligate halophilic bacterium. I. Ionic replacement of sodium chloride requirements. *J. Bact.* **64**, 713.

FLANNERY, W. L., DOETSCH, R. N. & HANSEN, P. A. (1953). Salt desideratum of *Vibrio costicolus*, an obligate halophilic bacterium. II. Effect of salts on the oxidation of glucose. *J. Bact.* **66**, 526.

FODA, I. O. & VAUGHN, R. H. (1950). Salt tolerance in the genus *Aerobacter*. *Food Tech.*, Champaign, **4**, 182.

FRANK, M. & HESS, E. (1941). Studies on salt fish. VI. Halophilic brown molds of the genus *Sporendonema* emend. Ciferri et Redaelli. *J. Fish. Res. Bd Can.* **5**, 287.

GIBBONS, N. E. & BAXTER, R. M. (1953). The relation between salt concentration and enzyme activity in halophilic bacteria. *Proc. VIth int. Congr. Microbiol.*, Rome, **1**, 210.

GOLIKOWA, S. M. (1930a). Eine Gruppe von obligat halophilen Bakterien, gezüchtet in Substraten mit hohen NaCl-Gehalt. *Zbl. Bakt.* Abt. II, **80**, 35.

GOLIKOWA, S. M. (1930b). A group of obligate halophiles isolated from salted Astrakhan herring. (In Russian.) *Trav. Lab. ichth. Astrakhan*, **7**, 71.

HARRISON, F. C. & KENNEDY, M. E. (1922). The red discoloration of cured codfish. *Trans. roy. Soc. Can.* **16**, 101.

HEINTZELER, I. (1939). Das Wachstum der Schimmelpilze in Abhängigkeit von den Hydraturverhältnissen unter verschiedenen Aussenbedingungen. *Arch. Mikrobiol.* **10**, 92.

HESS, E. (1942). Studies on salt fish. II. Effect of environment upon the growth of red halophilic bacteria. *J. Fish. Res. Bd Can.* **6**, 10.

HOF, T. (1935). Investigations concerning bacterial life in strong brines. *Rec. Trav. bot. néerl.* **32**, 92.

HOROWITZ-WLASSOWA, L. M. (1931*a*). Über die Rolle der Bakterienflora der Lake beim Pökeln mit Berücksichtigung der Frage der Halophilie in der Bakterienwelt. *Z. Untersuch. Lebensmitt.* **62**, 596.

HOROWITZ-WLASSOWA, L. M. (1931*b*). Über die Rotfärbung gesalzener Därme ('der rote Hund'). *Zbl. Bakt.* Abt. II, **85**, 12.

HOUWINK, A. L. (1956). Flagella, gas vacuoles, and cell wall structure in *Halobacterium halobium*. An electron microscope study. *J. gen. Microbiol.* **15**, 146.

INGRAM, M. (1938). The effect of sodium chloride on a bacterial enzyme which destroys lactic acid. *Rep. Fd Invest. Bd, Lond.*, p. 72.

INGRAM, M. (1939). The endogenous respiration of *Bacillus cereus*. II. The effect of salts on the rate of absorption of oxygen. *J. Bact.* **38**, 613.

INGRAM, M. (1940). The endogenous respiration of *Bacillus cereus*. III. The changes in the rate of respiration caused by sodium chloride, in relation to the hydrogen-ion concentration. *J. Bact.* **40**, 683.

INGRAM, M. (1947). A theory relating the action of salts on bacterial respiration to their influence on the solubility of proteins. *Proc. roy. Soc.* B, **134**, 181.

INGRAM, M. (1950). Osmophilic yeasts from concentrated orange juice. *J. gen. Microbiol.* **4**, ix.

JOSLYN, M. A. & CRUESS, W. V. (1929). A comparative investigation of certain film-forming fungi. *Hilgardia*, **4**, 201.

KAPLAN, J. G. (1955). The alteration of intracellular enzymes. I. Yeast catalase and the Euler effect. *Exp. Cell Res.* **8**, 305.

KATZNELSON, H. & LOCHHEAD, A. G. (1952). Growth factor requirements of halophilic bacteria. *J. Bact.* **64**, 97.

KATZNELSON, H. & ROBINSON, J. (1955). Observations on the respiratory activity of certain obligately halophilic bacteria with high salt requirements. *J. Bact.* **71**, 244.

KLEBAHN, H. (1919). Die Schädlinge des Klippfisches. *Mitt. Inst. allg. Bot. Hamb.* **4**, 11.

KLUYVER, A. J. & BAARS, J. K. (1932). On some physiological artefacts. *Proc. Acad. Sci. Amst.* **35**, 370.

KROEMER, K. & KRUMBHOLZ, G. (1931). Untersuchungen über osmophile Sproßpilze. I. Beiträge zur Kenntnis der Gärungsvorgänge und der Gärungserreger der Trockenbeerenauslesen. *Arch. Mikrobiol.* **2**, 352.

KROEMER, K. & KRUMBHOLZ, G. (1932). Untersuchungen über osmophile Sproßpilze. II. Das Verhalten von Sproßpilzen in Nährlösungen mit hohen Neutralsalzkonzentrationen. *Arch. Mikrobiol.* **3**, 384.

KUROCHKIN, B. I. & EMILIANCHIK, K. G. (1935). Fuchsin discoloration in freshly salted fish. (In Russian.) *Probl. Nutrit., Moscow*, **5**, 92.

LABRIE, A. & GIBBONS, N. E. (1937). Studies on salt fish. II. The effect of salt concentration on preservation. *J. biol. Bd Can.* **3**, 439.

LEFEVRE, E. & ROUND, L. A. (1919). A preliminary report upon some halophilic bacteria. *J. Bact.* **4**, 177.

LERCHE, W. (1937). Untersuchungen über Entwicklung und Fortpflanzung in der Gattung *Dunaliella*. *Arch. Protistenk.* **88**, 236.

LOCHHEAD, A. G. (1934). Bacteriological studies on the red discoloration of salted hides. *Canad. J. Res.* **10**, 275.

LOCHHEAD, A. G. & FARRELL, L. (1930). Soil as a source of infection of honey by salt-tolerant yeasts. *Canad. J. Res.* **3**, 51.

LOCHHEAD, A. G. & HERON, D. A. (1929). Microbiological studies of honey. *Bull. Dep. Agric. Can.* no. 116, new series.

LOCHHEAD, A. G. & LANDERKIN, G. B. (1942). Nutrilite requirements of osmophilic yeasts. *J. Bact.* **44**, 343.

LODDER, J. & KREGER VAN RIJ, N. J. W. (1952). *The Yeasts.* Amsterdam: North Holland Publishing Co.

MAGER, J., KUCZYNSKI, M., SCHATZBERG, G. & AVI-DOR, Y. (1956). Turbidity changes in bacterial suspensions in relation to osmotic pressure. *J. gen. Microbiol.* **14**, 69.

MALEVICH, O. A. (1936). A new species of halophilic mould isolated from salted fish: *Oospora Nikitinskii* n.sp. (In Russian.) *Microbiology, Moscow,* **5**, 813.

MITCHELL, P. & MOYLE, J. (1955). Osmotic function and structure in bacteria. *Sixth Symp. Soc. gen. Microbiol.* p. 150.

MOORE, H. N. (1940). The use of silica gels for the cultivation of halophilic organisms. *J. Bact.* **40**, 409.

MOORE, H. N. (1941). The use of silica gels for the cultivation of halophilic organisms. II. Quantitative determinations. *J. Bact.* **41**, 317.

MOSSEL, D. A. A. & INGRAM, M. (1955). The physiology of the microbial spoilage of foods. *J. appl. Bact.* **18**, 232.

MRAK, E. M. & BONAR, L. (1938). A note on yeast obtained from slimy sausage. *Food Res.* **3**, 615.

MRAK, E. M. & PHAFF, H. J. (1948). Yeasts. *Annu. Rev. Microbiol.* **2**, 1.

MÜLLER, G. (1950). Halophile Bakterien und Salzkonserven. *Dtsch. Lebensmitt-Rdsch.* **3**, 60.

NICKERSON, W. J. (1943). *Zygosaccharomyces acidifaciens*: a new acetifying yeast. *Mycologia,* **35**, 65.

NUNHEIMER, T. D. & FABIAN, F. W. (1940). Influence of organic acids, sugars and sodium chloride upon strains of food poisoning staphylococci. *Amer. J. publ. Hlth,* **30**, 1040.

O'BRIEN, F. E. M. (1948). Control of humidity by saturated salt solutions. *J. sci. Instrum.* **25**, 73.

PENSO, G. (1947). Il rosso dei baccalari—Etiologia, commestibilita, bonifica e prevenzione. *R.C. Ist. sup. Sanit.* **10**, 563.

PETROWA, E. K. (1933). Mikrobiologie des Kochsalzes. *Arch. Mikrobiol.* **4**, 326.

PETROWA, E. K. (1935). Étude sur le pléomorphisme de l'agent du rouge de poisson salé. *Ann. Inst. Pasteur,* **55**, 255.

PETTER, H. F. M. (1932). Over roode en andere bacteriën van gezouten visch. Dissertation, Utrecht.

PHAFF, H. J., MILLER, M. W. & SHIFRINE, M. (1956). The taxonomy of yeasts isolated from *Drosophila* in the Yosemite region of California. *Leeuwenhoek ned. Tijdschr.* **22**, 145.

PJETURSSON, S. H. & DAMM, H. (1935). Fakultativ halophile Hyphomyceten auf Salzfischen. *Dtsch. tierärztl. Wschr.* **43**, 239.

PRESTON, R. D. (1952). *The Molecular Architecture of Plant Cell Walls,* p. 82. London: Chapman and Hall.

RECCA, J. & MRAK, E. M. (1952). Yeasts occurring in citrus products. *Food Tech., Champaign,* **6**, 450.

RIPPEL, A. (1947). *Mikrobiologie.* Jena: Springer.

ROBINSON, J. (1952). The effects of salts on the nitritase and lactic acid dehydrogenase activity of *Micrococcus halodenitrificans. Canad. J. Bot.* **30**, 155.

ROBINSON, J. & GIBBONS, N. E. (1952). The effect of salts on the growth of *Micrococcus halodenitrificans. Canad. J. Bot.* **30**, 147.

ROBINSON, J., GIBBONS, N. E. & THATCHER, F. S. (1952). A mechanism of halophilism in *Micrococcus halodenitrificans*. *J. Bact.* **64**, 69.

ROBINSON, J. & KATZNELSON, H. (1953). Aspartate-glutamate transaminase in a red halophilic bacterium. *Nature, Lond.*, **172**, 672.

RUBENTSCHIK, L. (1929). Zur Frage der aeroben Zellulosezersetzung bei hohen Salzkonzentrationen. *Zbl. Bakt.* Abt. II, **76**, 305.

RUBINSTEIN, B. B. (1932). The kinetics of intracellular carbohydrate oxidation of *Sarcina lutea*. *J. cell. comp. Physiol.* **2**, 27.

SACKETT, W. G. (1919). Honey as a carrier of intestinal diseases. *Bull. Colo. agric. Exp. Sta.* no. 252.

SALTON, M. R. J. (1955). Bacterial cell walls. *Sixth Symp. Soc. gen. Microbiol.* p. 81.

SCARR, M. P. (1951). Osmophilic yeasts in raw beet and cane sugars and intermediate sugar-refining products. *J. gen. Microbiol.* **5**, 704.

SCARR, M. P. (1954). Studies on the taxonomy and physiology of osmophilic yeasts isolated from the sugar cane. Dissertation, London.

SCHACHINGER, L. & HEISS, R. (1951). Osmotischer Wert und Mikroorganismenwachstum in Zuckerlösungen. *Arch. Mikrobiol.* **16**, 347.

SCHELHORN, M. VON (1950a). Untersuchungen über den Verderb wasserarmer Lebensmittel durch osmophile Mikroorganismen. I. Verderb von Lebensmittel durch osmophile Hefen. *Z. Untersuch. Lebensmitt.* **91**, 117.

SCHELHORN, M. VON (1950b). Untersuchungen über den Verderb wasserarmer Lebensmittel durch osmophile Mikroorganismen. II. Mitteilung. *Z. Untersuch. Lebensmitt.* **91**, 338.

SCHELHORN, M. VON (1951). Control of microorganisms causing spoilage in fruit and vegetable products. *Advanc. Food Res.* **3**, 429.

SCHOOP, G. (1934). Salzbakterien. *Dtsch. tierärztl. Wschr.* **42**, 205.

SCHOOP, G. (1935). Obligat halophile Mikroben. *Zbl. Bakt.* Abt. I, Orig. **134**, 14.

SCHOOP, G. (1937). Salzpilz (Torula epizoa) auf Lebensmitteln. *Dtsch. tierärztl. Wschr.* **45**, 621.

SCOTT, W. J. (1953). Water relations of *Staphylococcus aureus* at 30° C. *Aust. J. biol. Sci.* **6**, 549.

SCOTT, W. J. (1956). The water relations of food spoilage microorganisms. *Advanc. Food Res.* (in the Press).

SHERMAN, J. M. & HOLM, G. E. (1922). Salt effects in bacterial growth. II. The growth of *Bact. coli* in relation to H-ion concentration. *J. Bact.* **7**, 465.

SHEWAN, J. M. (1938). The reddening of salt fish. *Rep. Fd Invest. Bd, Lond.*, p. 113.

SHEWAN, J. M. (1942). Some bacteriological aspects of the handling, production and distribution of food. *Chem. & Ind. (Rev.)*, **61**, 312.

SMITH, W. W. & ZOBELL, C. E. (1937). Direct microscopic evidence of an autochthonous bacterial flora in Great Salt Lake. *Ecology*, **18**, 453.

SMITHIES, W. R. & GIBBONS, N. E. (1955). The deoxyribose nucleic acid slime layer of some halophilic bacteria. *Canad. J. Microbiol.* **1**, 614.

SMITHIES, W. R., GIBBONS, N. E. & BAYLEY, S. T. (1955). The chemical composition of the cell and cell wall of some halophilic bacteria. *Canad. J. Microbiol.* **1**, 605.

SPIEGELBERG, C. H. (1944). Sugar and salt tolerance of *Clostridium pasteurianum* and some related anaerobes. *J. Bact.* **48**, 13.

STATHER, F. & LIEBSCHER, E. (1929). Zur Bakteriologie des Rotwerdens gesalzener Rohäute. *Collegium, Haltingen*, **713**, 437.

STILLE, B. (1948). Grenzwerte der relativen Feuchtigkeit und des Wassergehaltes getrockneter Lebensmittel für den mikrobiellen Befall. *Z. Untersuch. Lebensmitt.* **88**, 9.

STUART, L. S. (1935). The morphology of bacteria causing reddening of salted hides. *J. Amer. Leath. Chem. Ass.* **30**, 226.

STUART, L. S. (1938). Isolation of halophilic bacteria from soil, water and dung. *Food Res.* **3**, 417.

STUART, L. S. (1940*a*). The growth of halophilic bacteria in concentrations of sodium chloride above three molar. *J. agric. Res.* **61**, 259.

STUART, L. S. (1940*b*). Effect of protein concentration and cysteine on growth of halophilic bacteria. *J. agric. Res.* **61**, 267.

STUART, L. S., FREY, R. W. & JAMES, L. H. (1933). Microbiological studies of salt in relation to the reddening of salted hides. *Tech. Bull. U.S. Dep. Agric.* no. 383.

STUART, L. S. & JAMES, L. H. (1938). The effect of Eh and sodium chloride concentration on the physiology of halophilic bacteria. *J. Bact.* **35**, 381.

TANNER, F. W. & EVANS, F. L. (1933). Effect of meat curing solutions on anaerobic bacteria. I. Sodium chloride. *Zbl. Bakt.* Abt. II, **88**, 44.

TOMKINS, R. G. (1929). Studies of the growth of moulds. *Proc. roy. Soc.* B, **105**, 375.

VAISEY, E. B. (1954). Osmophilism of *Sporendonema epizoum*. *J. Fish. Res. Bd Can.* **11**, 901.

VELU, H. & BALOZET, L. (1929). Production expérimentale d'un agent du rouge des salaisons par mutation brusque de *Bacillus prodigiosus*. *C.R. Soc. Biol., Paris,* **100**, 1095.

VENKATARAMAN, R. & SREENIVASAN, A. (1954). Studies on the red halophilic bacteria from salted fish and salt. *Proc. Indian Acad. Sci.* **39**, 17.

VERHOEVEN, W. (1952). Aerobic spore-forming nitrate-reducing bacteria. Dissertation. Delft: Waltman.

WALTER, H. (1931). *Die Hydratur der Pflanze.* Jena: Gustav Fischer.

WARE, G. C., CHILDS, E. & SMITH, H. M. (1955). The effect of salt concentration on the growth of bacteria in dilute nutrient solutions. *J. appl. Bact.* **18**, 446.

WEBER, M. M. (1949). Red halophilic micro-organisms. A problem on the biochemical foundation of ecological specialization. *Biol. Rev. C.C.N.Y.* **1**, 9.

WHALLEY, H. C. S. DE & SCARR, M. P. (1947). Micro-organisms in refined sugar and intermediate products. *Chem. & Ind.* (*Rev.*), **66**, 531.

WINSLOW, C-E. A. & HAYWOOD, E. T. (1931). The specific potency of certain cations with reference to their effect on bacterial viability. *J. Bact.* **22**, 49.

WINSLOW, C-E. A., WALKER, H. H. & SUTERMEISTER, M. (1932). The influence of aeration and of sodium chloride upon the growth curve of bacteria in various media. *J. Bact.* **24**, 185.

YAMADA, T. & SHIIO, I. (1953). Effects of salt concentration on the respiration of a halotolerant bacterium. *J. Biochem., Tokyo,* **40**, 327.

THE ACTION OF PRESSURE AND TEMPERATURE*

FRANK H. JOHNSON

*Biology Department, Princeton University, Princeton, N.J.
and Marine Biological Laboratory, Woods Hole, Mass.*

INTRODUCTION

Ecology deals with the mutual relationships between organisms and their environment, at all levels of complexity. The ultimate goal of ecology, as of other branches of biology, is to interpret all accessible phenomena in terms of the structure and behaviour of molecules. Since the states and reactivities of biological molecules are subject to the influence of the immediate chemical and physical environment, there is, so to speak, an 'ecology' of molecules which constitutes a basic aspect of the broader problems, and this aspect is emphasized in the discussions which follow.

From the present viewpoint, it is appropriate as well as convenient to consider the ecological significance of pressure and temperature under one heading. It would be appropriate to include also chemical factors such as pH, growth substances, salt concentration, etc., inasmuch as their effects are in principle or in fact subject to modification by pressure and temperature, and a full understanding of their action requires reference to all the significant parameters. Since they are dealt with at length elsewhere in the Symposium, discussion of these other factors in the present paper will be limited to a few data that seem especially relevant to the problems of temperature and pressure.

Interrelationships in the biological action of temperature and pressure have become apparent only within recent years. Even now, the importance of pressure as a variable of both fundamental theoretical interest and ecological importance remains to be fully appreciated, inasmuch as contemporary books and extended discussions pertaining to ecology, comparative physiology, oceanography, deep-sea life, etc., often include the influence of temperature on living organisms with scarcely more than a passing reference to pressure. The reasons for this situation are several, some obvious but others less so. In the interests of clarifying the present status as well as of envisioning likely avenues of future research, a brief review of the background and theory of biological pressure-temperature

* Aided in part by a contract (Nonr 1353(00), Project NR 165–233) between the Office of Naval Research and Princeton University.

relationships should be helpful. As a further point of clarity it is worth keeping in mind the kind of pressure, namely, purely hydrostatic, that is under discussion. Unlike pressure on gaseous systems, increased hydrostatic pressure on condensed systems, with no gas phase present, results in no change in concentration of dissolved substances beyond the extent of compressibility of the solvent. For water, throughout the range of pressures and temperatures that are of physiological interest, the compressibility is slight.

THE BACKGROUND OF BIOLOGICAL RESEARCH ON PRESSURE AND TEMPERATURE

For nearly half a century after Arrhenius (1889) published his theory concerning the influence of temperature on chemical reaction rates, and after Regnard (1891) coincidentally published a monograph concerning the influence of increased pressure on biological processes, research progressed independently in these seemingly unrelated fields of endeavour. The Arrhenius equation was soon applied to biological reactions (cf. Arrhenius, 1907, 1915; Bělehrádek, 1935), and because of the obvious importance of temperature, the availability of a quantitative theory of its influence on chemical rates, the relative ease of measuring its effects, and a virtually unlimited array of biological systems conveniently at hand, a vast literature on the subject accumulated. Pressure, on the other hand, enjoyed none of these inviting advantages. The only obvious natural environment where it might be significant was the sea, and there was no quantitative, physical chemical theory for interpreting its influence on reaction rates.

The discovery of living forms from depths of about 6000 m. in the sea inspired Regnard (1884a, b, c, d) and Certes (1884a, b, c) to undertake laboratory experiments in regard to the effects of increased hydrostatic pressure on a wide variety of biological processes which by 1891 included the activity and viability of aquatic organisms, enzyme action, fermentation, putrefaction, muscle contraction, nerve conduction, hatching of fish eggs, etc. Unfortunately, none of their experiments with increased pressure involved organisms from the deep sea; the various difficulties of obtaining and studying such organisms no doubt led these early investigators, as many subsequent ones, to concentrate their efforts on specimens from near the surface of the land or waters. Fortunately, the assembly of equipment employed early was unsuited for pressures exceeding those naturally occurring in the depths. As it turns out, this range of pressures, up to roughly 1000 atm., is of physiological interest, and although the early experiments did not take temperature into account, they demonstrated a number of phenomena of distinct interest. In general, they showed that under a few hundred atmospheres the rates of some processes were retarded, others accelerated; with rise in pressure, stimulation and then inhibition at still higher pressures sometimes occurred; and the effects were reversible on release of pressure provided the period of compression was not too long nor the pressure too high, in which event serious damage or death of organisms took place.

The general results described by Regnard and Certes were confirmed, extended and refined by later investigators, among whom was Fontaine (1930), who concluded a lengthy study of the effects of pressures up to 800 atm. on respiration, development, permeability, muscle contraction, photosynthesis, etc., of marine and other organisms, with the expressed hope that the importance of the results would lead to other researches, towards a solution of the mysterious and seductive problem of life in the great depths.

In the meantime, however, emphasis in research with pressure had begun to take a different turn. As methods became available, higher and higher pressures were studied, much beyond those to which any living organism, so far as anyone knows, is ever subjected in nature. Such pressures, of several thousand atmospheres and higher, are not *prima facie* of ecological or physiological interest. Yet, perhaps because of the added importance of possible practical applications, they have attracted the greater amount of attention and their effects, e.g. the denaturation of proteins at room temperature, the killing of bacteria, the inactivation of viruses, destruction of enzyme activity, modification of antigens, antibodies, nucleic acids, etc., are more widely known. These results are of much interest, but a more widespread familiarity with them than with those of lower pressures has had one unfortunate consequence, namely, a mistaken general impression that essentially the only results of increased hydrostatic pressure are of the kind just mentioned.

Although a detailed consideration of the very high pressures is beyond the scope of the present discussion* it is important to note that, with

* A summary review of the literature up to about 1950–1, along with discussion of the theory, is available in a recent book by Johnson, Eyring & Polissar (1954). Since 1950, most publications on the subject have come from investigators in France and in Russia. The former group includes Atanasiu, Basset, Barbu, Bordet, Chromé, Dubert, Joly, Macheboeuf, Rebeyrotte, Robert, Sclizewicz, Talwar and Vignais whose papers have appeared chiefly in the *Annales de l'Institut Pasteur*, the *Bulletin de la Société de Chimie Biologique* and the *Comptes Rendus hebdomadaires des Séances de l'Académie des Sciences*. The latter group includes Bresler, Finogenov, Frenkel, Glikina, Ivanov, Kasatochkin, Koniov, Selezneva and Tongur, whose papers have appeared chiefly in *Biokhimiya*, *Doklady Akademii Nauk*, and *Izvestiia Akademii Nauk, S.S.S.R., Seriia Fizicheskaia*.

respect to biological materials and processes, there are two different ranges of increased hydrostatic pressures, roughly those below and those above about 1000 atm. respectively, whose net effects may be entirely different and take place via different mechanisms. Under certain conditions, for example, protein denaturation may be retarded or reversed by the lower pressures, as discussed presently. Between 1000 and 5000 atm. the two types of effects probably overlap, the extent depending on the materials involved and the conditions, including temperature, of the experiment. Only the lower pressures will be dealt with in the remainder of this paper.

Had the Arrhenius (1889) equation included an explicit basis for interpreting the influence of pressure on chemical reaction rates, the picture might have been different when Bělehrádek (1935) published a detailed, critical monograph on the biological effects of temperature with no reference to pressure, and Cattell (1936) published a review of the biological effects of pressure with all but no reference to temperature. It was not until 1935, however, that advances in quantum physics and other fields led to a fully rational theory—the theory of absolute reaction rates—for understanding the influence of pressure as well as temperature on rate processes in general (Eyring, 1935; Polanyi & Evans, 1935; Glasstone, Laidler & Eyring, 1941). At the same time, Brown (1934, 1935) was inquiring into the pressure-temperature relationships of muscle contraction and found not only that the effects of increased pressure could be modified by temperature, which had been observed a short while earlier (Cattell & Edwards, 1930, 1932), but that these effects were correlated with the specific temperature-activity relationship of the muscle involved, i.e. similar effects were noted within different temperature ranges which more or less corresponded to those prevailing in the normal habitats of the respective organisms from which the muscles were obtained. Research on luminous bacteria (Johnson, Brown & Marsland, 1942a; Brown, Johnson & Marsland, 1942; Eyring & Magee, 1942) revealed similar phenomena in the process of bioluminescence and provided data suitable for application of the modern rate theory. A new relationship was also encountered, namely, between hydrostatic pressure and the action of narcotics (Johnson, Brown & Marsland, 1942b).

Pressure, temperature, biological specificity and chemical environment of living cells were thus brought together as fundamentally interrelated factors, along with a quantitative physical chemical theory. In the ensuing years, pressure-temperature relationships have been investigated in regard to some representative biological processes, including specific enzyme activity *in vivo* and *in vitro*, protoplasmic sol-gel equilibria, denaturation of proteins and bacteriophage, bacterial reproduction and disinfection, cell division of marine eggs, cardiac rhythmicity and others (cf. Johnson & Lewin, 1946 *a,b,c,d*; ZoBell & Johnson, 1949; ZoBell & Oppenhimer, 1950; Johnson, Eyring & Polissar, 1954; Marsland, 1950, 1956). On the basis of suggestive evidence, and in anticipation of the possibility that microbial organisms from the deep sea or from deep oil-well brines might be found to exhibit specific adaptations for life under increased pressure, the word 'barophilic' was coined to describe such organisms (Johnson, 1948; ZoBell & Johnson, 1949). In due course, modifications such as 'stenobarophilic' and 'eurybarophilic' may become useful.

THE PHYSICAL CHEMICAL THEORY OF PRESSURE AND TEMPERATURE IN BIOLOGICAL REACTIONS

According to the theory of absolute reaction rates, any chemical rate process proceeds through the formation of an unstable intermediate complex of the reactants, referred to as the activated complex or the transition state, having a lifetime of the order of 10^{-13} sec. Once formed, the activated complex decomposes at a universal rate which is the same for all reactions and is given by the expression kT/h, where k is the Boltzmann constant, i.e. the gas constant R over Avogadro's number N, T is the absolute temperature and h is Planck's constant. The probability that the activated complex will decompose to products of the reaction rather than to a reconstitution of the reactants is given by the transmission coefficient κ, which for most reactions is equal to unity or nearly so. The specific reaction rate k' is determined by the fraction of the population of molecules in the activated state at any moment multiplied by the universal rate of decomposition and by the probability of successful reaction, and this fraction is a function of a quasi-equilibrium, whose constant is designated $K^{\ddagger}$, between the normal and activated states. Although the equilibrium of activation is conceptually different from the thermodynamic equilibrium of a reversible reaction, as well as from that of the Arrhenius theory, it behaves in the manner of an ordinary equilibrium constant and for all practical purposes can be treated as such. Thus, we have $K^{\ddagger} = e^{-\Delta F^{\ddagger}/RT}$, analogous to $K = e^{-\Delta F/RT}$ of thermodynamics, $\Delta F^{\ddagger}$ and ΔF being the free energy of activation and of reaction respectively. The specific reaction rate is therefore given by the following relation:

$$k' = \kappa \frac{kT}{h} K^{\ddagger} = \kappa \frac{kT}{h} e^{-\Delta F^{\ddagger}/RT}. \tag{1}$$

Moreover, since $\Delta F^{\ddagger} = \Delta H^{\ddagger} - T\Delta S^{\ddagger}$ and $\Delta H^{\ddagger} = \Delta E^{\ddagger} + p\Delta V^{\ddagger}$, we have

$$k' = \kappa \frac{kT}{h} e^{-\Delta H^{\ddagger}/RT} e^{\Delta S^{\ddagger}/R} = \kappa \frac{kT}{h} e^{-\Delta E^{\ddagger}/RT} e^{-p\Delta V^{\ddagger}/RT} e^{\Delta S^{\ddagger}/R}. \qquad (2)$$

In (2), $\Delta H^{\ddagger}$, $\Delta S^{\ddagger}$, $\Delta E^{\ddagger}$ and $\Delta V^{\ddagger}$ are the heat, entropy, energy and volume changes, respectively, of activation, and p is pressure.

Equation (2) provides the quantitative basis for the influence of temperature and pressure on reaction rates. The numerical value of $\Delta H^{\ddagger}$ differs only slightly, by the factor RT, from that of μ in the Arrhenius equation (3):

$$v = Ae^{-\mu/RT}, \qquad (3)$$

in which v is the velocity of reaction and A is an empirical constant which was replaced in the extended Arrhenius theory by PZ, P representing a probability or steric factor and Z the number of collisions. In equation (2) the fact that various chemical reactions characterized by very different activation energies may nevertheless take place at similar rates at a given temperature is accounted for by differences in the entropy of activation. Thus at normal pressure the constant A of the Arrhenius equation is approximately equal to $\kappa \dfrac{kT}{h} e^{\Delta S^{\ddagger}/R}$. For reactions to proceed at measurable rates at ordinary temperatures, the value of $\Delta F^{\ddagger}$ must fall roughly between 20 and 30 kcal.

Biological reactions are catalysed or ultimately controlled by large molecules, viz. enzymes, proteins and nucleic acids. While an enzyme lowers the effective activation energy, it introduces additional factors through which the overall rate may be modified by pressure and temperature. The chief points are as follows.

First, although ordinary chemical reactions are usually accompanied by only small volume changes, of the order of a few c.c./mole at most, and their rates are therefore affected only slightly by pressures up to 1000 atm., reactions involving large molecules may be accompanied by large volume changes, amounting to as much as 100 c.c./mole or more, and their rates are then markedly influenced by such pressures. The large volume changes could result either from the summation of electrostriction associated with the ionization of a number of groups, or from more or less drastic changes in molecular configuration, as in a partial unfolding of protein superstructure that possibly accompanies the combination of certain enzymes with their substrates and also the process of protein denaturation. Moreover, the initial action of proteases apparently involves a loosening of the native configuration of the substrate in a manner akin to denaturation (Linderstrøm-Lang 1950). The initial change may involve a volume increase (cf. ribonuclease action; Chantrenne, Linderstrøm-Lang & Vandendriessche, 1947). The subsequent cleavage of peptid bonds is accompanied by a volume decrease of reaction (Linderstrøm-Lang & Jacobsen, 1941).

Secondly, any enzyme-catalysed process involves at least three reactions,

$$E+S \underset{k_2}{\overset{k_1}{\rightleftharpoons}} ES \overset{k_3}{\rightarrow} E+P, \tag{4}$$

in which the overall velocity v may be expressed, in accordance with the Michaelis-Menten (1913) theory, as follows:

$$v = \frac{k_3 k_1 (S) (E_0)}{k_2 + k_3 + k_1 (S)}. \tag{5}$$

Here (S) is substrate concentration, (E_0) is the total amount of enzyme $(E)+(ES)$ and P the products of the reaction. From (5) it is evident that the net effect of pressure may undergo fancy variations, depending not only on the values of $\Delta H^{\ddagger}$, $\Delta S^{\ddagger}$ and $\Delta V^{\ddagger}$ pertaining to the three rate constants, but also, as Laidler (1951) has pointed out, depending on the concentration of substrate. Similarly, complications in temperature relationships may occur.

Thirdly, the amount of E_0 in equation (5) is subject to the influence of pressure, temperature and inhibitors or other chemical agents which combine with the enzyme in a manner affecting its catalytic activity. Any enzyme is subject to thermal inactivation, the temperature required for an appreciable effect depending both on the specific enzyme and its chemical environment. In a number of instances it has been shown that the thermal inactivation is reversible on cooling, and may be properly represented as a reversible protein denaturation with equilibrium constant K_1 between the catalytically active E_n and inactive E_d states respectively. The reversible

$$E_n \overset{K_1}{\rightleftharpoons} E_d \tag{6}$$

denaturation reaction is usually associated with, and may be obscured by, a rate process of irreversible destruction. Both reactions are likely to have high heats and entropies, of reaction and activation respectively, much higher than those of the enzyme reaction itself.

On very short exposures to relatively high temperatures, the equilibrium change, whereby the amount of active enzyme is reversibly reduced, is primarily responsible for the decrease in observed rate of enzyme action at temperatures exceeding the 'optimum'. At these higher temperatures, when the change from native to denatured states is accompanied by a large volume increase, the rate of the observed reaction may be increased several fold by raising the hydrostatic pressure from atmospheric to a few hundred atmospheres, as in bacterial luminescence (Johnson *et al.* 1942*a*, *b*; Strehler & Johnson, 1954), or to a somewhat less extent in some other systems such as invertase (Eyring, Johnson & Gensler, 1946), salivary amylase (Schneyer, 1952) and trypsin (Fraser & Johnson, 1950). Likewise, where the irreversible destruction is characterized by a large volume increase of activation, the rate is reduced by increased pressure, as has been shown to occur in certain proteins, e.g. serum globulin (Johnson & Campbell, 1945, 1946), and tobacco mosaic virus (Johnson, Baylor & Fraser, 1948). With bacteriophage, however, opposite effects of pressure on the rate of thermal inactivation have been noted, that of coli phage T5 being decreased but that of T7 being increased (Foster, Johnson & Miller, 1949). Moreover, in the presence of chemical agents, such as urea, that promote denaturation at room temperature, the effects of pressure are more complicated; the net effect may be nil, or an increase or a decrease in rate or amount of denaturation (Schlegel & Johnson, 1949; Wright & Schomaker, 1948; Simpson & Kauzmann, 1953).

At temperatures considerably below that of maximum activity of an enzyme, the value of K_1 is generally insignificant and equation (5) is applicable. Under conditions wherein the substrate concentration is essentially constant and the rate is limited by the amount of active enzyme, the overall velocity may be expressed as follows:

$$v = bk'(S)(E), \qquad (7)$$

in which b is a proportionality constant and k' the rate constant as given be equation (2). As long as neither (S) nor (E) vary, and appreciable complications do not arise from equation (5), the rate changes with temperature and pressure in proportion to the change in k'. When, with rise in temperature, K_1 of the reversible denaturation becomes significant, equation (7) must be extended as follows:

$$v = \frac{bk'(S)(E_0)}{1 + K_1} = \frac{b\kappa \dfrac{kT}{h} e^{-\Delta F^{\ddagger}/RT}(S)(E_0)}{1 + e^{-\Delta F_1/RT}}. \qquad (8)$$

This equation is sufficient to describe with some accuracy the quantitative relation between temperature and rates of certain processes limited by enzyme activity, from temperatures well below to those well above the optimum. Similarly, a reversal in the observed effects of pressure at relatively low and high temperatures, respectively, is understandable on the basis of a difference in the volume change of activation pertaining to k' and the volume change of reaction pertaining to K_1, the latter being insignificant at the low temperatures.

Certain inhibitors, X, such as sulphanilamide acting on bacterial luminescence, combine reversibly with the limiting enzyme through an equilibrium, whose constant may be represented as K_2, independently of the denaturation equilibrium with constant K_1. Others, U, such as urethane or alcohol, establish one or more equilibrium combinations with the enzyme, and often catalyse a rate process of irreversible destruction in addition. For simplicity, the equilibrium constants involving U may be designated as K_3. Letting r equal the average number of molecules of X, and s the average number of molecules of U that combine per enzyme molecule, equation (8) becomes

$$V = \frac{bk'(S)(E_0)}{1 + K_1 + K_2(X)^r + K_1 K_2(X)^r + K_1 K_3(U)^s}, \tag{9}$$

provided there is no interaction between X and U (cf. Johnson, Eyring & Kearns, 1943). Inhibitory actions illustrated by X and U have been referred to as type I and type II, respectively (Johnson, Eyring & Williams, 1942).* Typically, the former leads to a pronounced increase in observed activation energy and a slight increase in the temperature of maximum rate, whereas the latter leads to a pronounced decrease in observed activation energy and a marked lowering of the temperature of maximum rate, the extent of these effects in all cases depending, of course, on concentration of the inhibitor.

Formulations useful for determining the numerical values of the constants in equation (9) have been derived and applied to data obtained with intact cells and isolated systems. Although undoubtedly over-simplified when applied to such processes as respiration, growth, luminescence, etc., of living cells, in many instances complicated biological processes vary under the influence of temperature or pressure in remarkable conformance to the simple theory which postulates a few limiting reactions that vary in importance with the conditions involved. While the actual number of constants in equations (8) or (9) may seem large, chemical theory requires that they be no fewer for the reactions postulated, and it is unlikely that the constants are so numerous *per se* as to permit the quantitative description of biological rates which arise from unrelated mechanisms. Moreover, amid the multitude of reactions that govern the distribution and activities of micro-organisms in natural

---

* A detailed discussion with the pertinent literature references is given by Johnson *et al.* (1954).

environments, it is reasonable to expect that, under given conditions, the operation of a relatively few reactions in the manner formulated above may constitute the major limiting factors.

The capacity and mechanisms of adaptation to special conditions is another problem, but one to which the basic physical-chemical theory applies no less. Furthermore, experimental evidence indicates that the rate of microbial mutation—one of the important aspects of adaptation —is subject to modification by pressure as well as temperature, e.g. the influence of pressure on mutagenic action of nitrogen mustards on *Neurospora* (McElroy & de la Haba, 1949), and the influence of temperature on spontaneous mutation in *Phytomonas stewartii* (Lincoln, 1947) and on the mutagenic action of Fe^{2+} on *Escherichia coli* (Catlin, 1953).

THE PRESSURE-TEMPERATURE RANGE OF NATURAL HABITATS

It is a fairly safe assumption that micro-organisms occur in nature wherever there is any other form of life, as well as in some environments where no other form of life can long survive. The extremes of pressure and temperature in places from which bacteria have been isolated range from arctic areas in which the temperature is far below freezing most of the time, never much higher, and the pressure is normally of no significance (McLean, 1918; Darling & Siple, 1941; McBee & McBee, 1956), to deep oil-well brines where the temperature is perpetually high and pressures reach several hundred atmospheres (Bastin, 1926; Bastin & Greer, 1930; Ginter, 1930; Müller & Schwartz, 1949; Ekzertsev, 1951; ZoBell, 1952a). Hot springs at 89–90° under somewhat less than 1 atm. (Setchell, 1903; Copeland, 1936; Egorova, 1938) and cold abysses of the ocean at less than 3° under several hundred to more than 1000 atm. of pressure, are again opposite extremes where living bacteria have been found (Certes, 1884a; Fischer, 1894; ZoBell, 1952b).

The limits of these extremes as natural habitats cannot be precisely stated, inasmuch as time as well as pressure and temperature is a factor. Moreover, it is not always possible to distinguish with certainty between organisms that represent survivors of accidental dispersal and those of a native population. The occurrence of thermophiles in the Arctic (Egorova, 1938; McBee & McBee, 1956) and in deep ocean-bottom cores (Bartholomew & Rittenberg, 1949) as well as their widespread distribution in soils where the temperature is generally below the minimum for their cultivation in the laboratory, is a case in point (Gaughran, 1947; Clegg & Jacobs, 1953; Allen, 1953). Temperature relationships of growth, however, may be modified by nutritional factors or vice versa (Robbins & Kavanagh, 1944; Barnett & Lilly, 1948; Borek & Waelsch, 1951; Ware, 1951; Maas & Davis, 1952; Kasai, 1953; Campbell, 1954; Campbell & Williams, 1953a, b), and possibly the growth of thermophiles in nature may take place very slowly at temperatures lower than in artificial media (Koch & Hoffman, 1912; Black & Tanner, 1928; Hansen, 1933). Conceivably, therefore, organisms with the same physiological potentialities can develop at a low temperature under certain conditions in nature, such as the presence of unknown chemical influences and perhaps absence of unknown chemical inhibitors, but only at a relatively high temperature with the usual methods of laboratory cultivation.

Although the vast majority of living microbes probably exist under the more or less familiar conditions of moderate temperature and no significant pressure, the largest ecological unit in the world, comprising more than half the total area of the earth, lies between 3000 and 6000 m. deep in the oceans, at pressures between 300 and 600 atm., where there is no light except for an unknown amount of bioluminescence (cf. Clark & Wertheim, 1956), and where the temperature is always less than 4° (Bruun, 1951, 1956). Below this is the 'hadal' zone (Bruun, 1956), making up about 1 % of the total area of the earth, under pressures of 600–1100 atm. The actual number and varieties of micro-organisms, as well as their rates of growth and metabolic activities in oceanic depths, constitute challenging problems about which little is yet known. While essentially the same cold temperatures may exist at the bottoms of some fresh-water lakes, the deepest one known, Lake Baikal in Siberia, has a maximum pressure of less than 200 atm. at a depth of 1741 m. (Brooks, 1950).

Laboratory studies indicate an enormous variation in the extent to which different species of micro-organisms are more or less permanently restricted to conditions comparable to the environment in which they are found, as witnessed, on the one hand, by familiar examples of the 'fastidiousness' of certain haemophilic pathogens, and on the other hand by the extraordinary capacity of Desulfovibrio desulfuricans (now Sporovibrio desulfuricans) reversibly to acquire the ability to grow with the characteristics of a halophile at ordinary temperatures and of a thermophile in ordinary media, respectively (Kluyver & Baars, 1932; Starkey, 1938). Kluyver & Baars discussed evidence for the laboratory existence of 'physiological artefacts', i.e. organisms isolated by selective factors or special enrichments but unable to grow in nature with the same characteristics. In a similar sense, morphological artefacts no doubt occur also, inasmuch as this organism in its mesophilic state consists morphologically of small, asporogenous vibrios or spirals but in its thermophilic state consists of larger, granulated vibrios that produce spores. Temperature and pressure are as much instruments of the enrichment method as are specific nutrients or other chemical factors. Thus, the proportion of described species that in one respect or another constitute true artefacts is a moot question.

Even though the example of *Desulfovibrio* is unusual in recorded experience, it serves to emphasize the potentialities of microbial adaptation to different temperature ranges, in this instance over a relatively short period of time. Much slower mechanisms of adaptation were evidently involved in another classic example, that of the flagellates which Dallinger (1887), over a period of 7 years, succeeded in acclimatizing to a temperature of 70° instead of their usual best temperature of *c*. 15°. The adapted organisms would quickly die when transferred to a nutritive medium at 15°. Given sufficient time for the various mechanisms of adaptation to operate at slow as well as rapid rates in nature, there is nothing incredible about indigenous populations in the environmental extremes referred to above. Indeed, evidence exists (ZoBell, 1956, personal communication) that bacteria recovered from oil-well brines at a depth of *c*. 3000 m. can grow in the laboratory at 104° under 1000 atm. of pressure.

TEMPERATURE RELATIONSHIPS AT NORMAL PRESSURE

In general, the range of temperatures favourable to growth and metabolism of a micro-organism are at least roughly correlated with its habitat. Growth and certain other processes, however, e.g. adaptive enzyme formation (Knox, 1950) are apt to have a somewhat narrower range than that for enzyme activity. With specific enzymes the difference is sometimes quite marked, e.g. the formic dehydrogenase of *Escherichia coli*, which has a maximum rate at about 80°, some 35° higher than the maximum temperature for growth (Johnson & Lewin, 1946*a*). Conversely, various enzymes may function normally at temperatures much below those at which growth is measurable, e.g. at 13° in thermophiles (Gaughran, 1949). Bacterial luminescence continues perceptibly at −11 to −20° (Harvey, 1913, 1940; Morrison, 1924–5) which is considerably lower than the several below-freezing minimum temperatures that have been reported for growth of micro-organisms (Rubentschik, 1925; Haines, 1930, 1931; Butkevitsch, 1932; Berry & Magoon, 1934; ZoBell & Feltham, 1935). In a given species of luminous bacteria the temperature of maximum light intensity is lower than that of maximum respiratory activity (Root, 1932, 1934–5), and in some instances is lower than the maximum temperature for growth, at which maximum non-luminous cells develop (Beijerinck, 1916; Root, 1934–5).

Among different species of luminous bacteria, under similar extra-cellular conditions, the maximum intensity of luminescence in non-proliferating cells differs by 10 to 15°, as illustrated by the species represented in Fig. 1 (Johnson *et al.* 1942*a*). In this figure the

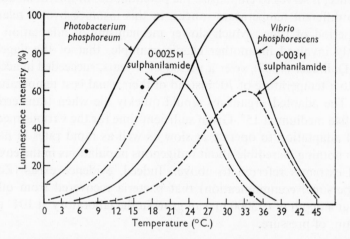

Fig. 1. Temperature-activity curves for the intensity of luminescence in a psychrophilic, marine species (*Photobacterium phosphoreum*), and a mesophilic, 'fresh-water' species (*Vibrio phosphorescens*) of luminous bacteria, in phosphate buffered salt solution believed to be isotonic for the respective organisms. Broken lines indicate the luminescence intensity of aliquot suspensions of cells containing moderately inhibitory concentrations of sulphanil-amide for the respective species. The three large solid points indicate the intensity during rapid cooling of a suspension of *P. phosphoreum* cells after a brief exposure to 34° (Johnson *et al.* 1942*a*).

maximum intensity for each species has arbitrarily been expressed as 100 %, although the average brightness per cell differed. The curves can be described fairly well by equation (8)* on the assumption that the rate of a limiting enzyme reaction increases with temperature in accordance with the Arrhenius equation (3) or with equation (2), and the overall brightness goes through a maximum ('optimum')

* In application to data on processes in living cells, the numerical value of $\Delta S^{\ddagger}$ cannot be readily obtained, but on the assumption that it does not vary much with temperature, it can be lumped together with κ, k, h, and the proportionality constant b, into an unknown constant c, yielding a useful form of the equation, as follows:

$$v = \frac{cTe^{-\Delta H^{\ddagger}/RT}}{1 + e^{-\Delta H_1/RT}\, e^{\Delta S_1/R}} = \frac{cTe^{-\Delta E^{\ddagger}/RT}\, e^{-p\Delta V^{\ddagger}/RT}}{1 + e^{-\Delta E_1/RT}\, e^{-p\Delta V_1/RT}\, e^{\Delta S_1/R}}.$$

because of the more rapid increase, with rise in temperature, in the amount of reversibly denatured enzyme. Differences in values of heats and entropies pertaining to k' and K_1, respectively, are found for the two curves with different temperature optima.

Fig. 1 illustrates also the extent to which luminescence is inhibited by a given concentration of sulphanilamide. The fact that the concentrations employed are so similar for these two species is probably a coincidence, inasmuch as the luminescence of other species varies in sensitivity to this drug at the optimal temperatures. The influence of temperature on the amount of inhibition, however, is similar for each of the several species that have been studied (Johnson, Eyring & Williams, 1942), i.e. the heats and entropies pertaining to K_2 (equation (9)) do not vary greatly. In general, the temperature relative to the biological temperature-activity curve of the system in the species involved is significant, rather than the actual temperature itself, in understanding the influence of enzyme inhibitors and activators. In the present instance, an essentially similar relationship in the two species is shifted a few degrees on the temperature scale. The effects of pressure, also, vary with respect to the specific temperature-activity curve, as discussed presently.

Rates of growth or cell division among several bacterial species and one mould, with pronounced differences in their respective optimal temperatures (each taken arbitrarily as 100 %), are plotted as the logarithm against $1/T$ in Fig. 2.* The actual maximum rates, in terms of generation time, are subject to considerable variation in each species, depending upon the nature of the culture medium and conditions of the experiment. For example, the minimum generation time of *Escherichia coli* according to Barber's (1908) data is 17 min., while according to Johnson & Lewin's (1946 c) data it is 40 min. Barber's experiments were all started with a single cell in a broth medium, whereas Johnson & Lewin's were started with a few thousand cells per ml. in a chemically defined, semi-synthetic medium. In both cases the rate of reproduction was uniform over the period of observation, and the number of cells was too small throughout to cause any appreciable change in the medium. These are important considerations for experiments on growth rates. Information based on the growth of cultures over long periods of time and wide differences in numbers of cells is useful in other respects, for it generally involves profound changes in the chemical environment of the cells as well as complicated changes in numerous rates of individual reactions.

* The points in Figs. 2, 4, 5 and 6 for the most part represent averaged values, in a number of instances estimated from smooth curves of published figures.

The short periods of observation in Johnson & Lewin's experiments made it possible to demonstrate a quantitative reversal, on cooling, of thermal bacteriostasis at 45°. Application of equation (8) was thus justified, and the calculated curve (Fig. 2), throughout the range of temperature from about 18 almost to 45°, conformed to the data within the limits of experimental error.

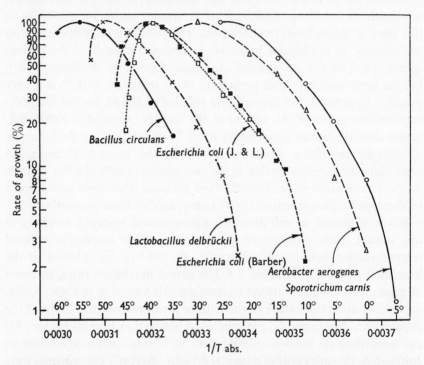

Fig. 2. Influence of temperature on rates of growth, relative to the observed maximum as 100 in each, of different species of bacteria and a mould. The data were obtained from the following sources: Allen (1953), *Bacillus circulans*; Slator (1916), *Lactobacillus delbrückii*; Barber (1908), *Escherichia coli* (solid squares); Johnson & Lewin (1946), *E. coli* (hollow squares); Greene & Jezeski (1954), a strain of *Aerobacter aerogenes*; Haines (1930), *Sporotrichum carnis*.

The positions of the optima on the temperature scale (Fig. 2) and the slopes of the curves on either side of these optima are subject to modification as in luminescence (Johnson, Eyring, Steblay, Chaplen, Huber & Gherardi, 1945) by pH and other chemical factors (Johnson & Lewin, 1947) as well as by pressure (Johnson & Lewin, 1946*d*; see below).

The general similarity of the curves in Fig. 2 is not surprising. They show that the activation energy for growth in favourable media, throughout the range of below-optimal temperatures permitting between about

10 and 90 % of the rate at the optimum, is not very different among various species and is within the range commonly encountered for enzyme action.

An impressive feature of Fig. 2 is the fairly sudden increase in slope of the line for each species at the relatively low temperatures, i.e. below those temperatures at which the rate is approximately 10 % of the maximum, regardless of the actual temperature at which the change takes place. The steep slopes indicate activation energies much higher than are usually associated with enzyme activity. With *Lactobacillus delbrückii*, for example, the slope of a straight line between the points at 25 and 22° gives a μ value of some 77,000 calories. Extrapolation of this line to lower temperatures would indicate generation times of roughly 6 hr. at 15°, 67 days at 10°, and 26 years at 5°, at which point, if not above, the cell might die of old age, for there is no doubt that optimum temperatures for longevity exist in general.

The reasons for the sharp drop in growth rate at temperatures low relative to the optimum are largely conjectural and they probably stem from more than one cause. A contributory factor possibly consists in differences, with temperature of growth, in the degree of saturation of fatty constituents synthesized (Bělehrádek, 1935; Gaughran, 1947). In various organisms the lipid constituents are more saturated and have higher melting-points, after growth at higher than at lower temperatures. It is reasonable to believe that growth and cell division would be more difficult with intracellular lipids in a solid than in a more fluid state. For this hypothesis to suffice in the present instance, however, it would be necessary to postulate a similar degree of unsaturation in the lipids of *Sporotrichum carnis* growing at 0° and in *Lactobacillus delbrückii* growing at 25°. An alternative hypothesis seems worth suggesting, namely, that inability to develop at the low temperatures results in part from solation of systems whose gelation is required in the process of cell division and perhaps growth. This hypothesis stems from the critical pressure-temperature relationship of cytoplasmic gel strength which is directly correlated with the ability of egg cells to divide (Marsland, 1950, 1956), as discussed in the next section. Analogous relationships possibly exist with respect to sol-gel changes in the degree of polymerization of nucleic acids. Consistent with this notion is the observation that bacterial nuclei round up, reversibly, under the influence of increased concentration of salts in the medium surrounding the cells, as well as at low temperatures or in the presence of metabolic inhibitors (Johnson & Gray, 1949; Whitfield & Murray, 1956). It will be interesting to find out if bacterial nuclei round up under increased pressures, analogous to the reversible rounding and fusion of *Tradescantia* chromosomes, at certain phases of meiosis, under 200–400 atm. (Pease, 1946). The evidence indicates that in bacteria the nuclear substances behave like an anionic gel whose state of aggregation or dispersal varies, without necessarily damaging the viability of the cell, with the internal ionic environment that is regulated by metabolic devices controlling the influx and efflux of electrolytes, as in cells of higher plants and animals (Whitfield & Murray, 1956; Cowie & Roberts, 1955; Shanes, 1955). It will be interesting to learn, perhaps with ultra-micro-electrodes no larger than Wamoscher's (1930) needles, about the electrical polarization across the bacterial cell membrane.

An effort to account, at the molecular level, for differences among biological species in rates of growth at low temperatures thus invokes a wide array of interrelationships: metabolism, properties and reactions of specific molecules, chemical environment, temperature and pressure. The same is true for growth and viability at the upper limits of temperature.

Diminution in growth rates at temperatures above an optimum are evidently attributable primarily to the thermal instability of proteins, enzymes and nucleic acids, in part reversible but in part not reversible, and characterized as a rule by high heats of reaction or of activation. Because of the unusually high temperatures involved, the problem in 'extreme' thermophiles is of especial interest, although there is a virtually imperceptible gradation between the optimum temperatures of these organisms and those of mesophiles (Morrison & Tanner, 1924; Smith, Gordon & Clark, 1952; Allen, 1950, 1953). At high temperatures it is to be expected that essentially all reaction rates will be relatively fast, even though the net rates of enzyme reactions may become slow again because of reversible and irreversible decreases in the amount of active catalysts. Allen (1950, 1953) has stressed the dynamic nature of thermophily, i.e. rapid synthesis and repair along with rapid destruction. The same concept applies, at lower temperatures and lower absolute rates, to mesophiles and psychrophiles also, inasmuch as the rate of growth at maximal temperatures in all cases is limited by differences in the effects of temperature upon constructive and destructive reactions, and the point at which the latter overtake the former depends upon the activity and thermal stability of the systems. While the stability is in part dynamic, the stability of non-metabolizing systems is subject also to profound modification by slight changes in the chemical environment. For example, coli phage T5, with no metabolism of its own, is rapidly inactivated at temperatures only above 70° in broth, but is rapidly inactivated at 30° in 0·1 M-NaCl. At 50° the rate of inactivation is a million times faster in 0·1 M-NaCl than in broth or in 2 M-NaCl or in 0·003 M-Ca^{2+} or Mg^{2+} (Adams, 1949; Lark & Adams, 1953). In view of the potent effect of Ca^{2+} in this instance, it appears likely that the greater concentration of Ca^{2+} in bacterial spores than in vegetative cells is a fundamentally important factor in the thermal resistance of spores (Curran, Brunstetter & Myers, 1943).

Here again, complex, though in principle understandable, interrelationships between biologically specific molecular structures and the chemical environment are evident in the influence of temperature. The significance of genetically controlled molecular structure is apparent in certain 'temperature mutants' of *Neurospora*, of which a considerable number are now known (Catcheside, 1951; Horowitz & Leupold, 1951). Also in bacteria, a mutant of *Escherichia coli* requiring addition of pantothenate for growth above 30° produces at lower temperatures an altered, excessively heat-labile pantothenate-synthesizing enzyme. In extracts, its activity and thermal stability are unaffected by the presence of extracts containing the more heat-resistant, corresponding enzyme of the wild type (Maas & Davis, 1952). Similarly, the thermal stability of tyrosinase in *Neurospora* is under genic control (Horowitz & Fling, 1953). Very likely the same is true of the greater heat stability of certain enzymes from thermophilic bacteria (Militzer, Sonderegger, Tuttle & Georgi, 1949, 1950; Militzer, Tuttle & Georgi, 1951; Militzer & Tuttle, 1952; Marsh & Militzer, 1956 *a*, *b*), although association of the enzyme with particulate matter is apparently a factor in some of these instances, as it is in the greater thermal stability of alanine racemase from spores than from vegetative cells of *Bacillus subtilis* (Stewart & Halvorson, 1954).

The thermal stability of nucleic acids, because of their fundamental role in synthesis (cf. Gale, 1953, 1955), is of no less importance to growth and viability than that of proteins and enzymes. In a favourable ionic environment, desoxyribonucleic acid (DNA) from animal and microbial sources is stable at temperatures up to between 80 and 90°, above which it denatures at rapidly increasing rates as the temperature is raised further (Goldstein & Stern, 1950; Zamenhof, Alexander & Leidy, 1953; Zamenhof, Griboff & Marullo, 1954; Doty & Rice, 1955). The stability is markedly influenced, however, by salt concentration, pH and the buffer system, as well as other factors (Zamenhof *et al.* 1953, 1954; Reichmann, Bunce & Doty, 1953). Few data are yet available regarding a possible correlation between the thermal stability of nucleic acids and the temperature range of growth or of the habitat of different organisms. The fact that DNA from starfish testes denatures irreversibly in very dilute NaCl at 35 to 40° (Thomas, 1954) is suggestive evidence of such a correlation. Moreover, yeast DNA is more stable to acid, down to pH 3·7 (at the temperature of the experiment), than calf thymus DNA, which is stable down to only pH 5·8, possibly indicating a correlation with intracellular pH (Zamenhof & Chargaff, 1950).

PRESSURE-TEMPERATURE-INHIBITOR RELATIONSHIPS

Interrelations between pressure, temperature and the action of certain chemical agents on a typical biological process directly under enzyme control can be conveniently illustrated with bacterial luminescence, for which the available data are most extensive. Moreover, it has recently become possible (Strehler, 1953) to study this process in cell-free extracts. Luminescence of extracted enzyme preparations requires flavine mono-nucleotide (FMN) and a long-chain aliphatic aldehyde; addition of reduced diphosphopyridine nucleotide (DPNH) then results in a sustained, steady-state luminescence which, in all important respects, is like that of the living cells (Strehler, 1955; Hastings & McElroy, 1955).

Fig. 3 shows, for comparison, the variation in intensity of steady-state luminescence in cells of *Photobacterium phosphoreum* (Brown *et al.* 1942) and in extracts of *Achromobacter fischeri* (Strehler & Johnson, 1954) at different pressures and temperatures and in the absence of known inhibitors. The former species has a 'normal' optimum tempera-ture for luminescence a few degrees lower than that of the latter species, and it will be noted that the pressure-temperature relationships are essentially similar in the cells and extracts, except that a given effect occurs at a lower temperature in the species having the lower optimum. All the effects illustrated in this figure are reversible, provided the exposures to high temperatures or pressures are only brief.

At low temperatures, increasing pressure causes an exponential decrease in luminescence intensity, whereas at the high temperatures pressure causes an increase in observed intensity, relative to the control arbitrarily taken as 100 % at normal pressure and all temperatures. The actual intensity of this control varied with temperature, of course, in the manner usually found for enzyme reactions, as illustrated in Fig. 4, which includes the variation of intensity with temperature under an increased pressure of 7000 lb./sq.in. Fig. 4 also shows the temperature-activity curves for the intensity at normal and 7000 lb./sq.in. pressure after adding 0·5M alcohol to the cell suspension.*

* The reason for the slight 'stimulation' by alcohol at 0° is obscure. It occurs also in the extracted system (Strehler & Johnson, 1954).

The relationships shown in Figs. 3 and 4 have been interpreted as follows. At low temperatures the major effect of pressure is on the limiting enzyme reaction, which in accordance with equation (8) proceeds with a volume increase of activation $\Delta V^{\ddagger}$ of 51·5 c.c./mole at 0° (Eyring & Magee, 1942). With rise in temperature near to and exceeding the optimum, the amount of reversibly denatured enzyme becomes rapidly more important as a limiting factor in the overall rate of light

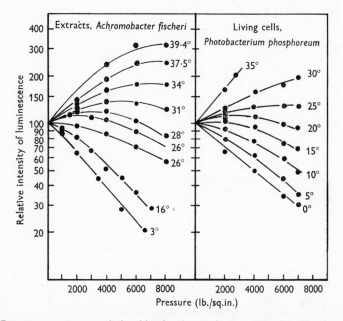

Fig. 3. Pressure-temperature relationships for the steady-state intensity of luminescence in cell suspensions of *Photobacterium phosphoreum* and in cell-free extracts of *Achromobacter fischeri*, respectively. The intensity at normal pressure is arbitrarily taken as 100 at each temperature (Strehler & Johnson, 1954; data for cells of *P. phosphoreum* from Brown *et al.* 1942).

emission. Under pressure, the equilibrium shifts in favour of the undenatured state, thus increasing the amount of active enzyme and therefore increasing the intensity of luminescence. The volume increase of reaction ΔV_1 according to equation (8) amounts to 64·6 c.c./mole at 35°. Equation (8) is sufficient to describe with considerable accuracy the intensity of luminescence from 0 to 36° at pressures between normal and 7000 lb./sq.in., provided a temperature dependence of $\Delta V^{\ddagger}$ and ΔV_1 is taken into account (Eyring & Magee, 1942). While this temperature dependence of $\Delta V^{\ddagger}$ and ΔV_1 could be real, it probably indicates that the theoretical equation is over-simplified.

At temperatures above the optimum at atmospheric pressure, irreversible destruction of the luminescent system takes place at rates which increase with temperature in the manner typical of irreversible protein denaturation. These rates are retarded by increased pressure to an extent indicating a volume increase of activation amounting to

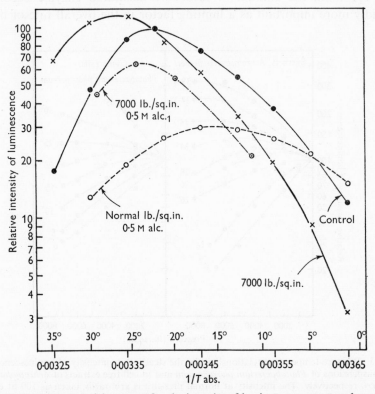

Fig. 4. Temperature-activity curves for the intensity of luminescence, at normal pressure and 7000 lb./sq.in. respectively, in cells of *Photobacterium phosphoreum* suspended in buffered salt solution, with and without the addition of 0·5 M ethyl alcohol. The control curve, for normal pressure without the addition of alcohol, represents the average of several curves with many points obtained in repeated experiments. Points on the other curves represent the same percentage difference, with respect to the averaged control, as with respect to the control in the experiment involved. The data are from figures in Johnson *et al.* (1954).

71 c.c./mole in the formation of the activated complex of the molecules whose destruction results in the loss of luminescence (Johnson *et al.* 1945).

Relationships similar to those of Fig. 3 were found by Brown (cf. Johnson *et al.* 1954) for muscle tension. In both these examples, and to some extent in regard to specific enzyme reactions *in vitro*, increasing the pressure has been found to have the same kind of effect as lowering the temperature, at temperatures both above and below the optimum. A note of caution is in order, however, against generalizing that pressure and cold have the same effect. Their influence on bacterial growth rates, for example, is more complicated (*vide infra*), and as yet the data on biological pressure-temperature relationships are too few to justify broad generalizations.

The presence of alcohol or other narcotics of similar nature markedly alters the pressure-temperature relationships of luminescence. At normal pressure the inhibition tends to increase rapidly with rise in temperature. The effect of pressure is to reduce the amount of inhibition. This effect is most conspicuous at the higher temperatures represented in Fig. 4, but the statement holds also for the lower temperatures where the amount of inhibition under pressure appears to be greater than that at normal pressure (between 10 and 15° in Fig. 4). At the lower temperatures the total effect includes a large contribution of the action of pressure in retarding the limiting enzyme reaction rate. The total reduction in intensity under pressure in the presence of alcohol at low temperatures is less than the sum of the alcohol inhibition at normal pressure plus the inhibition due to pressure in absence of alcohol. Variations in the amount of pressure and concentration of alcohol at different temperatures lead to complex variations in intensity which, however, are generally understandable on the basis of equation (9). The equation is over-simplified in not taking into account more than a single equilibrium between the enzyme and alcohol, whereas the evidence indicates that several equilibria are established, as discussed in detail elsewhere (Johnson *et al.* 1954).

Qualitatively, the action of alcohol may be pictured as promoting a reversible protein denaturation of the limiting enzyme. At higher temperatures, or with higher concentrations of alcohol at lower temperatures, alcohol catalyses irreversible thermal denaturations of certain enzymes and proteins, through reactions that proceed with large volume increases of activation as shown by their retardation under pressure (Johnson *et al.* 1954).

The action of urethane on luminescence is much like that of alcohol, and it resembles also the action of unfavourable alkalinity (Fig. 5). Sulphanilamide or moderate acidity, however, act differently on this system; the inhibitor apparently dissociates with rise in temperature, K_2 of equation (9) decreasing independently of K_1's increasing, with the results that the amount of inhibition decreases with rise in temperature up to and beyond the normal optimum, the observed activation energy for luminescence becomes greater, and the temperature of maximum intensity becomes slightly higher.

Figs. 4 and 5 illustrate how greatly the observed activation energy and temperature of maximum observed activity of a process directly under enzyme control may vary with pressure and the chemical environment. Such variations would be expected to be significant, or in some instances perhaps the determining factors of metabolic activities and growth in natural environments.

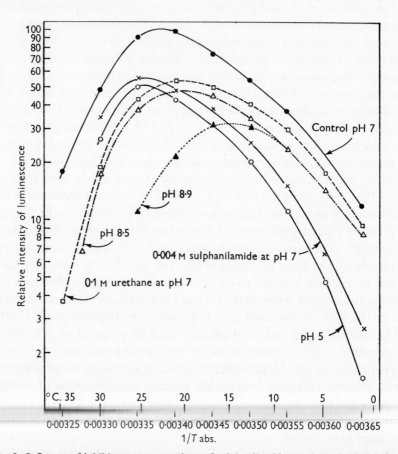

Fig. 5. Influence of inhibitory concentrations of sulphanilamide, urethane, hydrogen ions, and hydroxyl ions on the temperature-activity curve for luminescence intensity of cells of *Photobacterium phosphoreum* suspended in phosphate buffered NaCl solution. The data are from Johnson *et al.* (1954) treated as in Fig. 4.

Growth and reproduction are manifestly subject to control by factors beyond the activity of enzymes. In consequence, the pressure-temperature relationships of growth are more complicated than those of a simpler process such as luminescence. For example, with *Escherichia coli* in the early logarithmic growth phase, a pressure of 1000 lb./sq.in., during short periods of time,* depresses the rate of reproduction at temperatures below, and accelerates the rate at temperatures above the optimum, as in luminescence, whereas a pressure of 5000 lb./sq.in. depresses the rate at all temperatures (Fig. 6). At temperatures leading to a measurable rate of thermal disinfection either in growing cultures

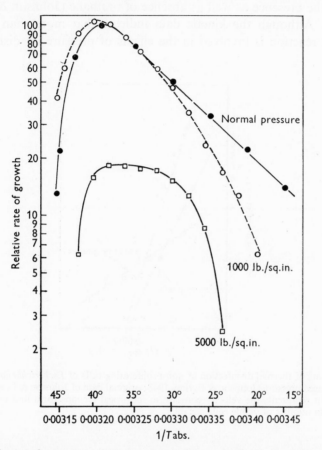

Fig. 6. Influence of pressure on the temperature activity curve for the rate of reproduction of *Escherichia coli* in an inorganic salts, glucose, asparagine medium. The data are replotted, in the manner of Figs. 4 and 5, from Johnson & Lewin (1942c, d).

* The influence of pressure on uniform growth rates of aerobic bacteria, or of facultative anaerobes whose growth rate is influenced by oxygen tension, can be satisfactorily determined only with small populations of cells in the early logarithmic phase. In order to include an initial supply of oxygen adequate to insure aerobic growth of a culture maintained continuously under pressure, from the time of inoculation with a relatively small inoculum to the development of visible turbidity, an air or oxygen bubble included in the culture tube at the start would very probably have to be larger in volume than that of the medium. Moreover, the abnormally high initial oxygen tension might be expected of itself to inhibit growth of some organisms, depending on their sensitivity to higher than normal tensions (Bean, 1945) and on the temperature (Thaysen, 1934).

Johnson & Lewin, 1946d) or in a non-proliferating state (Johnson & Lewin, 1946b), the rate is retarded under pressure (Fig. 7). Similarly, the rate of spore disinfection at temperatures above 90° is retarded by pressure (Johnson & ZoBell, 1949a). Small concentrations of urethane accelerate disinfection at high temperatures, and pressure retards the rate in the presence as well as absence of urethane (Johnson & ZoBell, 1949b). Although the kinetic data indicate that more than a single limiting reaction is involved in the effects of pressure on disinfection,

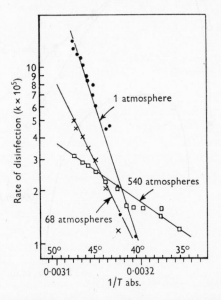

Fig. 7. Rate of thermal disinfection of non-proliferating cells of *Escherichia coli* at normal and increased pressure (Johnson & Eyring, 1948; original data of Johnson & Lewin, 1946b). Each point represents the velocity constant in reciprocal seconds for a first order rate of decrease in number of viable cells per ml.

this action is probably related to the retardation of thermal denaturation of proteins under pressure. It is an interesting possibility that similar mechanisms are responsible, in part, for the ability of bacteria (sulphate reducers) to survive and perhaps grow in deep oil-well brines mentioned above.

While the nature of the reactions accounting for the greater sensitivity of growth than of enzyme activity to pressure remains largely a matter of speculation, two possibilities suggest themselves, namely, synthetic reactions and sol-gel changes.

In regard to the effects of pressure on biosynthesis, practically no data are yet available pertaining to isolated systems.* Suggestive evidence resides in the fact that phage synthesis in *Escherichia coli* appears to be stopped, in part reversibly, by 600 atm. at 38° (Foster & Johnson, 1951). At this temperature the net rate of enzyme reactions in the infected cell would not be expected to be seriously reduced under this pressure, by analogy with the pressure-temperature data available with respect to luminescence and some other systems. In addition, pressure might be expected to interfere with biosynthesis on general principles. For template mechanisms must be involved in the synthesis of biologically specific molecules, and both complexly folded proteins (Pauling & Corey, 1951 *a, b, c, d, e, f*; Linderstrøm-Lang, 1952) and plectonemically coiled nucleic acids (Watson & Crick, 1953; Dekker & Schachman, 1954) must exist in at least partially unfolded or uncoiled states in the process. Such changes in states very likely involve volume changes, and pressure would then tend to stabilize one state whereas both are required. Temperature, of course, would likewise have an effect in accordance with the difference in heat and entropy of the two states, and the temperature relationship would again be subject to modification by the chemical environment.

In regard to the role of sol-gel changes, a fundamental pressure-temperature relationship has been found with respect to gel strength and ability of egg cells to divide (Marsland, 1950, 1956; Marsland & Landau, 1954). The cytoplasmic gels undergo solation at low temperatures or high pressures. As the temperature is raised, the amount of pressure required for a given extent of solation increases. A minimum gel strength is required for cell division, and both vary with temperature and pressure in the manner illustrated in Fig. 8. Division of the cell can take place only at those combinations of temperature and pressure that are represented below the respective lines; above these lines cytoplasmic division is blocked or reversed. Variations in the quantitative relationships among eggs of different animals are evident in differences in the slopes of the lines and in the position of these lines with respect to the temperature scale. Such differences are no doubt under genetic control and have

---

* Interpretation of the synthesis of proteins under pressures of 5000–6000 atm. at 37–38° reported by Bresler and his co-workers (Bresler, Glikina, Konikov, Selezneva & Finogenov, 1949, and later papers) is not clear. The same results were not obtained in similar experiments by other investigators (Talwar & Macheboeuf, 1954). Relevant to the problem is the observation that an even lower pressure of *c.* 700 atm. causes purified serum globulin, denatured at 65°, to go partly back into aqueous solution slowly at room temperature (Johnson & Campbell, 1946; cf. also Tongur, 1952). Moreover, an optimum pressure at 7500 atm. occurs for the rate of denaturation of tobacco mosaic virus (TMV), as judged by insolubilization (Lauffer & Dow, 1941). Denatured, insoluble TMV was formed only slowly at either 5000 or 10,000 atm., although loss of infectivity took place throughout this range of pressures. Evidently, denaturation and solubility of the product are both influenced by pressure.

some adaptive significance, but they can be modified to a greater or lesser extent by the chemical environment. The addition of small concentrations of adenosine triphosphate, for example, raises the pressure needed to block division of *Arbacia* or *Chaetopterus* eggs by about 500 lb./sq.in. at each temperature (Landau, Marsland & Zimmerman, 1955).

Studies similar to the above are lacking with respect to bacteria but they are not unfeasible and they should be rewarding, especially because the range of temperature and pressure in microbial physiology so far

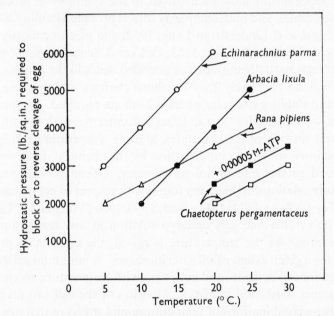

Fig. 8. Pressure-temperature relationship for blocking or reversing the cleavage of egg cells of different animals. The data are from Marsland & Landau (1954).

exceeds that of any other organisms. Data of this kind pertaining to deep-sea bacteria and to extreme thermophiles, for example, would be particularly interesting.

A main objective in the foregoing discussions has been to indicate the usefulness of studying not only the various individual factors of ecological significance, at both the level of molecules and organisms, but also the various parameters of these factors, in an effort to understand their interrelationships. While the ultimate goal of ecology—interpretation of all interrelationships in terms of the structure and behaviour of molecules —is still only a faint smudge on a distant horizon, the progress of modern physics, chemistry and biology contains an encouraging hint of eventual success.

REFERENCES

ADAMS, M. H. (1949). The stability of bacterial viruses in solutions of salt. *J. gen. Physiol.* **32**, 579.

ALLEN, MARY B. (1950). The dynamic nature of thermophily. *J. gen. Physiol.* **33**, 205.

ALLEN, MARY B. (1953). The thermophilic aerobic sporeforming bacteria. *Bact. Rev.* **17**, 125.

ARRHENIUS, S. (1889). Über die Reaktionsgeschwindigkeit bei der Inversion von Rohrzucker durch Säuren. *Z. phys. Chem.* **4**, 226.

ARRHENIUS, S. (1907). *Immunochemistry.* New York: Macmillan.

ARRHENIUS, S. (1915). *Quantitative Laws in Biological Chemistry.* London: Bell.

BARBER, M. A. (1908). The rate of multiplication of *Bacillus coli* at different temperatures. *J. infect. Dis.* **5**, 379.

BARNETT, H. L. & LILLY, V. G. (1948). The interrelated effects of vitamins, temperature and pH upon vegetation growth of Sclerotinia camelliae. *Amer. J. Bot.* **35**, 297.

BARTHOLOMEW, J. W. & RITTENBERG, S. C. (1949). Thermophilic bacteria from deep ocean bottom cores. *J. Bact.* **57**, 658.

BASTIN, E. S. (1926). The presence of sulfate reducing bacteria in oil field waters. *Science*, **63**, 21.

BASTIN, E. S. & GREER, F. E. (1930). Additional data on sulfate-reducing bacteria in soils and waters of Illinois oil fields. *Bull. Amer. Ass. Petrol. Geol.* **14**, 153.

BEAN, J. W. (1945). Effects of oxygen at increased pressure. *Physiol. Rev.* **25**, 1.

BEIJERINCK, M. W. (1916). Die Leuchtbakterien der Nordsee im August und September. *Folia microbiol.* **4**, 15.

BĚLEHRÁDEK, J. (1935). *Temperature and Living Matter.* Berlin: Borntraeger.

BERRY, J. A. & MAGOON, C. A. (1934). Growth of microorganisms at and below 0°. *Phytopathology*, **24**, 780.

BLACK, L. A. & TANNER, F. W. (1928). A study of thermophilic bacteria from the intestinal tract. *Zbl. Bakt.* (2 Abt.), **75**, 360.

BOREK, E. & WAELSCH, H. (1951). The effect of temperature on the nutritional requirement of microorganisms. *J. biol. Chem.* **190**, 191.

BRESLER, S. E., GLIKINA, M. V., KONIKOV, N. A., SELEZNEVA, N. A. & FINOGENOV, P. A. (1949). (Synthesis of proteins and peptides under pressure; cf. *Chem. Abstr.* **43**, 7988*b*.) *Inzvest. Akad. Nauk. S.S.S.R.*, Serr. Fiz., **13**, 392.

BROOKS, J. L. (1950). Speciation in ancient lakes. *Quart. Rev. Biol.* **25**, 30, 131.

BROWN, D. E. (1934). The pressure-tension-temperature relation in cardiac muscle. *Amer. J. Physiol.* **109**, 16.

BROWN, D. E. (1935). Cellular reactions to high hydrostatic pressure. *Annual Report of Tortugas Lab.*, *Carnegie Inst. Wash.* p. 76.

BROWN, D. E., JOHNSON, F. H. & MARSLAND, D. A. (1942). The pressure-temperature relations of bacterial luminescence. *J. cell. comp. Physiol.* **20**, 151.

BRUUN, A. F. (1951). The Philippine Trench and its bottom fauna. *Nature, Lond.*, **168**, 692.

BRUUN, A. F. (1956). The abyssal fauna: Its ecology, distribution and origin. *Nature, Lond.*, **177**, 1105.

BUTKEVITSCH, V. S. (1932). Methodik der bakteriologischen Meeresuntersuchungen und einige Angaben über die Verteilung der Bakterien im Wasser und in den Boden des Barents Meeres. *Trans. Oceanogr. Inst. Moscow*, **2** (no. 2), 5. (Russian, with German summary.)

CAMPBELL, L. L. (1954). The growth of an 'obligate' thermophile at 36° C. *J. Bact.* **68**, 505.

CAMPBELL, L. L. & WILLIAMS, O. B. (1953*a*). The effect of temperature on the nutritional requirements of facultative and obligate thermophilic bacteria. *J. Bact.* **65**, 141.

CAMPBELL, L. L. & WILLIAMS, O. B. (1953*b*). Observations on the biotin requirement of thermophilic bacteria. *J. Bact.* **65**, 146.

CATCHESIDE, D. G. (1951). *The Genetics of Microorganisms.* London: Pitman.

CATLIN, B. W. (1953). Response of *Escherichia coli* to ferrous ions. I. Influence of temperature on the mutagenic action of Fe^{2+} for a streptomycin-dependent strain. *J. Bact.* **65**, 413.

CATTELL, McK. (1936). The physiological effects of pressure. *Biol. Rev.* **11**, 441.

CATTELL, McK. & EDWARDS, D. J. (1930). The influence of hydrostatic pressure on the contraction of cardiac muscle in relation to temperature. *Amer. J. Physiol.* **93**, 97.

CATTELL, McK. & EDWARDS, D. J. (1932). Conditions modifying the influence of hydrostatic pressure on striated muscle, with special reference to the role of viscosity changes. *J. cell. comp. Physiol.* **1**, 11.

CERTES, A. (1884*a*). Sur la culture, à l'abri des germes atmosphériques, des eaux et des sédiments rapportés par les expéditions du 'Travailleur' et du 'Talisman'; 1882–1883. *C.R. Acad. Sci., Paris*, **98**, 690.

CERTES, A. (1884*b*). Note relative à l'action des hautes pressions sur la vitalité des microorganismes d'eau douce et d'eau de mer. *C.R. Soc. Biol., Paris*, **36**, 220.

CERTES, A. (1884*c*). De l'action des hautes pressions sur les phénomènes de la putréfaction et sur la vitalité des microorganismes d'eau douce et d'eau de mer. *C.R. Acad. Sci., Paris*, **99**, 385.

CHANTRENNE, H., LINDERSTRØM-LANG, K. & VANDENDRIESSCHE, L. (1947). Volume change accompanying the splitting of ribonucleic acid by ribonuclease. *Nature, Lond.*, **159**, 877.

CLARK, G. L. & WERTHEIM, G. K. (1956). Measurements of illumination at great depths and at night in the Atlantic Ocean by means of a new bathyphotometer. *Deep-Sea Res.* **3**, 189.

CLEGG, L. F. L. & JACOBS, S. E. (1953). Environmental and other aspects of adaptation in thermophiles. *Adaptation in Micro-organisms. Third. Symp. Soc. gen. Microbiol.* p. 306.

COPELAND, J. J. (1936). Yellowstone thermal myxophyceae. *Ann. N.Y. Acad. Sci.* **36**, 1.

COWIE, D. B. & ROBERTS, R. B. (1955). Permeability of micro-organisms to inorganic ions, amino acids, and peptides. In *Electrolytes in Biological Systems* (A. M. Shanes, ed.), pp. 1–34. Washington: Amer. Physiol. Soc.

CURRAN, H. R., BRUNSTETTER, B. C. & MYERS, A. T. (1943). Spectrochemical analysis of vegetative cells and spores of bacteria. *J. Bact.* **45**, 485.

DALLINGER, W. H. (1887). The President's Address. *J.R. micr. Soc.* **7**, 185.

DARLING, C. A. & SIPLE, P. A. (1941). Bacteria of Antarctica. *J. Bact.* **42**, 83.

DEKKER, C. A. & SCHACHMAN, H. (1954). The macromolecular structure of desoxyribonucleic acid: an interrupted two-strand model. *Proc. nat. Acad. Sci., Wash.*, **40**, 894.

DOTY, P. & RICE, S. A. (1955). Denaturation of desoxypentose nucleic acid. *Biochim. biophys. Acta*, **16**, 446.

EGOROVA, A. A. (1938). Thermophile bacteria in Arctic. *C.R. Acad. Sci. U.R.S.S.* **19**, 649.

EKZERTSEV, V. A. (1951). (Microscopic examination of bacterial flora in oil-bearing facies of the Secondary Baku; cf. *Chem. Abstr.* **46**, 9830*i*.) *Microbiologya, Moscow*, **20**, 324.

EYRING, H. (1935). The activated complex in chemical reactions. *J. chem. Phys.* **3**, 107.

EYRING, H., JOHNSON, F. H. & GENSLER, R. L. (1946). Pressure and reactivity of proteins, with special reference to invertase. *J. phys. Chem.* **50**, 453.

EYRING, H. & MAGEE, J. L. (1942). Application of the theory of absolute reaction rates to bacterial luminescence. *J. cell. comp. Physiol.* **20**, 169.

FISCHER, B. (1894). Die Bakterien des Meeres nach den Untersuchungen der Plankton-Expedition. *Erbebn. Plankton-Exped. Humb. Stiftung.* Kiel and Leipsig: Lipsius and Tischer.

FONTAINE, M. (1930). Recherches expérimentales sur les réactions des êtres vivants aux fortes pressions. *Ann. Inst. Océanogr. Monaco, N.S.,* **8**, 1.

FOSTER, RUTH A. C. & JOHNSON, F. H. (1951). Influence of urethane and of hydrostatic pressure on the growth of bacteriophages T2, T5, T6 and T7. *J. gen. Physiol.* **34**, 529.

FOSTER, R. A. C., JOHNSON, F. H. & MILLER, V. K. (1949). The influence of hydrostatic pressure and urethane on the thermal inactivation of bacteriophage. *J. gen. Physiol.* **33**, 1.

FRASER, D. & JOHNSON, F. H. (1951). The pressure-temperature relationship in the rate of casein digestion by trypsin. *J. biol. Chem.* **190**, 417.

GALE, E. F. (1953). Assimilation of amino acids by Gram-positive bacteria and some actions of antibiotics thereon. *Advance. Protein Chem.* **8**, 287.

GALE, E. F. (1955). From amino acids to proteins. In *Symposium on Amino Acid Metabolism* (W. D. McElroy and B. Glass, eds.). Baltimore: Johns Hopkins University Press.

GAUGHRAN, E. R. L. (1947). The thermophilic microorganisms. *Bact. Rev.* **11**, 189.

GAUGHRAN, E. R. L. (1949). Temperature activation of certain respiratory enzymes of stenothermophilic bacteria. *J. gen. Physiol.* **32**, 313.

GINTER, R. L. (1930). Causative agents of sulphate reduction in oil-well waters. *Bull. Amer. Ass. Petrol. Geol.* **14**, 139.

GLASSTONE, S., LAIDLER, K. J. & EYRING, H. (1941). *The Theory of Rate Processes.* New York: McGraw-Hill.

GOLDSTEIN, G. & STERN, K. (1950). Experiments on the sonic, thermal and enzymic depolymerization of desoxyribosenucleic acid. *J. Polym. Sci.* **5**, 687.

GREENE, V. W. & JEZESKI, J. J. (1954). Influence of temperature on the development of several psychrophilic bacteria of dairy origin. *Appl. Microbiol.* **2**, 110.

HAINES, R. B. (1930). The influence of temperature on the rate of growth of *Sporotrichum carnis* from −10° to +30° C. *J. exp. Biol.* **8**, 379.

HAINES, R. B. (1931). The influence of temperature on the rate of growth of saprophytic actinomyces. *J. exp. Biol.* **9**, 45.

HANSEN, P. A. (1933). The growth of thermophilic bacteria. *Arch. Mikrobiol.* **4**, 23.

HARVEY, E. N. (1913). The temperature limits of phosphorescence of luminous bacteria. *Biochem. Bull.* **2**, 456.

HARVEY, E. N. (1940). *Living Light.* Princeton: Princeton University Press.

HASTINGS, J. W. & McELROY, W. D. (1955). Purification and properties of bacterial luciferase. In *The Luminescence of Biological Systems* (F. H. Johnson, ed.). Washington: Amer. Ass. Adv. Sci.

HOROWITZ, N. H. & FLING, M. (1953). Genetic determination of tyrosinase thermostability in *Neurospora*. *Genetics*, **38**, 360.

HOROWITZ, N. H. & LEUPOLD, U. (1951). Some recent studies bearing on the one gene-one enzyme hypothesis. *Cold Spr. Harb. Symp. quant. Biol.* **16**, 65.

JOHNSON, F. H. (1948). Bioluminescence: a reaction rate tool. *Sci. Mon., Wash.,* **67**, 225.

JOHNSON, F. H., BAYLOR, M. B. & FRASER, D. (1948). The thermal denaturation of tobacco mosaic virus in relation to hydrostatic pressure. *Arch. Biochem.* **19**, 237.

JOHNSON, F. H., BROWN, D. E. & MARSLAND, D. A. (1942a). A basic mechanism in the biological effects of temperature, pressure and narcotics. *Science*, **95**, 200.

JOHNSON, F. H., BROWN, D. E. & MARSLAND, D. A. (1942b). Pressure reversal of the action of certain narcotics. *J. cell. comp. Physiol.* **20**, 269.

JOHNSON, F. H. & CAMPBELL, D. H. (1945). The retardation of protein denaturation by hydrostatic pressure. *J. cell. comp. Physiol.* **26**, 43.

JOHNSON, F. H. & CAMPBELL, D. H. (1946). Pressure and protein denaturation. *J. biol. Chem.* **163**, 689.

JOHNSON, F. H. & EYRING, H. (1948). The fundamental action of pressure, temperature, and drugs on enzymes, as revealed by bacterial luminescence. *Ann. N.Y. Acad. Sci.* **49**, 376.

JOHNSON, F. H., EYRING, H. & KEARNS, W. (1943). A quantitative theory of synergism and antagonism among diverse inhibitors, with special reference to sulfanilamide and urethane. *Arch. Biochem.* **3**, 1.

JOHNSON, F. H., EYRING, H. & POLISSAR, M. J. (1954). *The Kinetic Basis of Molecular Biology*. London: Chapman and Hall.

JOHNSON, F. H., EYRING, H., STEBLAY, R., CHAPLIN, H., HUBER, C. & GHERARDI, G. (1945). The nature and control of reactions in bioluminescence. With special reference to the mechanism of reversible and irreversible inhibitions by hydrogen and hydroxyl ions, temperature, pressure, alcohol, urethane, and sulfanilamide in bacteria. *J. gen. Physiol.* **28**, 463.

JOHNSON, F. H., EYRING, H. & WILLIAMS, R. W. (1942). The nature of enzyme inhibitions in bacterial luminescence: sulfanilamide, urethane, temperature and pressure. *J. cell. comp. Physiol.* **20**, 247.

JOHNSON, F. H. & GRAY, D. H. (1949). Nuclei and large bodies of luminous bacteria in relation to salt concentration, osmotic pressure, temperature and urethane. *J. Bact.* **58**, 675.

JOHNSON, F. H. & LEWIN, I. (1946a). The action of quinine on dehydrogenases of *E. coli*. *J. cell. comp. Physiol.* **28**, 1.

JOHNSON, F. H. & LEWIN, I. (1946b). The disinfection of *E. coli* in relation to temperature, hydrostatic pressure and quinine. *J. cell. comp. Physiol.* **28**, 23.

JOHNSON, F. H. & LEWIN, I. (1946c). The growth rate of *E. coli* in relation to temperature, quinine and coenzyme. *J. cell. comp. Physiol.* **28**, 47.

JOHNSON, F. H. & LEWIN, I. (1946d). The influence of pressure, temperature and quinine on the rates of growth and disinfection of *E. coli* in the logarithmic growth phase. *J. cell. comp. Physiol.* **28**, 77.

JOHNSON, F. H. & LEWIN, I. (1947). The rates of growth and disinfection of *Escherichia coli* in relation to pH, quinine and temperature. *Leeuwenhoek J. Microbiol. Seerl.* **12**, 177.

JOHNSON, F. H. & ZOBELL, C. E. (1949a). The retardation of thermal disinfection of *Bacillus subtilis* spores by hydrostatic pressure. *J. Bact.* **57**, 353.

JOHNSON, F. H. & ZOBELL, C. E. (1949b). The acceleration of spore disinfection by urethan and its retardation by hydrostatic pressure. *J. Bact.* **57**, 359.

KASAI, G. J. (1953). Growth response of microorganisms to vitamins at different temperatures. *J. infect. Dis.* **92**, 58.

KLUYVER, A. J. & BAARS, J. K. (1932). On some physiological artefacts. *Proc. K. Akad. Wet. Amst.* **35**, 370.

KNOX, R. (1950). Tetrathionase: the differential effect of temperature on growth and adaptation. *J. gen. Microbiol.* **4**, 388.

KOCH, A. & HOFFMAN, C. (1912). Über die Verschiedenheit der Temperaturansprüche thermophiler Bakterien im Boden und in künstlichen Nährsubstraten. *Zbl. Bakt.* (2. Abt.), **31**, 433.

LAIDLER, K. J. (1951). The influence of pressure on the rates of biological reactions. *Arch. Biochem.* **30**, 226.

LANDAU, J. V., MARSLAND, D. A. & ZIMMERMAN, A. M. (1955). The energetics of cell division: effects of adenosine triphosphate and related substances on the furrowing capacity of marine eggs (*Arbacia* and *Chaetopterus*). *J. cell. comp. Physiol.* **45**, 309.

LARK, K. G. & ADAMS, M. H. (1953). The stability of phages as a function of the ionic environment. *Cold Spr. Harb. Symp. quant. Biol.* **18**, 171.

LAUFFER, M. A. & DOW, R. B. (1941). The denaturation of tobacco mosaic virus at high pressures. *J. biol. Chem.* **140**, 509.

LINCOLN, R. E. (1947). Mutation and adaptation of *Phytomonas stewartii*. *J. Bact.* **54**, 745.

LINDERSTRØM-LANG, K. (1950). Structure and enzymatic breakdown of proteins. *Cold Spr. Harb. Symp. quant. Biol.* **14**, 117.

LINDERSTRØM-LANG, K. (1952). Proteins and enzymes. *Stanf. Univ. Publ., Univ. Ser., Med. Sci.* **6**, 1.

LINDERSTRØM-LANG & JACOBSEN, C. F. (1941). The contraction accompanying enzymatic breakdown of proteins. *C.R. Lab. Carlsberg*, **24**, 1.

MAAS, W. K. & DAVIS, B. D. (1952). Production of an altered pantothenate-synthesizing enzyme by a temperature-sensitive mutant of *Escherichia coli*. *Proc. nat. Acad. Sci., Wash.*, **38**, 785.

McBEE, R. H. & McBEE, V. H. (1956). The incidence of thermophilic bacteria in Arctic soils and waters. *J. Bact.* **71**, 182.

McELROY, W. D. & DE LA HABA, G. (1949). The effect of pressure on induction of mutations by nitrogen mustard. *Science*, **110**, 640.

McLEAN, A. L. (1918). Bacteria of ice and snow in Antarctica. *Nature, Lond.*, **102**, 35.

MARSH, C. & MILITZER, W. (1956*a*). Thermal enzymes. VII. Further data on an adenosinetriphosphatase. *Arch. Biochem. Biophys.* **60**, 433.

MARSH, C. & MILITZER, W. (1956*b*). Thermal enzymes. VIII. Properties of a heat-stable inorganic phosphatase. *Arch. Biochem. Biophys.* **60**, 439.

MARSLAND, D. A. (1950). The mechanisms of cell division; temperature-pressure experiments on the cleaving eggs of Arbacia punctulata. *J. cell. comp. Physiol.* **36**, 205.

MARSLAND, D. (1956). Protoplasmic contractility in relation to gel structure: temperature-pressure experiments on cytokinesis and amoeboid movement. *Internat. Rev. Cytol.* **5**, 199.

MARSLAND, D. A. & LANDAU, J. V. (1954). The mechanisms of cytokinesis: temperature-pressure studies on the cortical gel system in various marine eggs. *J. exp. Zool.* **125**, 507.

MICHAELIS, L. & MENTEN, M. L. (1913). Die Kinetik der Invertinwirkung. *Biochem. Z.* **49**, 333.

MILITZER, W., SONDEREGGER, T. B., TUTTLE, L. C. & GEORGI, C. E. (1949). Thermal enzymes. *Arch. Biochem.* **24**, 75.

MILITZER, W., SONDEREGGER, T. B., TUTTLE, L. C. & GEORGI, C. E. (1950). Thermal enzymes. II. Cytochromes. *Arch. Biochem.* **26**, 299.

MILITZER, W. & TUTTLE, L. C. (1952). Thermal enzymes. IV. Partial separation of an adenosinetriphosphatase from an apyrase fraction. *Arch. Biochem. Biophys.* **39**, 379.

MILITZER, W., TUTTLE, L. C. & GEORGI, C. E. (1951). Thermal enzymes. III. Apyrase from a thermophilic bacterium. *Arch. Biochem. Biophys.* **31**, 416.

MORRISON, E. L. & TANNER, F. W. (1924). Studies on thermophilic bacteria. *Bot. Gaz.* **77**, 171.

MORRISON, T. F. (1924–5). Studies on luminous bacteria. II. The influence of temperature on the intensity of the light of luminous bacteria. *J. gen. Physiol.* **7**, 741.

MÜLLER, A. & SCHWARTZ, W. (1949). Untersuchungen zur Erdölbakteriologie. I. *Arch. Mikrobiol.* **14**, 291.

PAULING, L. & COREY, R. B. (1951*a*). The structure of synthetic polypeptides. *Proc. nat. Acad. Sci., Wash.*, **37**, 241.

PAULING, L. & COREY, R. B. (1951*b*). The pleated sheet, a new layer configuration of polypeptide chains. *Proc. nat. Acad. Sci., Wash.*, **37**, 251.

PAULING, L. & COREY, R. B. (1951*c*). The structure of feather rachis keratin. *Proc. nat. Acad. Sci., Wash.*, **37**, 256.

PAULING, L. & COREY, R. B. (1951*d*). The structure of hair, muscle, and related proteins. *Proc. nat. Acad. Sci., Wash.*, **37**, 261.

PAULING, L. & COREY, R. B. (1951*e*). The structure of fibrous proteins of the collagen-gelatin group. *Proc. nat. Acad. Sci., Wash.*, **37**, 272.

PAULING, L. & COREY, R. B. (1951*f*). The polypeptide-chain configuration in hemoglobin and other globular proteins. *Proc. nat. Acad. Sci., Wash.*, **37**, 282.

PEASE, D. C. (1946). Hydrostatic pressure effects upon the spindle figure and chromosome movement. II. Experiments on the meiotic divisions of *Tradescantia* pollen mother cells. *Biol. Bull., Woods Hole*, **91**, 145.

POLANYI, M. & EVANS, M. G. (1935). Some applications of the transition state method to the calculation of reaction velocities, especially in solution. *Trans. Faraday Soc.* **31**, 875.

REGNARD, P. (1884*a*). Note sur les conditions de la vie dans les profondeurs de la mer. *C.R. Soc. Biol., Paris*, **36**, 164.

REGNARD, P. (1884*b*). Note relative à l'action des hautes pressions sur quelques phénomènes vitaux (mouvement des cils vibratiles, fermentation). *C.R. Soc. Biol., Paris*, **36**, 187.

REGNARD, P. (1884*c*). Sur la cause de la rigidité des muscles soumis aux très hautes pressions. *C.R. Soc. Biol., Paris*, **36**, 310.

REGNARD, P. (1884*d*). Effet des hautes pressions sur les animaux marins. *C.R. Soc. Biol., Paris*, **36**, 394.

REGNARD, P. (1891). *Recherches expérimentales sur les conditions physiques de la vie dans les eaux.* Paris: Librairie Acad. Med.

REICHMANN, M. E., BUNCE, B. H. & DOTY, P. (1953). The changes induced in sodium desoxyribonucleate by dilute acid. *J. Polym. Sci.* **10**, 109.

ROBBINS, W. J. & KAVANAGH, F. (1944). Temperature, thiamine and growth of *Phycomyces. Bull. Torrey bot. Cl.* **71**, 1.

ROOT, C. W. (1932). The relation between respiration and light intensity of luminous bacteria, with special reference to temperature. I. Temperature and light intensity. *J. cell. comp. Physiol.* **1**, 195.

ROOT, C. W. (1934–5). The relation between respiration and light intensity of luminous bacteria with special reference to temperature. II. Temperature and oxygen consumption. *J. cell. comp. Physiol.* **5**, 219.

RUBENTSCHIK, L. (1925). Ueber die Lebenstätigkeit der Urobakterien bei einer Temperatur unter 0° C. *Zbl. Bakt.* (2. Abt.), **64**, 166.

SCHLEGEL, F. McK. & JOHNSON, F. H. (1949). The influence of temperature and hydrostatic pressure on the denaturation of methemoglobin by urethanes and salicylate. *J. biol. Chem.* **178**, 251.

SCHNEYER, L. H. (1952). Effects of hydrostatic pressure and selected sulfhydryl inhibitors on salivary amylase. *Arch. Biochem. Biophys.* **41**, 345.

SETCHELL, W. A. (1903). The upper temperature limits of life. *Science*, **17**, 934.

SHANES, A. B. (ed.) (1955). *Electrolytes in Biological Systems.* Washington: Amer. Physiol. Soc.

SIMPSON, R. B. & KAUZMANN, W. J. (1953). Kinetics of protein denaturation. I. Behavior of the optical rotation of ovalbumin in urea solutions. *J. Amer. chem. Soc.* **75**, 1539.

SLATOR, A. (1916). The rate of growth of bacteria. *J. chem. Soc.* **109**, 2.

SMITH, N. R., GORDON, R. E. & CLARK, F. E. (1952). *Aerobic Sporeforming Bacteria.* U.S. Dep. Agric., Agric. Monograph, no. 16.

STARKEY, R. L. (1938). A study of spore formation and other morphological characteristics of *Vibrio desulfuricans. Arch. Mikrobiol.* **9**, 268.

STEWART, B. T. & HALVORSON, H. O. (1954). Studies on the spores of aerobic bacteria. II. The properties of an extracted heat-stable enzyme. *Arch. Biochem. Biophys.* **49**, 168.

STREHLER, B. L. (1953). Luminescence in cell-free extracts of luminous bacteria and its activation by DPN. *J. Amer. chem. Soc.* **75**, 1264.

STREHLER, B. L. (1955). Factors and biochemistry of bacterial luminescence. In *The Luminescence of Biological Systems* (F. H. Johnson, ed.). Washington: Amer. Ass. Adv. Sci.

STREHLER, B. L. & JOHNSON, F. H. (1954). The temperature-pressure-inhibitor relations of bacterial luminescence in vitro. *Proc. nat. Acad. Sci., Wash.,* **40**, 606.

TALWAR, G. P. & MACHEBOEUF, M. (1954). A propos des travaux de Bresler sur la synthèse des protéines sous hautes pressions. *Ann. Inst. Pasteur,* **86**, 169.

THAYSEN, A. C. (1934). Preliminary note on the action of gases under pressure on the growth of microorganisms. I. Action of oxygen under pressure at various temperatures. *Biochem. J.* **28**, 1330.

THOMAS, R. (1954). Recherches sur la dénaturation des acides desoxyribo-nucléïques. *Biochem. Biophys. Acta.* **14**, 231.

TONGUR, V. S. (1952). (Regeneration of egg albumins under pressure; cf. *Chem. Abstr.* **47**, 643 h.) *Biochemistry, Leningrad,* **17**, 495.

WÁMOSCHER, L. (1930). Versuche über die Struktur der Bakterienzelle. *Z. Hyg. InfecktKr.* **111**, 422.

WARE, G. C. (1951). Nutritional requirements of *Bacterium coli* at 44°. *J. gen. Microbiol.* **5**, 880.

WATSON, J. D. & CRICK, F. H. C. (1953). A structure for desoxyribose nucleic acid. *Nature, Lond.,* **171**, 737.

WHITFIELD, J. F. & MURRAY, R. G. E. (1956). The effects of the ionic environment on the chromatin structures of bacteria. *Canad. J. Microbiol.* **2**, 245.

WRIGHT, G. G. & SCHOMAKER, V. (1948). Studies on the denaturation of antibody. IV. The influence of pH and certain other factors on the rate of inactivation of staphylococcus antitoxin in urea solutions. *J. biol. Chem.* **175**, 169.

ZAMENHOF, S., ALEXANDER, H. E. & LEIDY, G. (1953). Studies on the chemistry of the transforming principle. I. Resistance to physical and chemical agents. *J. exp. Med.* **98**, 373.

ZAMENHOF, S. & CHARGAFF, E. (1950). Studies on the diversity and the native state of desoxypentose nucleic acids. *J. biol. Chem.* **186**, 207.

ZAMENHOF, S., GRIBOFF, G. & MARULLO, N. (1954). Studies on the heat resistance of desoxyribonucleic acids to physical and chemical factors. *Biochim. biophys. Acta,* **13**, 459.

ZOBELL, C. E. (1952a). Part played by bacteria in petroleum formation. *Sediment. Petrol.* **22**, 42.

ZOBELL, C. E. (1925b). Bacterial life at the bottom of the Philippine trench. *Science,* **115**, 507.

ZOBELL, C. E. & FELTHAM, CATHERINE B. (1935). The occurrence and activity of urea-splitting bacteria in the sea. *Science,* **81**, 234.

ZOBELL, C. E. & JOHNSON, F. H. (1949). The influence of hydrostatic pressure on the growth and viability of terrestrial and marine bacteria. *J. Bact.* **57**, 179

ZOBELL, C. E. & OPPENHEIMER, C. H. (1950). Some effects of hydrostatic pressure on the multiplication and morphology of marine bacteria. *J. Bact.* **60**, 771.

THE ECOLOGICAL SIGNIFICANCE OF ANTIBIOTIC PRODUCTION

P. W. BRIAN

*Akers Research Laboratories, Imperial Chemical Industries Ltd.,
Welwyn, Hertfordshire*

INTRODUCTION

Antibiotics are produced by many fungi, actinomycetes and bacteria, and by a few micro-organisms of other groups. As soon as this was generally realized the question was asked—*are these substances produced under natural conditions and, if so, has their production any ecological consequences?* (Lucas, 1944; McIlwain, 1944; Salisbury, 1944). This was not just idle curiosity. Many cases are known of antagonism between microbes in their natural habitats, the mechanism of which is little understood, and antibiotic production suggests a possible mechanism. The question therefore is natural, logical and one that can be answered experimentally. I can see no scientific or philosophical justification for the view (Waksman, 1945a, 1948, 1951) that the question assumes wilful or purposive behaviour on the part of the antibiotic-producing organism or that it verges upon a vitalistic ideology. Nevertheless, there are many sound reasons for thinking it likely that the answer to both parts of the question is 'no'. Most natural habitats are impoverished in comparison with the luxurious nutrient conditions of laboratory culture. Rigorous monoculture is usually required for production of antibiotics in the laboratory or factory, but populations in natural habitats are very mixed. It is my purpose in this review to present and assess the available evidence which is now much more abundant than at the time of earlier reviews (Brian, 1949a, b; Hessayon, 1953a). The main habitat that has been investigated is soil, and I shall devote the greater part of my space to a consideration of the possible role of antibiotics in microbial antagonisms in soil. In addition, to indicate that it is not purely a problem of soil microbiology, I shall deal very briefly with organisms in two other habitats—autotrophic organisms in water and parasitic fungi in the tissues of higher plants.

SOIL

I do not propose to review in detail the great amount of work on microbial antagonism in soil; this has already been done elsewhere (Brian, 1949a; Garrard & Lochhead, 1938; Garrett, 1939, 1944, 1950, 1951, 1955, 1956; Harley, 1948; Katznelson, Lochhead & Timonin, 1948; Krasilnikov, 1954; Waksman, 1945b; Weindling, 1946). I shall briefly describe in general terms the circumstances in which one well-known antagonism develops—that between root-inhabiting fungi, in particular root parasites, and saprophytic soil micro-organisms. We owe our understanding of this situation, above all, to the work of Garrett.

In soil, saprophytic microbial life is governed by Malthusian principles. Numbers continually tend to a maximum determined by the available food supply. Life is therefore to be visualized as consisting of periods of quiescence when all suitable organic matter has been used up, alternating with periods of rapid multiplication when food again becomes available in the form of plant or animal debris. The size of microbial populations therefore fluctuates in time and space, peaks being determined by the position and availability of substrates. These 'flare-ups' of activity must be periods of intense competition. Those organisms which have an aptitude to utilize substrates which cannot be utilized by other species will be able to escape this intense competition to some extent and any such aptitude should be favoured by natural selection. The root-parasitic fungi represent one such evolutionary escape from the rigours of saprophytic life (Garrett, 1944, 1950). But their escape is only temporary and, in the case of parasites of annual plants, only lasts for one growing season. A time comes when the host is mature, fragments of the dead plant containing the parasite are distributed in the soil and the parasite has to enter a saprophytic period of existence. It may be physiologically quite capable of saprophytic life, but some form of competition develops between the established parasite in the plant fragment and saprophytes in the surrounding soil. In general, the root parasites seem to have lost, in the course of evolution, some of their competitive saprophytic ability, and in the face of this competition there is a general tendency for numbers and vigour of infective units to decline in this stage. The root parasites are also at a disadvantage in that because of the competition of the soil-inhabiting saprophytes their capacity to colonize other particles of dead plant tissue is reduced. One can thus envisage that the antagonism between root-parasitic fungi and soil saprophytes is not something that takes place evenly throughout the soil but is concentrated in space in the immediate vicinity of available organic substrates. I make this point because, if antibiotic production is of significance in this antagonism, that too is likely to be similarly localized.

Antagonism is also almost certainly of great significance when appropriate living seed or root tissues again become available to the parasite, as on the surface of these, too, there is a great concentration of saprophytic organisms, their numbers presumably dependent upon substrates diffusing from the root or seed tissues (Rovira, 1956a). Here also is a potential site for antibiotic production (Brian, Wright, Stubbs & Way, 1951; Wright, 1956c).

Mixed culture experiments have resulted in species of organism being isolated which are especially active as antagonists to root parasites. These include species of *Pseudomonas*, spore-forming aerobic bacilli, species of *Streptomyces*, and fungi of such genera as *Trichoderma*, *Penicillium* and *Aspergillus*. These are precisely those groups where antibiotic production is most well known. They are also characteristically species capable of rapidly exploiting organic matter whether in the form of dead plant or animal tissues or of root excretions (Rovira, 1956b); in other words, they are characteristic 'zymogenous' organisms. In itself, the observation that antagonists in soil are often antibiotic producers affords some indirect evidence that antibiotic production is ecologically significant. Other indirect evidence can be found, but without direct evidence it is of limited value. I propose therefore to proceed immediately to review experimental work bearing directly on this point.

Direct evidence of antibiotic production in soil

Experimental studies on antibiotic production in soil, and on soil conditions likely to affect production have, naturally enough, proceeded from the study of simple systems to more complex ones. Though there has been some overlap in time between these various stages, I propose to discuss results in the logical order of these stages, viz. (1) in sterilized soil supplemented with organic matter; (2) in unsupplemented sterile soil; (3) in soil containing its normal microflora, with various amounts of organic supplement. There has also been a trend from considering soil as a whole towards considering special local environments in the soil.

Sterile supplemented soil

A list is given in Table 1 of micro-organisms which have been found to produce antibiotics in sterilized soil supplemented with organic matter. This includes a wide range of fungi and actinomycetes; the number of bacteria is fewer, but only a few have been examined. In fact only one organism tested—a streptomycin-producing strain of *Streptomyces griseus*—has failed to produce detectable quantities of an antibiotic. Even in this case it is probable that streptomycin was produced but was difficult or impossible to extract because of adsorption on clay colloids (see below). In many of the examples cited, the sole organic supplement was glucose; this indicates that in sterile soil nutrient concentrations, other than that of a carbon source, are sufficient to support vigorous microbial growth and antibiotic synthesis. Indeed, Gregory, Allen, Riker & Peterson (1952*a*) record that their *Bacillus* sp. B6 produced more antibiotic in supplemented sterile soil than in more conventional culture media, and the yield of griseofulvin obtained in soil-cornmeal cultures of *Penicillium nigricans* (Brian *et al.* 1951) equalled that in the most favourable liquid culture media.

Table 1. *Production of antibiotics in sterile supplemented soil*

(Antibiotics are named in parentheses unless satisfactory evidence
of identity was obtained.)

Organism	Antibiotic	References
Fungi		
Aspergillus clavatus	(patulin)	Grossbard, 1952; Gottlieb, Siminoff & Martin, 1952
A. terreus	(citrinin?)	Grossbard, 1952
Penicillium nigricans	griseofulvin	Brian *et al.* 1951; Wright, 1955
P. patulum	(patulin)	Grossbard, 1948, 1949, 1952; Gregory *et al.* 1952*a*
Trichoderma viride	(gliotoxin)	Gregory *et al.* 1952*a*; Evans & Gottlieb, 1955
T. viride	gliotoxin	Wright, 1952, 1954
Trichothecium roseum	(trichothecin)	Hessayon, 1953*b*
Actinomycetes		
Streptomyces antibioticus	(actinomycin)	Grossbard, 1948
S. griseus	(actidione)	Gottlieb *et al.* 1952
S. venezuelae	chloramphenicol	Gottlieb & Siminoff, 1952
Streptomyces sp. A67	(unknown)	Gregory *et al.* 1952*a*
Streptomyces spp.	actinomycin	Stevenson, 1954*a*, 1956
Streptomyces spp. 290, 287 and B	(unknown)	Krasilnikov, 1954
Bacteria		
Bacillus sp. B6	(unknown)	Gregory *et al.* 1952*a*
Pseudomonas fluorescens	(unknown)	Lewis, 1929

(Species examined but not found to produce antibiotics: *Streptomyces griseus* (Streptomycin strain) Siminoff & Gottlieb, 1951.)

In most cases the antibiotic produced in soil has not been identified, but the production of griseofulvin, gliotoxin, chloramphenicol and actinomycin has been proved by specific bioassay, behaviour on paper chromatograms, or by actual isolation.

Sterile soil without supplement

Most micro-organisms which produce abundant antibiotic in supplemented sterile soil have failed to produce detectable quantities of antibiotics in unsupplemented sterile soil (see Table 2). This is to some extent due to losses in extraction and insensitive methods of assay. Nevertheless, a few fungi and actinomycetes have been shown to produce antibiotics under such conditions of low nutrient status. Three antibiotics produced in such circumstances have been identified. Gottlieb & Siminoff (1952) showed that chloramphenicol is produced by *Streptomyces venezuelae*, and identified the antibiotic with some certainty by chemical assay and by its behaviour on paper chromatograms. Wright (1954), using similar techniques, showed that *Trichoderma viride* will produce gliotoxin, and Stevenson (1954*b*) demonstrated the presence of actinomycin by specific effects on the morphology of fungal germ tubes. In none of these cases was the amount of antibiotic produced nearly as great as that produced in supplemented sterile soil, confirming that shortage of organic material, mainly carbon sources, limits production of antibiotics in soil.

Table 2. *Production of antibiotics in sterile soil without supplement*

(Antibiotics are named in parentheses unless satisfactory evidence of identity was obtained.)

Organism	Antibiotic	References
Fungi		
Penicillium patulum	(patulin)	Gregory *et al.* 1952*a*
Trichoderma viride	(gliotoxin)	Evans & Gottlieb, 1955
T. viride	gliotoxin	Wright, 1954
Trichothecium roseum	(trichothecin)	Hessayon, 1951, 1953*b*
Actinomycetes		
Streptomyces antibioticus	actinomycin	Stevenson, 1954*b*
S. venezuelae	chloramphenicol	Gottlieb & Siminoff, 1952; Erhlich, Anderson, Coffey & Gottlieb, 1951, 1955
Streptomyces sp.	(unknown)	Krasilnikov, 1954

(Species examined but not found to produce antibiotics: *Aspergillus clavatus* (Gottlieb *et al.* 1952); *A. terreus* (Grossbard, 1949); *Penicillium nigricans* (Wright, 1954); *P. patulum* (Grossbard, 1948, 1952); *Trichoderma lignorum* (Gregory *et al.* 1952*a*); *Streptomyces aureofaciens* (Martin & Gottlieb, 1952); *S. griseus* (actidione strain) (Gottlieb *et al.* 1952); *S. griseus* (Streptomycin strain) (Siminoff & Gottlieb, 1951); *S. rimosus* (Martin & Gottlieb, 1952); *Streptomyces* sp. A67 (Gregory *et al.* 1952*a*); *Bacillus* sp. B6 (Gregory *et al.* 1952*a*).)

Soil containing normal microflora

It has been almost universal experience that little or no antibiotic production can be demonstrated in normal soil, even if supplemented, by the techniques which have proved successful in work with sterile soil, viz. bioassay of expressed soil water or of solvent extracts of the soil. On a few occasions, antibiotic production has been demonstrated by such methods, usually in soils highly supplemented with organic material (Table 3). Gregory *et al.* (1952*a*) showed that *Penicillium patulum*, *Streptomyces* sp. A67 and *Bacillus* sp. B6 produced antibiotics in a sandy soil supplemented with 0·5 % (w/v) soybean meal, 0·52 % (w/v) glucose and 0·15 % (w/v) cornsteep liquor; in no case was the antibiotic identified. Krasilnikov (1954) demonstrated a trace of antibiotic in a heavily supplemented soil inoculated with a *Streptomyces* sp. Wright (1952, 1954) demonstrated production of gliotoxin, identified by paper chromatography, in two types of soil supplemented by clover-meal. At least 1 % clover-meal was needed and even then the yield of gliotoxin was much less than in a similarly supplemented sterile soil, and less even than that produced in an unsupplemented but sterile soil.

Table 3. *Production of antibiotics in soil containing full normal microflora*

(Antibiotics are named in parentheses unless satisfactory evidence of identity was obtained.)

Organism	Antibiotic	References
Fungi		
Penicillium frequentans	frequentin	Wright, 1956*a*
P. gladioli	gladiolic acid	Wright, 1956*a*
P. patulum	(patulin)	Gregory *et al.* 1952*a*
Trichoderma viride	gliotoxin	Wright, 1952, 1954, 1956*a,c*
T. viride	(viridin)	Wright, 1956*c*
Actinomycetes		
Streptomyces sp. A67	(unknown)	Gregory *et al.* 1952*a*
Streptomyces sp. 287	(unknown)	Krasilnikov, 1954
Bacteria		
Bacillus sp. B6	(unknown)	Gregory *et al.* 1952*a*

(Species examined but not found to produce antibiotics: *Penicillium nigricans* (Wright, 1954); *P. patulum* (Grossbard, 1950); *Trichoderma viride* (Gregory *et al.* 1952*a*; Evans & Gottlieb, 1955); *Streptomyces aureofaciens* (Wright, 1956*c*); *S. griseus* (Wright, 1956*c*); *S. venezuelae* (Ehrlich *et al.* 1952, 1953; Wright, 1956*c*); *Streptomyces* spp. (Stevenson, 1954*a*).)

On the basis of these results one might conclude that antibiotic production in soil is only likely to reach significant proportions in soils very heavily enriched with organic matter—more heavily enriched than would occur naturally or than could be contemplated in normal agricultural practice. But the recent results of Wright (1956*a*, *b*, *c*) throw a new light on the subject. The results already summarized show clearly that the supply of organic matter limits antibiotic production in soil and that very rarely will the organic matter content of soil be of a quality and quantity suitable to stimulate appreciable antibiotic production, if one considers a bulk of soil as a whole. This does not preclude the possibility of local concentrations being produced in the vicinity of a suitable carbon source and, since many soil micro-organisms tend to be concentrated in such sites, the antibiotic formed may have profound though spatially restricted ecological effects. Wright has developed two techniques for detecting antibiotic production in such restricted sites.

The first of these (Wright, 1956 *a*, *b*) simulates conditions in fragments of dead plant debris. Small lengths of straw were buried in normal soil inoculated with *Trichoderma viride*. After a suitable period the straw sections were dug up, extracted with ether and run on paper chromatograms; the antibiotic gliotoxin was found in quite considerable concentration—far higher than in the surrounding soil. This result is of special interest, since the work of Garrett and his colleagues on saprophytic survival of root pathogens has largely been based on similar experimental situations.

In Wright's second technique (1956 *a*, *c*) viable seeds (mustard, wheat and pea) were used as an example of a natural source of organic carbon compounds available to soil micro-organisms. Seeds were inoculated with spores of various micro-organisms; they were then sown and, after an interval, dug up again and the whole seeds or the seed coats extracted as in the case of the straw sections. By this technique, production of the fungal antibiotics frequentin, gladiolic acid and gliotoxin was demonstrated. On the other hand, actinomycetes potentially capable of producing aureomycin, streptomycin and chloramphenicol failed to produce antibiotics in seed coats.

Factors affecting antibiotic production in soil

The data so far quoted indicate that various soil conditions affect the amount of antibiotic produced. Some of these are dealt with in greater detail below.

Availability of carbon source

Results already presented show that antibiotic production in soil is limited by the supply of suitable organic carbon compounds. There is also evidence that the increased production of antibiotics in soil after heat sterilization is in part due to improved nutrient status. Wright (1954) showed that, within limits, the yield of gliotoxin in soil infected with *Trichoderma viride* was related to the length of heat treatment prior to inoculation. Relatively short periods of steaming were sufficient to sterilize the soil but much longer periods were needed to secure maximum yields of the antibiotic. The heat treatment increased the ammonia-nitrogen content of the soil markedly, but this was not responsible for higher yields of gliotoxin. Heating is known also to increase the soluble phosphate, sulphate and organic carbon concentrations in the soil; there was some evidence that the increased available organic carbon content was responsible for increased antibiotic production.

Effect of soil microflora on antibiotic production

The main reason why less antibiotic is produced in untreated soil than in sterile soil is that the normal soil microflora interferes in various ways. Two forms of interference can be envisaged: (1) inhibition of growth of the antibiotic-producing organism and hence inhibition of synthesis of the antibiotic; (2) metabolic breakdown of the antibiotic when formed. It is probable that both of these processes occur; the second is dealt with in a subsequent section of this paper.

Wright (1954) has shown that the first process is of importance in connexion with production of griseofulvin in soil by *Penicillium nigricans*. In her experiments, griseofulvin was only produced in sterile, supplemented soil. Introduction of other soil fungi at the same time as *P. nigricans* in some cases markedly influenced griseofulvin production. Several antibiotic-producing fungi prevented growth of *P. nigricans* and so reduced griseofulvin production. Some which produce no antibiotic, including the rapidly growing Phycomycete *Mucor ramannianus* and an antibiotically inactive strain of *Trichoderma viride*, were also antagonistic. In other pairs, *Penicillium nigricans* was dominant, preventing growth of the other. Thus one has to envisage a complex web of antagonisms existing in mixed cultures, the potential antagonistic properties of one species being influenced by others. Similar but even more complex interrelationships between antagonistic actinomycetes have been described by Lochhead & Landerkin (1949) and Peterson (1954).

Adsorption

In the presence of soil the inhibitory properties of an antibiotic may be much reduced. In many cases this has been shown to be due to adsorption of the antibiotic on clay colloids, so that concentrations of the antibiotic in the soil water are much reduced (Siminoff & Gottlieb, 1951; Gottlieb & Siminoff, 1952; Martin & Gottlieb, 1952, 1955; Krasilnikov, 1954; Jefferys, 1952; Gregory *et al.* 1952a; Skinner, 1956). This is particularly true of actinomycete antibiotics with basic properties, such as streptomycin, terramycin, aureomycin, neomycin, actinomycin and viomycin and some of the bacterial polypeptide antibiotics. Neutral and acidic antibiotics are not adsorbed to the same extent; nine such antibiotics studied by Jefferys (1952) were not adsorbed, whereas under similar conditions streptomycin was strongly adsorbed. It should not be concluded that an adsorbed antibiotic is necessarily biologically inert, since Pramer & Starkey (1951) were able to show that streptomycin strongly adsorbed in soil and unextractable by solvent techniques, was in fact still inhibitory to bacterial cells sufficiently near to the clay-streptomycin complex.

Chemical and biological breakdown of antibiotics in soil

Many antibiotics are highly labile substances and are rapidly degraded in soil. This may be due to intrinsic instability in aqueous solution at the pH of the soil; the instability in soil of such antibiotics as penicillin, viridin, gliotoxin, frequentin and albidin is partially or wholly explained in this way (Jefferys, 1952). In addition, many antibiotics, including some of considerable chemical stability, are biologically degraded in soil. A list of those which appear to be biologically degraded, in so far as they are inactivated more rapidly in normal soil than in sterilized soil, is given in Table 4. It is highly probable that all antibiotics are susceptible to biological attack in soil; though fradicin and actidione have been reported (Gregory et al. 1952a) to be highly stable in several soils, on some occasions at least actidione rapidly disappears (Gottlieb et al. 1952) and the same probably applies to fradicin. Streptomycin adsorbed on clay colloids is still susceptible to biological attack (Pramer & Starkey, 1951).

Table 4. *Antibiotics which are biologically degraded in soil*

Antibiotic	References
Actinomycin	Waksman & Woodruff, 1942
Albidin	Jefferys, 1952
Biomycin (= aureomycin)	Krasilnikov, 1954
Chloramphenicol	Gottlieb & Siminoff, 1952; Ehrlich et al. 1953; Smith & Worrel, 1950
Frequentin	Jefferys, 1952
Globisporin	Krasilnikov, 1954
Griseofulvin	Brian et al. 1951; Jefferys, 1952
Mycophenolic acid	Jefferys, 1952
Patulin*	Grossbard, 1952; Gottlieb et al. 1952; Jefferys, 1952
Penicillin	Jefferys, 1952; Krasilnikov, 1954
Streptomycin	Pramer & Starkey, 1951; Krasilnikov, 1954
Terramycin	Krasilnikov, 1954

* Synonyms = clavacin, expansine.

Relation between antibiotic production and microbial antagonism

Are antibiotics produced by micro-organisms in soil? I think we can now fairly claim that in certain circumstances some are produced. The only nutrient limiting factor appears to be a suitable organic carbon source. This requirement is met in pieces of plant debris (e.g. the wheat-straw fragment in the experiments of Wright), in seed coats (Wright, 1956c) and probably in the rhizospheres of some plants, where sugars and amino acids are known to be present (Rovira, 1956a). In soils containing no other organisms most antibiotic producers will produce easily detectable quantities of an antibiotic if a carbon source is present, but even in these highly simplified circumstances the concentration produced is determined by the balance of rate of synthesis of the antibiotic and rate of degradation; the latter process may be rapid if, for instance, the soil pH is one at which the antibiotic is unstable.

In a soil with a normal mixed microflora a more complex system prevails. The antibiotic producer has to compete with other saprophytes, some of which also produce antibiotics, with the consequence that there is an antagonism between antagonists. Some antibiotic producers, for example *Trichoderma viride*, are not seriously affected by this antagonism, but others, for example *Penicillium nigricans* (Wright, 1955), are markedly inhibited and will produce little or no antibiotic in mixed culture. The greater success of *Trichoderma viride* in such circumstances is probably due to its high intrinsic growth rate, to its capacity to produce antibiotics rapidly, and to its remarkable tolerance of fungitoxic compounds of all kinds. Such antibiotic as may be formed may be inactivated chemically or biologically, or may be adsorbed on clay colloids or humus, and all these processes may be proceeding simultaneously. The amount of antibiotic capable of exerting an ecological effect at any one place at any one time is thus determined by the balance of these forces. Antibiotics of relatively high intrinsic stability and resistance to biological degradation and those which are not adsorbed by soil colloids may well be more ecologically significant than others. The high activity of some actinomycetes as antagonists to root parasites (Johnson, 1954) may be an indication that adsorption of basic antibiotics is not an important limitation of their effectiveness.

All these processes in turn are affected by the nature of the soil. Thus, in any one soil certain organisms may be able to produce antibiotics, while others, though potentially capable of doing so, will not. In a different soil the organisms capable of producing antibiotics will be different. If antibiotic production is to be put to practical use, as, for example, in biological control of pathogenic fungi, this point is of fundamental importance.

While we can now say with some confidence that some micro-organisms can produce antibiotics in soil in quantities sufficient to account for some observed biological antagonisms, we have yet to show that the two phenomena are connected. The evidence is mainly indirect, probably necessarily so. Five kinds of observation are suggestive:

(1) The sites where competition between root parasites and soil saprophytes is most intense are in fragments of organic matter, on root surfaces (rhizosphere) and seed surfaces (spermatosphere). A high proportion of the saprophytic bacteria, actinomycetes and fungi isolated from such sites can produce antibiotics.

(2) In experiments where root parasites and antibiotic-producing saprophytes have been inoculated together into sterile soil, the anti-biotic producers have frequently been shown to reduce the survival or infective vigour of the parasite (Gregory *et al.* 1952*a, b*; Grossbard, 1947, 1952; Johnson, 1954; van Luijk, 1938; Stevenson, 1954*a*; Tveit & Wood, 1955; Weindling & Fawcett, 1936; Wright, 1956*a*).

(3) Organisms shown to be antagonistic to root pathogens in soil have been found to produce antibiotics *in vitro* (Tveit & Moore, 1954).

(4) Where antibiotic-producing strains of a given species have been compared with strains producing no antibiotic as antagonists to root pathogens in soil, the antibiotic-producing strains have been found to be the more effective antagonists (Wright, 1956*a*).

(5) Soil conditions unfavourable for accumulation of a given anti-biotic have been shown to reduce the antagonistic activity of the organism producing the antibiotic (Weindling, 1934).

Accumulated observations of this kind afford considerable support to the view that antibiotic production plays a part in biological antagonism of the kind we have been discussing. However, to statements (2), (3) and (4) above, certain exceptions are known. On occasion, for instance, antibiotic-producing organisms have not behaved as anta-gonists. Slykhuis (1947) found that a strain of *Penicillium urticae* antagonistic to *Fusarium culmorum in vitro* did not reduce the infectivity of the *Fusarium* to cereal or grass seedlings. This could, of course, be a reflexion of the fact that soil conditions were unsuitable for production of the antibiotic. Again, the failure of Wright (1956*a*) to obtain control of *Pythium* damping-off of mustard seedlings by seed inoculation with *Penicillium nigricans*, a common soil fungus producing the antibiotic griseofulvin, can be attributed to the known resistance of *Pythium* spp.

to that antibiotic. Under similar conditions species producing anti-biotics inhibitory to *Pythium* reduced the amount of disease.

Potent antagonists have sometimes not shown any indication of being antibiotic producers. An interesting example is quoted by Slykhuis (1947) who found species of *Phialophora* and *Acremonium* to be very effective antagonists to *Fusarium culmorum* in soil, yet were not antagonistic *in vitro*, nor did they produce culture filtrates on liquid media toxic to *F. culmorum*. Other mechanisms of antagonism must exist. These could include competition for nutrients or active parasitism, as has been recorded for *Trichoderma* (Aytoun, 1953; Weindling, 1932). Similar conclusions can be drawn from the fact that non-producing strains, of species usually producing antibiotics, can also act as antagonists in soil (Siminoff & Gottlieb, 1951; Wright, 1956a).

Discussion of antagonism between soil saprophytes and root para-sites usually tends to centre round the survival of the latter in dead plant tissue or their capacity to colonize other organic fragments during their saprophytic, declining phase. Equally important micro-environments, whose selective forces are probably no less intense, are related to incep-tion of the parasitic phase. These are particularly important in any attempt to use knowledge of biological antagonism to obtain biological control of soil-borne disease. Slykhuis (1947) has shown the importance of the seed coat as a food base for parasitic attack on cereal and grass seedlings. The antagonists which he studied appeared to reduce infection with *Fusarium culmorum* by competing with the parasite for a foothold in the seed coat. By reducing the mass of parasite mycelium in the seed coat the intensity of infection of the seedling was much reduced. This observation explains the successful control of seed-borne and soil-borne diseases following seed inoculation with antagonists (Gregory *et al.* 1952b; Rehm, 1953; Tveit & Wood, 1955; Winter, 1951; Wright, 1956d). Competition between antagonists and root parasites in the rhizosphere probably influences infection at later stages of growth of the host. As yet, satisfactory methods for influencing the rhizosphere microflora have not been developed, but this is probably the key to successful biological control of root disease.

WATER

Several observations suggest that antibiotic production may assume importance in shallow waters and in the plankton of lakes and oceans. The examples I shall give stretch somewhat the usual definition of an antibiotic, but they are nevertheless relevant to my general theme. The antibiotic-producing organism in each case is autotrophic. Consequently, availability of a carbon source is not a limiting factor in antibiotic production as it was in the case of soil saprophytes.

The first example concerns cases of severe mortality of fish, occasionally observed in shallow, brackish waters in Europe and elsewhere (Otterstrom & Steemann-Nielsen, 1940). Wherever this has occurred it has been found to be associated with a great increase in numbers of a brownish phytoflagellate *Prymnesium parvum*. Filtered water from the lakes was highly toxic to fish. A number of severe recent incidences of this trouble in fish-breeding ponds in Israel have made it possible to study the causes in greater detail (Shilo & Aschner, 1953). It is now quite certain that under certain conditions *Prymnesium* multiplies rapidly and at the same time produces an exotoxin. This exotoxin is a large molecule, probably protein, and specifically toxic to gill-breathing animals. The level of toxin is in part determined by a balance between the rate of production by *Prymnesium* and destruction of the toxin by bacteria; it may also be adsorbed on the bottom mud. Thus the factors affecting accumulation of this fish poison are very similar to those affecting production of antibiotics in soil and, though the toxin is not perhaps what we would ordinarily call an antibiotic, since it is not known to be toxic to other micro-organisms, its ecological significance in nature is similar to that which I have suggested for true antibiotics. Other phytoflagellates (Gunter, Williams, Davis & Smith, 1948; Sommer, Monnier, Riegel, Stanger, Mold, Wikholm & Kivalis, 1948) and blue-green algae (Shelubsky, 1951) produce fish toxins but these are endocellular and have no effect until the organisms are eaten or until the toxin is liberated by autolysis after death.

A closer analogy to the situation in soil is provided by the observations of Lefèvre, Jakob & Nisbet (1952), who find that in cultures of certain algae extracellular metabolites accumulate, toxic to other species. Similar materials accumulate in natural shallow waters and are considered to be factors contributing to observed phases of dominance of a single algal species. Little chemical work has been done on these antibiotic substances and it is not known whether or not they are similar to the fatty acid antibiotics produced by *Chlorella* (Spoehr, Smith, Strain, Milner & Hardin, 1949). Other examples of antagonism between organisms of the phytoplankton probably based on antibiotic production are given by Lucas (1947).

PLANT PARASITES

Antibiotic production has been recorded much more often from saprophytic fungi than from plant-parasitic fungi, but this may merely be due to the fact that many more of the former have been examined (Brian, 1951). Be that as it may, some plant parasites do produce antibiotics *in vitro*; in some cases they also produce them in tissues of host plants.

The most certain case involves the parasite *Penicillium expansum*, which causes storage rots of apples and some other fruits. Brian, Elson & Lowe (1956) have shown that strains of this mould capable of producing patulin in culture also produce it in considerable concentration in rotted apple tissue. Furthermore, they have examined natural rots caused by *P. expansum* and have found that an antibiotic with the same activity spectrum as patulin is usually present. Here then is an antibiotic which must be produced under natural conditions in considerable quantities. Similarly, Brian, Elson, Hemming & Wright (1952) have produced evidence that some strains of *Alternaria solani* may produce alternaric acid in infected tomato fruits, and Lakshminarayan & Subramanian (1955) have detected fusaric acid in tomato plants infected with *Fusarium vasinfectum*.

It may be that the production of these substances in the plant tissues is concerned with development of pathological symptoms in the host, because all are phytotoxic as well as toxic to other fungi and to bacteria. In the case of patulin production it is unlikely that this is the case and solid evidence is wanting in the other cases. However, it is possible, and this may be worth further investigation, that production of these materials tends to discourage secondary invasion by other microorganisms, thus, as it were, reserving territory for the primary parasite.

ANTIBIOTICS AND EVOLUTION

I think that the evidence presented above is sufficient for us to conclude that some antibiotics are naturally occurring substances and that they do exert an ecological effect, expressed in various kinds of microbial antagonism. I propose to conclude with a much more speculative consideration of the possible evolutionary consequences of antibiotic production, referring particularly to the soil microflora.

Antibiotics are metabolic products of micro-organisms which are secreted, or which diffuse or leak out of the cells which produce them, so altering or conditioning the surrounding medium, whether it is an agar gel in a Petri dish or a water film surrounding a particle of organic matter in the soil. They are in this respect just one kind of a variety of metabolites which similarly leak out. Others may be vitamins, sugars or even such simple substances as inorganic salts or carbon dioxide, all of which alter the environment and so affect the lives of neighbouring micro-organisms. There is no ecological distinction save in scale between this kind of modification of the environment and that produced by secretions or excretions of higher plants and animals, but whereas most metabolites tend to leak out of microbial cells, the process is more canalized and controlled in higher organisms, particularly in those that have adopted a terrestrial life. Antagonism between microbes based on antibiotic production is thus in every way comparable with root competition between species of higher plants where it is based on the production of phytotoxic root excretions. The natural production of antibiotics and the ecological effects consequent upon this production are but an example of the more general phenomenon described by Lucas (1944, 1947, 1949) as production of 'ectocrine' substances, substances which have an extracellular regulating or correlating effect analogous to the regulating effect of endocrine secretions within more highly differentiated organisms.

In soil, as Stanier (1953) has pointed out, micro-organisms tend to live in micro-environments, discontinuous in space and time. I have already suggested that it is in such micro-environments that antibiotics will most probably be produced in nature. Though in terms of our time-scale a small concentration of antibiotic produced in a fragment of dead plant tissue may have a short life, by the time scale of microbes growing and multiplying in that micro-environment its presence may be highly significant. A succession of such transient concentrations of antibiotics in those very loci where microbial reproduction is most rapid, may be expected to have a significant selective effect and, as Waksman (1951) has said, we should expect evolutionary adaptation to have taken place. Unfortunately, data which would enable us to judge whether this has happened are scarce. Certainly penicillin-resistant or penicillin-destroying bacteria abound in soil, but the significance of this, or of the fact that penicillin-sensitive bacteria are also abundant, is uncertain unless we know whether these organisms are likely to be found in the same micro-environment as penicillin-producing moulds. It would be more profitable to consider a group of organisms with similar basic nutrient requirements and inhabiting the same kind of micro-environment, such as the saprophytic soil fungi and root-parasitic fungi in the saprophytic phase of their life history. Some information on such a group has been collected by Jefferys, Brian, Hemming & Lowe (1953).

The organisms likely to experience the greatest concentrations of antibiotic are those producing them and it is therefore significant, if not unexpected, that each of the nine antibiotic-producing fungi studied by Jefferys *et al.* were highly tolerant of the antibiotics they themselves produce. Equally striking was the fact that the antibiotic producers as a group were far more resistant to the several antibiotics they produce than were a group of plant pathogenic fungi. This greater sensitivity of plant pathogens was first noted by Garrett (1950). A particularly interesting example of the ecological consequences of such sensitivity has been found by Butler (1953). He was seeking to explain the different saprophytic colonizing abilities of two cereal root-rot fungi, *Curvularia ramosa* which is a vigorous competitive saprophyte and *Helmintho-sporium sativum* which is a much weaker saprophyte. The difference could not be explained in terms of growth rate, or by the ability of the stronger saprophyte to produce antibiotics. It was associated with much stronger resistance of *Curvularia ramosa* to a range of fungal antibiotics and to antagonistic effects of some common soil bacteria. Thus is seems possible that the greater susceptibility to anti-biotics of root pathogens, when compared with antibiotic-producing soil saprophytes, is to some extent responsible for their characteristically low competitive saprophytic ability. Significance is added to this difference between antibiotic-producing saprophytes and root parasites by the additional observation that a group of soil saprophytes believed not to produce antibiotics, including several widespread species of Mucorales, were as resistant to antibiotics as the antibiotic producers themselves. Consequently, although there must be a complex antago-nistic relationship between the soil saprophytes themselves, which has possibly led to a widespread evolutionary development of resistance to antibiotics, the main selective effect would now appear to be exerted on the root parasites in their saprophytic phase.

Why have the root parasites in general not developed an adaptive resistance as a result of this selective pressure? I find it difficult to find a satisfactory answer to this question. It may be true that by 'escaping' into plant tissues for the greater part of the year in the case of parasites of annual plants, or for longer periods in the case of parasites of perennials, the period of exposure to the selective pressure of antibiotic-producing saprophytes is much reduced. Nevertheless, resistance to antibiotics would appear to assist survival of a root parasite, as exemplified by the case of *Curvularia ramosa* described by Butler, and should surely be a valuable adaptation and one likely to be favoured by natural selection.

Alternatively, why have not root parasites developed the capacity to produce antibiotics, when in this way they might inhibit colonization of dead infected plant material by saprophytes? Some have, but I think it is understandable that, in general, they have not. Most antibiotics are generally toxic and most of those that have been tested have proved to be phytotoxic. Conversely, many of the toxins produced by plant pathogens, believed in some cases to be responsible for some of the disease symptoms, have been found to possess antimicrobial activity. In cases where plant parasites do produce phytotoxic substances in the host, these tend to kill cells immediately surrounding the infection so that the normal diffusion of nutrients from other parts of the host is prevented. The parasite in this way tends to isolate itself. There is some evidence that the more specialized plant parasites do not release toxic metabolites into the host tissue and so increase the possibilities of maintaining an equilibrium between host and parasite. If in the course of evolution there has been a tendency to select such forms this might be expected to override the advantages of antibiotic production in the saprophytic phase.

Having dealt with the selective effect of antibiotics on organisms naturally exposed to them, I must now take up the more problematical topic of the advantages that antibiotic production may confer on the producing organism. The general thesis that I have expounded is that organisms sensitive to antibiotics are at a disadvantage where they have to compete with antibiotic producers for limited substrates. If that conception is valid, I think it is reasonable to conclude that what is a disadvantage for one group of organisms may be an advantage to others. If that is so, the capacity to produce antibiotics must be expected to increase the likelihood of survival of a saprophytic species, though not necessarily of a parasitic species as I have suggested earlier, and so is likely to be favoured by selection. Has this happened? Waksman (1951) has discussed this point and has concluded: 'If an antibiotic is of help to the organism producing it, we would expect that the soil would be largely inhabited by antibiotic producing organisms. This is not the case.'

Let us look at this more closely. I have conceived antibiotic production to be confined in soil to micro-environments where suitable substrates occur, and I have instanced fragments of organic debris, seed surfaces and the rhizosphere as examples of such micro-environments. It is organisms inhabiting such micro-environments that we have to consider. Are those mainly antibiotic-producing organisms? There are no accurate data available on this point, but it is possible to get an approximate answer. It seems to me justifiable to assume that the

organisms isolated from soil by plating techniques are fairly representative of the more vigorous saprophytes inhabiting the kind of
micro-environment we have been discussing. Information is available
concerning the proportion of such organisms that produce antibiotics.
Benedict (1953) has tabulated the results of several surveys of actinomycetes isolated in this way, and it would seem that quite 50 % of the
cultures tested produced antibiotics. Similarly, Brian (1951) has shown
that of 526 species of microfungi (Basidiomycetes excluded), most of
which were soil fungi, 41 % produced antibiotics. If one bears in mind
that many of the active species are very common in soil, a percentage
based on isolates would be much larger. These results seem to me to
show that antibiotic production is, in fact, quite common among soil
saprophytes.

I do not think one would expect *all* soil saprophytes to be antibiotic
producers. After all, fitness does not usually depend on a single character
and the possession of such characters as resistance to antibiotics and
rapid growth rate, seen in some Mucorales, might well equal in value
the capacity to produce antibiotics. Consequently, I think it can be
said that the present-day occurrence of antibiotic-producing soil saprophytes is not incompatible with the view that the capacity to produce
antibiotics is a character conducing to fitness.

REFERENCES

AYTOUN, R. S. C. (1953). The genus *Trichoderma*: its relationship with *Armillaria
mellea* (Vahl ex Fries) Quel and *Polyporus schweinitzii* Fr., together with
preliminary observations on its ecology in woodland soils. *Trans. bot. Soc.
Edinb.* **36**, 99.
BENEDICT, R. G. (1953). Antibiotics produced by actinomycetes. *Bot. Rev.* **19**, 229.
BRIAN, P. W. (1949*a*). The production of antibiotics by microorganisms in relation
to biological equilibria in the soil. *Symp. Soc. exp. Biol.* **3**, 357.
BRIAN, P. W. (1949*b*). The production of antibiotics by soil microorganisms. *Chem.
& Ind. (Rev.)*, 391.
BRIAN, P. W. (1951). Antibiotics produced by fungi. *Bot. Rev.* **17**, 357.
BRIAN, P. W., ELSON, G. W., HEMMING, H. G. & WRIGHT, J. M. (1952). The phyto-
toxic properties of alternaric acid in relation to the etiology of plant diseases
caused by *Alternaria solani* (Ell. & Mart.) Jones & Grout. *Ann. appl. Biol.* **39**,
308.
BRIAN, P. W., ELSON, G. W. & LOWE, D. (1956). Production of patulin in apple
fruits by *Penicillium expansum*. *Nature, Lond.*, **178**, 263.
BRIAN, P. W., WRIGHT, J. M., STUBBS, J. & WAY, A. M. (1951). Uptake of anti-
biotic metabolites of soil microorganisms by plants. *Nature, Lond.*, **167**, 347.
BUTLER, F. C. (1953). Saprophytic behaviour of some cereal root-rot fungi.
II. Factors influencing saprophytic colonization of wheat straw. *Ann. appl.
Biol.* **40**, 298.
ERHLICH, J., ANDERSON, L. E., COFFEY, G. L. & GOTTLIEB, D. (1952). *Streptomyces
venezuelae*: soil studies. *Antibiot. Chemother.* **2**, 595.

186 P. W. BRIAN

EHRLICH, J., ANDERSON, L. E., COFFEY, G. L. & GOTTLIEB, D. (1953). *Streptomyces venezuelae*: further soil studies. *Antibiot. Chemother.* 3, 1141.

EVANS, E. & GOTTLIEB, D. (1955). Gliotoxin in soils. *Soil. Sci.* 80, 295.

GARRARD, E. H. & LOCHHEAD, A. G. (1938). Relationships between soil micro-organisms and soil-borne plant pathogens. A review. *Sci. Agric.* 18, 719.

GARRETT, S. D. (1939). Soil-borne fungi and the control of root disease. *Tech. Commun. Bur. Soil Sci., Harpenden*, no. 38.

GARRETT, S. D. (1944). *Root Disease Fungi*. Waltham, Massachusetts: Chronica Botanica Co.

GARRETT, S. D. (1950). Ecology of the root inhabiting fungi. *Biol. Rev.* 25, 254.

GARRETT, S. D. (1951). Ecological groups of soil fungi: A survey of substrate relationships. *New Phytol.* 50, 149.

GARRETT, S. D. (1955). Presidential address. Microbial Ecology of the soil. *Trans. Brit. mycol. Soc.* 38, 1.

GARRETT, S. D. (1956). *Biology of Root-infecting Fungi*. Cambridge University Press.

GOTTLIEB, D. & SIMINOFF, P. (1952). The production and role of antibiotics in the soil. II. Chloromycetin. *Phytopathology*, 42, 91.

GOTTLIEB, D., SIMINOFF, P. & MARTIN, M. M. (1952). The production and role of antibiotics in soil. IV. Actidione and clavacin. *Phytopathology*, 42, 493.

GREGORY, K. F., ALLEN, O. N., RIKER, A. J. & PETERSON, W. H. (1952a). Antibiotics as agents for the control of certain damping-off fungi. *Amer. J. Bot.* 39, 405.

GREGORY, K. F., ALLEN, O. N., RIKER, A. J. & PETERSON, W. H. (1952b). Antibiotics and antagonistic microorganisms as control agents against damping-off of Alfalfa. *Phytopathology*, 42, 613.

GROSSBARD, E. (1947). The control of plant diseases by microbial antagonism. *Rep. exp. Res. Sta. Cheshunt*, 1946, 32, 41.

GROSSBARD, E. (1948). The control of plant diseases by microbial antagonism. *Rep. exp. Res. Sta. Cheshunt*, 1947, 33, 29.

GROSSBARD, E. (1949). Investigations on microbial antagonism and antibiotic substances. *Rep. exp. Res. Sta. Cheshunt*, 1948, 34, 37.

GROSSBARD, E. (1950). Investigations on microbial antagonism and antibiotic substances. Progress report. *Rep. exp. Res. Sta. Cheshunt*, 1949, 35, 38.

GROSSBARD, E. (1952). Antibiotic production by fungi on organic manures and in soil. *J. gen. Microbiol.* 6, 295.

GUNTER, G., WILLIAMS, R. H., DAVIS, C. C. & SMITH, F. G. W. (1948). Catastrophic mortality of marine animals and coincident phytoplankton bloom on the west coast of Florida, November 1946 to August 1947. *Ecol. Monogr.* 18, 310.

HARLEY, J. L. (1948). Mycorrhiza and soil ecology. *Biol. Rev.* 23, 127.

HESSAYON, D. G. (1951). 'Double-action' of trichothecin and its production in soil. *Nature, Lond.*, 168, 998.

HESSAYON, D. G. (1953a). Fungitoxins in the soil. I. Historical. *Soil Sci.* 75, 317.

HESSAYON, D. G. (1953b). Fungitoxins in the soil. II. Trichothecin, its production and investigation in unsterilized soil. *Soil Sci.* 75, 395.

JEFFERYS, E. G. (1952). The stability of antibiotics in soils. *J. gen. Microbiol.* 7, 295.

JEFFREYS, E. G., BRIAN, P. W., HEMMING, H. G. & LOWE, D. (1953). Antibiotic production by the microfungi of acid heath soils. *J. gen. Microbiol.* 9, 314.

JOHNSON, L. F. (1954). Antibiosis in relation to *Pythium* root-rot of sugarcane and corn. *Phytopathology*, 44, 69.

KATZNELSON, H., LOCHHEAD, A. G. & TIMONIN, M. I. (1948). Soil microorganisms and the rhizosphere. *Bot. Rev.* 14, 543.

KRASILNIKOV, N. A. (1954). Formation and accumulation of antibiotic substances in soil. (Title translated.) *C.R. Acad. Sci. U.R.S.S.* 94, 957.

LAKSHMINARAYAN, K. & SUBRAMANIAN, D. (1955). Is fusaric acid a vivotoxin? *Nature, Lond.*, **176**, 697.

LEFÈVRE, M., JAKOB, H. & NISBET, M. (1952). Auto- et hétéroantagonisme chez les algues d'eau douce *in vitro* et dans les collections d'eau naturelles. *Ann. Sta. cent. Hydrobiol. appl.* **4**, 5.

LEWIS, I. M. (1929). Bacterial antagonism with special reference to the effect of *Pseudomonas fluorescens* on spore forming bacteria of soils. *J. Bact.* **17**, 89.

LOCHHEAD, A. G. & LANDERKIN, G. B. (1949). Aspects of antagonisms between microorganisms in soil. *Plant and Soil*, **1**, 271.

LUCAS, C. E. (1944). Excretions, ecology and evolution. *Nature, Lond.*, **153**, 378.

LUCAS, C. E. (1947). The ecological effects of external metabolites. *Biol. Rev.* **22**, 270.

LUCAS, C. E. (1949). External metabolites and ecological adaptation. *Symp. Soc. exp. Biol.* **3**, 336.

LUIJK, A. VAN (1938). Antagonism between various microorganisms and different species of the genus *Pythium*, parasitizing upon grasses and lucerne. *Meded. phytopath. Lab. Scholten*, **14**, 43.

MARTIN, N. & GOTTLIEB, D. (1952). The production and role of antibiotics in the soil. III. Terramycin and aureomycin. *Phytopathology*, **42**, 294.

MARTIN, M. & GOTTLIEB, D. (1955). The production and role of antibiotics in soil. V. Antibacterial activity of five antibiotics in the presence of soil. *Phytopathology*, **45**, 407.

MCILWAIN, H. (1944). Origin and action of drugs. *Nature, Lond.*, **153**, 300.

OTTERSTROM, C. V. & STEEMANN-NIELSEN, E. (1940). Two cases of extensive mortality in fishes caused by the flagellate *Prymnesium parvum* Carter. *Rep. Danish biol. Sta.* **44**, 5.

PETERSON, E. A. (1954). A study of cross antagonisms among some Actinomycetes active against *Streptomyces scabies* and *Helminthosporium sativum*. *Antibiot. Chemother.* **4**, 145.

PRAMER, D. & STARKEY, R. L. (1951). Decomposition of streptomycin. *Science*, **113**, 127.

REHM, H. J. (1953). Versuche zur Bekämpfung von Roggenfußkrankheiten (Fusariosen) durch Saatgutimpfung mit antibiotisch wirkenden Streptomyceten. *Z. PflKrankh.* **60**, 549.

ROVIRA, A. D. (1956a). Plant root excretions in relation to the rhizosphere effect. I. The nature of root exudate from oats and peas. *Plant & Soil*, **7**, 178.

ROVIRA, A. D. (1956b). Plant root excretions in relation to the rhizosphere effect. II. A study of the properties of root exudate and its effect on the growth of microorganisms isolated from the rhizosphere and control soil. *Plant & Soil*, **7**, 195.

SALISBURY, E. J. (1944). Antibiotics and competition. *Nature, Lond.*, **153**, 170.

SHELUBSKY, M. (1951). Observations on the properties of a toxin produced by Microcystis. *Proc. Int. Cong. theor. appl. Limnol.* **11**, 362.

SHILO, M. & ASCHNER, M. (1953). Factors governing the toxicity of cultures containing the phytoflagellate *Prymnesium parvum* Carter. *J. gen. Microbiol.* **8**, 333.

SIMINOFF, P. & GOTTLIEB, D. (1951). The production and role of antibiotics in the soil. I. The fate of streptomycin. *Phytopathology*, **41**, 420.

SKINNER, F. A. (1956). The effect of adding clays to mixed cultures of *Streptomyces albidoflavus* and *Fusarium culmorum*. *J. gen. Microbiol.* **14**, 393.

SLYKHUIS, J. T. (1947). Studies on *Fusarium culmorum* blight of crested wheat and Brome grass seedlings. *Canad. J. Res.* C, **25**, 155.

SMITH, G. N. & WORREL, C. S. (1950). The decomposition of chloromycetin (chloramphenicol) by microorganisms. *Arch. Biochem.* **28**, 232.

SOMMER, H., MONNIER, R. P., RIEGEL, B., STANGER, D. W., MOLD, J. D., WIKHOLM, D. M. & KIVALIS, E. S. (1948). Paralytic shellfish poison. I. Occurrence and concentration by ion exchange. *J. Amer. chem. Soc.* **70**, 1015.

SPOEHR, H. A., SMITH, J. H. C., STRAIN, H. H., MILNER, H. W. & HARDIN, G. H. (1949). Fatty acid antibacterials from plants. *Publ. Carneg. Instn*, no. 586, p.1.

STANIER, R. Y. (1953). Adaptation, evolutionary and physiological: or Darwinism among the microorganisms. *Third Symp. Soc. gen. Microbiol.* p. 1.

STEVENSON, I. L. (1954*a*). Antibiotic production of Actinomycetes in soil and their effect on root-rot of wheat (*Helminthosporium sativum*). *Rep. Eighth Bot. Congr. Paris*, 1954, sect. 21, p. 69.

STEVENSON, I. L. (1954*b*). Antibiotic production by Actinomycetes in soil demonstrated by morphological changes induced in *Helminthosporium sativum. Nature, Lond.*, **174**, 598.

STEVENSON, I. L. (1956). Antibiotic activity of Actinomycetes in soil and their controlling effects on root-rot of wheat. *J. gen. Microbiol.* **14**, 440.

TVEIT, M. & MOORE, M. B. (1954). Isolates of *Chaetomium* that protect oats from *Helminthosporium victoriae. Phytopathology*, **44**, 686.

TVEIT, M. & WOOD, R. K. S. (1955). The control of Fusarium blight in oat seedlings with antagonistic species of *Chaetomium. Ann. appl. Biol.* **43**, 538.

WAKSMAN, S. A. (1945*a*). Production and nature of antibiotic substances. *Harvey Lect.* **40**, 77.

WAKSMAN, S. A. (1945*b*). *Microbial Antagonisms and Antibiotic Substances.* New York: Commonwealth Fund.

WAKSMAN, S. A. (1948). Antibiotics. *Biol. Rev.* **23**, 452.

WAKSMAN, S. A. (1951). Biological aspects of antibiotics. In *Frontiers in Medicine: The March of Medicine* 1950. New York: Columbia University Press.

WAKSMAN, G. A. & WOODRUFF, H. B. (1942). The occurrence of bacteriostatic and bactericidal substances in the soil. *Soil Sci.* **53**, 233.

WEINDLING, R. (1932). *Trichoderma lignorum* as a parasite of other soil fungi. *Phytopathology*, **22**, 837.

WEINDLING, R. (1934). Studies on a lethal principle effective in the parasitic action of *Trichoderma lignorum* on *Rhizoctonia solani* and other soil fungi. *Phytopathology*, **24**, 1153.

WEINDLING, R. (1946). Microbial antagonism and disease control. *Soil Sci.* **61**, 23.

WEINDLING, R. & FAWCETT, H. S. (1936). Experiments in the control of *Rhizoctonia* damping-off of citrus seedlings. *Hilgardia*, **10**, 1.

WINTER, A. G. (1951). Untersuchungen über die Förderung der Jugendentwicklung des Hauptgetreidearten durch boden bewohnende Pilze. *Phytopath. Z.* **18**, 221.

WRIGHT, J. M. (1952). Production of gliotoxin in unsterilized soil. *Nature, Lond.* **170**, 673.

WRIGHT, J. M. (1954). The production of antibiotics in soil. I. Production of gliotoxin by *Trichoderma viride. Ann. appl. Biol.* **41**, 280.

WRIGHT, J. M. (1955). The production of antibiotics in soil. II. Production of griseofulvin by *Penicillium nigricans. Ann. appl. Biol.* **43**, 288.

WRIGHT, J. M. (1956*a*). Production of gliotoxin in soils. *Nature, Lond.*, **177**, 896.

WRIGHT, J. M. (1956*b*). The production of antibiotics in soil. III. Production of gliotoxin in wheatstraw buried in soil. *Ann. appl. Biol.* **44**, 461.

WRIGHT, J. M. (1956*c*). The production of antibiotics in soil. IV. Production of antibiotics in seed coats. *Ann. appl. Biol.* (in the Press).

WRIGHT, J. M. (1956*d*). Biological control of soil borne *Pythium* infection by seed inoculation. *Plant & Soil* (in the Press).

THE RELATIONS OF BACTERIOPHAGES
TO BACTERIAL ECOLOGY

E. S. ANDERSON

*Central Enteric Reference Laboratory and Bureau, Public Health
Laboratory Service, Colindale Avenue, London, N.W.9*

The bacteriophage has been regarded as an important factor in the ecology of its host bacteria practically from the time of its discovery. For many years its influence was thought to depend on the elimination of sensitive cell populations by what we now call virulent phages. Recent work has exposed other potentialities of phages, for example, their control of toxigenicity in *Corynebacterium diphtheriae* and their capacity for transferring genetic characters from one host cell to another. These functions, if they operated to any considerable extent in nature, could profoundly affect the relationships between the bacteria concerned and their natural hosts or environments.

D'Herelle believed that the progress of epidemic bacterial diseases was closely correlated with the presence of phages 'virulent' for the infecting organisms. In *The Bacteriophage* (English translation, 1926) he dealt *in extenso* with the beneficial effects of phage in bacillary dysentery, stating that the recovery of the patient commenced from the moment when the virulence of the phage dominated the resistance of the bacterium. He claimed that, in fatal cases of bacillary dysentery, phages were absent or of inadequate virulence or that the infecting bacterial strain had become resistant to the phage. He suggested that the immunity of healthy dysentery contacts was probably due to infection with the same phage as that responsible for the cure of the disease in patients.

D'Herelle believed many other bacterial diseases to be under the control of bacteriophages. He summed up in the following words (*The Bacteriophage*, p. 508): 'The history of an epidemic is, in the last analysis, the story of an infection with two micro-organisms. The epidemic ceases at the moment when all the susceptible individuals harbour a bacteriophage active for the causative organisms of the epidemic. Either the bacteriophage has acquired virulence in the body of the individual who harbours it, or this individual has been "contaminated" by a bacteriophage which has acquired a virulence in another organism for the specific bacterium involved.'

D'Herelle, then, was in no doubt concerning the importance of bacteriophages in microbial ecology. To the credulous reader of his publications in the 1920's, it must have seemed that the moment was at hand for the liberation of the animal world from bacterial diseases. Alas for this vain hope!

THE POSSIBLE ROLE OF PHAGES
IN MICROBIAL ECOLOGY

The following terms, most of which were defined by Jacob, Lwoff, Siminovitch & Wollman (1953) will be used in connexion with the action of phages on bacteria. *Lysogeny* (or *lysogenicity*) is the ability of a bacterial strain to produce bacteriophage and to transmit this property to its progeny. Lysogenic strains are not obviously phage-infected and are resistant to the phages they carry. *Lysogenization* is the production of the lysogenic state. Phages capable of entering into this relationship are known as *temperate* phages. They are detected by their ability to lyse other bacterial strains, which are called *indicator* strains. The latent form in which a phage is carried by a lysogenic strain is known as *prophage*. The initiation of the lytic cycle of phage reproduction in lysogenic cells by the application of ultra-violet radiation or other stimuli is known as *induction*. *Virulent* phages do not possess the power of forming lysogenic complexes with host cells and can undergo only lytic reproduction.

A phage may influence a bacterial population in the following ways:

(1) By the elimination of sensitive organisms, a virulent phage may cause the replacement of a population by a phage-resistant mutant differing in ecological potentialities from the original stock.

(2) A temperate phage may destroy a varying fraction of the original population and lysogenize the remainder. Apart from conferring protection against the phage concerned, lysogenization may cause specific character changes inseparably associated with the prophage; for example, the conversion of avirulent diphtheria bacilli to virulence, or an alteration in antigenic structure such as that found in the E group of salmonellas.

(3) Transduction of genetic properties may occur with or without lysogenization and may be effected by virulent or temperate phages.

All three of these influences may be regarded as selective. In the first case the selection is direct. In the second it is initially direct: protection of lysogenized cells against attack by phage; and then indirect: the endowment of lysogenized diphtheria bacilli with the property of toxigenicity which helps them to become established in the human host.

In the third instance the selective action is entirely indirect, since transduction is independent of lysogenization, and any ecological advantage conferred on the recipient cell will operate irrespective of whether the cell can resist attack by the phage.

The selective action of virulent phages

Bacterial diseases of animals

No instance exists in which it has been possible to observe the control of an epidemic disease by a virulent phage under natural conditions. Nevertheless, because of the impressive destruction of organisms by phage lysis in the laboratory, the temptation is always present to test the therapeutic effect of phages. The natural history of any disease susceptible to this form of treatment might be materially affected if the treatment were widely used.

The only disease that would seem to be a natural candidate for bacteriophage therapy or control is cholera, because the infection is primarily non-invasive and the causal organisms are largely restricted to the lumen of the gut where they are present in high concentrations in liquid exudate. Provided that other conditions in the intestine are favourable for phage multiplication, therefore, it might be expected that the presence of a virulent phage would cause massive destruction of the cholera vibrio. Moreover, the infection of water supplies with a suitable cholera phage should result in dissemination of the phage throughout the population. Thus the development of cholera might be prevented or attacks aborted because of the destruction of vibrios by the phage already present in the intestine of cholera-sensitive persons.

Asheshov and his co-workers (Asheshov, Asheshov, Khan & Lahiri, 1930; Asheshov, Khan & Lahiri, 1931; Asheshov, 1933; Asheshov, Asheshov, Khan, Lahiri & Chatterjee, 1933; Morison, 1932) tested the effect of phage on cases of cholera and on the development of cholera outbreaks. It was claimed that the administration of phage to patients in the first 24 hr. of the disease produced a significantly higher recovery rate than in control series. Moreover, the addition of phage to wells appeared to reduce the morbidity rate from cholera. Less favourable results were reported by Taylor (1930). As I have pointed out, the cholera vibrio is most abundant in the intestinal lumen, but some invasion of the epithelium may occur and the organisms may reach the mesenteric lymph nodes and the spleen. The destruction of organisms in such sites in the tissues may be essential for the specific treatment of cholera, but they may be inaccessible to bacteriophages. Although interest in the influence of phage on cholera appears to have waned, the problem remains *sub judice*. Most of the published evidence, which appeared largely during the early 1930's, seemed to indicate that phages might be beneficial in this condition, but few workers now consider that they affect the ecology of the cholera vibrio either under natural conditions or when they are administered artificially.

Topley, Wilson & Lewis (1925) tested the effect of a phage on mouse typhoid due to *Salmonella typhimurium*. They found no evidence that the course of epidemics or of the developed disease was influenced by the phage they used. Asheshov, Wilson & Topley (1937) found that if a Vi phage was given intraperitoneally or intravenously before, simultaneously with, or soon after the organisms, it protected mice against the lethal effect of *S. typhi*. Thus, phages appear to be able to act *in vivo* in other situations than the intestine. Fisk (1938), Yen & Chang (1941) and Yen (1949) supported these findings. Wahl & Terrade (1950) investigated the possibilities of phage treatment of *S. typhimurium* infections in mice. They found that a dosage of at least 6×10^6 particles was necessary for phage to appear in the circulation of healthy animals and that the phage rapidly disappeared from the blood, but that, in animals infected with *S. typhimurium*, phage multiplication occurred. On the whole, their experiments did not suggest that phages were effective in the treatment of mouse typhoid. In some cases phage-resistant organisms of unimpaired virulence appeared in the blood; in others, the organisms remained phage-sensitive.

A number of attempts have been made to treat typhoid fever with Vi phages (Knouf, Ward, Reichle, Bower & Hamilton, 1946; Archambault, 1948; Desranleau, 1948, 1949). Each worker has claimed success in his trial, but it is not generally accepted that the method is effective. There are obvious objections to the parenteral administration of phages. The lysates that are normally used contain nutrient broth, the metabolic by-products of the typhoid bacillus, dead bacterial bodies, the products of bacterial lysis and, lastly, the phage. Such lysates may cause severe non-specific reactions. In order to be effective, the phage must reach most infecting organisms within a short time—a difficult condition to satisfy when the bacteria are widely disseminated in a systemic infection and the reticulo-endothelial system of the patient is removing the phage as fast as it can. Moreover, neutralizing antibodies against phage are rapidly produced and it could thus be effective for only a few days. It may be added that, in the procedure recommended by one worker who used a mixture of Vi phages, if the patient's temperature had not reached 106–107° F. within 3–4 hr. of the first (intravenous) dose of phage, a further 1 ml. of lysate was injected. The reactions following such a heroic operation would seem to be due to non-specific protein shock rather than lysis of the infecting organisms by the phage. The clinical trials described were on the whole unsupported by controls.

The dubious results obtained in attempts to cure bacterial infections with phages suggest that the natural influence of these viruses in disease is negligible.

Phages and the nitrogen-fixing bacteria

It was suggested by Laird (1932) and Almon & Wilson (1933) that bacteriophages might be important in the symbiosis of root-nodule bacteria and leguminous plants, but these workers were unsuccessful in demonstrating a relationship. Demolon & Dunez (1933, 1935), on the other hand, isolated phage from nodules, roots and stems of lucerne plants that had been grown in 'lucerne-sick' soil for more than 1 year; it was, however, more difficult to isolate it from the roots of plants more than 3 years old or devoid of root nodules. They isolated phage from soils bearing old lucerne crops, but not from soils bearing young crops or supporting plants other than lucerne. They claimed that extension of the root system of lucerne permitted the formation of new root nodules and fixation of nitrogen in spite of the presence of phage, but that, once the root system was static, the whole root zone became permeated by phages and the rhizobia were eliminated. Lucerne affected in this way grew like a non-leguminous plant. Demolon & Dunez (1935) added the rider that the phages disappeared from such soil after about a further year, presumably because of the lack of a susceptible host. However, sterilized lucerne seeds planted by these workers in pots containing soils infected with a rhizobium phage showed root nodules when examined after 2 months' growth. This is in contradiction to their claims concerning the possible activity of bacteriophage in the rhizobium-lucerne relationship.

Vandecaveye & Katznelson (1936) were rather critical of the conclusions of Demolon & Dunez, but did think it possible for rhizobium phages to interfere with the activities of the root-nodule bacteria. They believed that the appearance of phages in soils showing reduced lucerne yields when the plants were older than 3 years suggested a possible causal relationship. They drew attention to the possible spread of phages by irrigation.

By exposing cultures of *Rhizobium trifolii* to phage, Kleczkowska (1950) selected a number of phage-resistant mutants. Many of these had lost the power of fixing nitrogen and a few had lost the ability to form root nodules. Kleczkowska suggested that failure of leguminous crops was unlikely to occur through the elimination of phage-sensitive rhizobia by phage action. However, she considered it possible that phages might be responsible for a rise in the proportion of rhizobium strains unable to fix nitrogen.

Dr Kleczkowska (personal communication) states that in her experience the rhizobium phage content of clover-sick soil is of a similar order to that of healthy clover soil, that is, less than 50 particles/g. of soil. The soil examined was taken from the roots of clover plants. In an experimental clover plot over 100 years old at Rothamsted the phage content is about 150 particles/g. When phage in a strength of 3×10^3 particles/g. was added to soil in pots the phage titre increased 10 to 100-fold in a month, but most of the rhizobia isolated remained phage-sensitive. In contrast, when phage and sensitive organisms were grown together in liquid medium, only phage-resistant bacteria could be isolated after 1 month. In Dr Kleczkowska's experience phage-resistant rhizobium strains constitute less than 50 % of the population in old clover-bearing soils. Most of the rhizobium phages examined hitherto have been virulent, but Marshall (1956) has recently reported lysogeny in *Rhizobium trifolii*.

Thus, it would seem that the importance of phages in the ecological relationship of nodule bacteria and the Leguminosae cannot be assessed at present. Laboratory experiments show that phages exert a selection pressure which might affect the efficiency of nitrogen fixation, but field observations hitherto have not provided convincing evidence that they do so.

The importance of phages to the lactic streptococci

Apart from the fact that they are found in milk, the other natural habitats of the lactic streptococci are obscure, although Stark & Sherman (1935) state that they are commonly found on some plants. For practical purposes it can be accepted that milk is now one of their major natural environments. These organisms are important to the cheese-making industry, because of the rapid acid- and clot-forming effect they exert on milk. The use of lactic streptococcal 'starters' is a widespread practice in cheese-making areas, especially for the production of cheddar and cottage cheeses. A commonly encountered difficulty in cheese manufacture is that of slow acid and clot formation. It has been shown that this is usually caused by infection of the starter culture by phage. This trouble is widespread, having been encountered in America, Canada, New Zealand and the United Kingdom (see, for example, Nichols & Wolf, 1946; Wolf, Nichols & Ineson, 1946; Nichols & Ineson, 1947 (England); Johns, 1942 (Canada); Babel, 1946a, b (United States); Whitehead & Hunter, 1941 (New Zealand)).

Conditions in cheese-making vats are, of course, ideal for phage growth—the sensitive organism present, a good medium in abundance, plenty of space and a suitable temperature for growth. The result is massive lysis of the starter culture with delay in the formation of acid and clot. The phage titres attained may exceed 10^{11} (Hunter, 1944). Phage-resistant mutants finally replace the original sensitive population and normal acid and clot may be produced, but this is not invariable and it appears that in some instances the resistant mutants have impaired acid-forming properties. In New Zealand, Whitehead & Hunter (1941, 1946) demonstrated that aerosols of infected whey were a frequent source of phage contamination of cheese vats. They were able to map out the distribution of phage in the air of a factory by exposing dishes of skim milk for as little as 10 sec. They also showed that the air surrounding a factory could be phage-contaminated up to 25 yards outside the building. Moreover, the phage infection might be disseminated throughout an entire dairying district because farmers used whey as a pig food; this whey frequently contained phage, and the cans in which it was carried were usually inadequately sterilized before being refilled with milk for delivery to the cheese factory. Disinfection of the atmosphere of factories by hypochlorite aerosols and ultra-violet irradiation was to some extent effective but was impracticable as a routine procedure. Whitehead & Hunter (1946) recommended that cheese-making rooms be constructed as far from the remainder of the factory as possible, and to the windward side of it, in order to restrict contamination by airborne phage.

A number of methods have been suggested for solving the problem. Rotation of starter strains (Anderson & Meanwell, 1945; Babel, 1946a, b; Whitehead & Hunter, 1947) and a mixture of starter strains (Nichols & Ineson, 1947) were proposed, on the assumption that when one strain was attacked by a phage, another resistant to the phage might be able to replace it. This is at best a temporary solution, however, because a phage able to attack the new dominant streptococcus will always appear after a period of weeks or months.

Hunter (1947) observed that cultures of Streptococcus cremoris could attain a state of 'peaceful co-existence', with bacteriophages. In this condition lysis did not take place or was restricted in amount, although the phages persisted in the culture. The organisms were still sensitive to the phages, however, and sensitive phage-free clones could be isolated from platings. Thus, the cells were neither resistant mutants nor were they lysogenic. The phage was easily lost on repeated subculture, when the strain again became susceptible to mass lysis by the same phage. The factors responsible for this co-existence of the cells and phage are unknown. One is familiar with the persistence of sensitive cells in mass lysates when the stage of logarithmic growth is past, but the phenomena described by Hunter seemed to occur equally well in logarithmic cultures. Hunter & Whitehead (1949) suggested that such phage-carrying cultures should be used as routine starter strains, because their acid production appeared to be normal. The protection conferred by the phage associated with the strains was specific and, if fresh phages infected the culture, massive lysis could again result.

Ford & Babel (1950) recommended persistence with a starter strain in the face of phage infection, until a phage-resistant mutant of satisfactory acid-forming properties emerged. However, infection with a new phage would recreate the difficulty. Overcast, Nelson & Parmelee (1951) suggested that a heavy initial seeding of cheese vats with starters might cause a rapid shift to an acid pH that would inhibit phage multiplication.

This problem remains essentially unsolved. The widespread use of lactic streptococci as cheese starters makes it probable that their artificial distribution exceeds their natural habitat, whatever that may be. Thus, the presence of bacteriophage infection can have important effects on the man-made ecology of these streptococci. It is, unfortunately, impossible to protect cheese factories against the influx of new phages. A streptococcus that has overcome its immediate problem by mutating to resistance to one phage, therefore, may soon find itself faced with the task of producing a mutant to another if it is to multiply freely in the massive culture conditions of the cheese vats.

Character conversion produced by lysogenization of bacteria

Virulence in Corynebacterium diphtheriae

One of the most intriguing stories that has emerged in recent years is that of the role of phages in the determination of toxigenicity in the diphtheria bacillus.

In 1951 Freeman observed that the lysogenization of avirulent strains with a particular phage endowed them with toxigenic power. Parsons & Frobisher (1951), Freeman & Morse (1952), Groman (1953), Groman & Lockart (1953), Barksdale & Pappenheimer (1954), Groman (1955), and Groman & Eaton (1955) have amplified and developed these findings, and Hewitt (1952, 1953, 1954a, b, c) has studied similar phenomena in other strains of *Corynebacterium diphtheriae*. The present position can be summarized as follows. Lysogenization of avirulent strains of *C. diphtheriae* with appropriate phages enables them to produce toxin. All lysogenized clones become toxigenic and all toxigenic clones are lysogenic. There is convincing evidence that the agent responsible for this conversion is the genetic content of the phage particle itself and that the conversion is not, as in the transduction of characters by phage in salmonellas, which we will discuss presently, due to the fortuitous carry-over of genetic material from a former host by the phage. The toxin-determining power of the phage in the *C. diphtheriae* system is possessed by every particle and is independent of the genome (that is, the genetic composition) of the strain on which the phage has been propagated. Repeated propagation of the phage on a non-toxigenic strain does not interfere with its ability to confer toxigenicity (Groman, 1955). Freeman & Morse (1952) showed that the strain C4 (non-toxigenic) and the lysogenized strain C4(β) (toxigenic) were antigenically indistinguishable by agglutinating antisera. The property of producing toxin is stable as long as a newly converted strain remains lysogenic, but Groman (1955) isolated non-lysogenic clones from a strain that had been converted to virulence, and showed that they had lost their toxigenicity. Groman & Eaton (1955) observed that the capacity to convert avirulent *C. diphtheriae* to toxigenicity behaved as a discrete genetic character in phage β, and segregated independently in recombination experiments with another phage. The property of toxigenic conversion seems to be a special quality of particular phages, and some phages have shown themselves to be devoid of it. The observations of the American workers were carried out on strains behaving as *C. diphtheriae mitis*, but Hewitt (1954b) claims to have demonstrated similar phenomena in strains that were serologically *gravis*.

Barksdale & Pappenheimer (1954) reported that the few naturally occurring toxigenic strains which they examined were lysogenic, but a large-scale investigation of this nature is needed, together with an examination of the toxin-determining power of the phages concerned. Dudley (1923) observed the occurrence of clinical diphtheria in a boy from whose throat an avirulent strain of *Corynebacterium diphtheriae* had been isolated for two months preceding his illness. He pointed out that the virulent strain isolated after the onset of the disease was, with the exception of its toxin production, indistinguishable from the avirulent organism isolated previously. There is a tempting inference that the avirulent strain had come into contact with a phage that could lysogenize it and convert it to virulence. Okell's (1929) observation that persons in a diphtheria outbreak could carry serologically similar virulent and avirulent diphtheria bacilli in the throat might also point in the same direction, although the thesis that the avirulent organism in such instances had lost the phage carried by the epidemic strain is equally or perhaps more tenable.

The position of the carrier of avirulent diphtheria bacilli has undergone a radical change as the result of this work. The placid acceptance that such avirulent strains have permanently lost their toxigenic power is no longer permissible. If a suitable phage could reach the organisms that they harbour, these carriers might become a source of danger to themselves and to the community. Fortunately, the virtual eradication of diphtheria by active immunization programmes has made this a subject of largely academic interest to all but the carrier himself. But if such a carrier were not immune to diphtheria he might, given the possibility of the phage-activated conversion of his strain to toxigenicity, be attacked by the organism with which he had formerly been living in harmony.

The phages of the diphtheria bacillus show considerable specificity (Hewitt, 1952) and at present we do not know of temperate phages carried by any other species that can attack *Corynebacterium diphtheriae* (see Howard & Jann, 1954). This introduces some difficulty into the conception of the evolution of toxigenic strains by lysogenization of those that are non-toxigenic, because it seems that contact with a lysogenic virulent strain would be required to initiate the change, unless phages carried by other organisms commonly found in the nasopharynx possess the necessary properties. However, the possibility must also be considered that phages derived from virulent diphtheria bacilli might gain access as airborne particles to the throats of carriers of avirulent strains.

Transduction

Zinder & Lederberg (1952) demonstrated the ability of phages to carry genetic characters to a new host; they called this phenomenon transduction. Zinder & Lederberg's original observations showed that many different types of character could be transduced: nutritional, fermentative, antigenic, and resistance to antibiotics. Only one character could be transduced by each phage particle, the efficiency of transduction being 10^{-6} to 10^{-7} per character per particle. The characters carried were controlled by the genome of the host on which the phage had been propagated before being applied to the organism to which the characters were to be transferred. It was suggested that this carriage was due to the accidental incorporation of genetic units of the host (genes or short chromosomal fragments) in the envelope of the phage during its maturation. It is thus possible that a phage lysate may carry the entire genome of the host on which it has been grown.

Stocker, Zinder & Lederberg (1953) carried out a detailed analysis of the transduction of motility and showed that simultaneous transductions of two characters affecting this property could occur. This suggested sufficiently close linkage between the genes governing the characters concerned to permit their transport by the phage as a single fragment. Lederberg & Edwards (1953), Kauffmann (1953) and Edwards, Davis & Cherry (1955) extended the observations on transduction of motility.

The foregoing transductions were mediated by temperate phages. Baron, Formal & Spilman (1953, 1955), however, have shown that Vi-phage II of *Salmonella typhi* (Craigie & Yen, 1938), which is a virulent phage incapable of entering into a lysogenic relationship with a host cell, can transduce nutritional, fermentative, drug resistance and antigenic characters to strains of the typhoid bacillus which can adsorb it but in which it cannot multiply. Similar observations have been made by Zinder (1955) on a virulent mutant of PLT-22, the original transducing phage of Zinder & Lederberg (1952). Thus it is possible to divorce transduction altogether from lyosogenicity. This indicates that in spite of its being included in the phage coat and injected into the cell with the phage deoxyribonucleic acid, the transduced-genetic fragment operates as an independent unit.

The field of investigation has recently widened to embrace *Escherichia coli* and *Shigella*. Lennox (1955) has demonstrated that the temperate phage P1 (Bertani, 1951), carried by the *E. coli* strain of Lisbonne & Carrère, will transduce characters from *Shigella shigae* strain Sh to a number of strains of *E. coli*, and from *E. coli* K-12 to strain Sh. The demonstration of transduction between *Escherichia* and *Shigella* is important because it suggests some genetic homology between the two bacterial groups. Lennox found that joint transductions occasionally occurred, and that the frequency of insertion of unselected markers into recipient strains conformed with their proximity to the selected markers as determined by sexual recombination experiments in the donor strains of *E. coli* studied.

Transduction of a rather different sort has been recently described by Morse (1954) and Morse, Lederberg & Lederberg (1955). When phage λ is induced to undergo lytic reproduction by ultra-violet irradiation of lysogenic cells, it has been found to transduce the restricted chromosomal region with which it is associated in *Escherichia coli* K-12, that is the loci for galactose fermentation, with an efficiency of 10^{-6}–10^{-7}. Gal⁻

organisms could be transduced to become Gal+. Many such Gal+ clones were unstable and segregated Gal- progeny. It seemed possible that they were heterozygous for a single locus or a short chromosomal segment. Such clones have been called *heterogenotes*. They were lysogenic for phage λ, but the phage they carried, when liberated by ultraviolet induction, had much higher transduction efficiency (approaching unity) for the Gal loci than had λ from the normal lysogenic K-12.

The exceptional features of this system are: only one group of associated loci is transduced; transduction can be carried out only by phage resulting from ultra-violet induction of lysogenic cells, and not by phage from the lytic multiplication following external infection of non-lysogenic cells; and the phage liberated from heterogenotes has a very much higher transduction efficiency than that from normal lysogenic cells, although its titre is constantly lower than the latter (about 5×10^8 as compared with 3×10^{10}). It is possible that the prophage, which is precipitated into the lytic developmental cycle by irradiation, is accompanied by the Gal chromosomal fragment with which it is associated in the lysogenic cell. However, the high transduction efficiency found in phage derived from heterogenotes would necessitate reproduction of the Gal locus *pari passu* with the phage, or its ability to retain genetic competence when divided between the phage progeny. Otherwise it must be argued that the burst size from heterogenotes after induction is very small—not more than ten particles per cell—in which case the Gal transducing fragment need only be retained by one particle. It is worth remembering in relation to the last suggestion that the phage yield from heterogenotes is low. These questions could probably be cleared up by experiment.

We can now contrast the systems of phage-mediated transduction in the Enterobacteriaceae and conversion to toxigenicity of *Corynebacterium diphtheriae*. In the diphtheria system, the converting activity is independent of the genome of the strain on which the phage has been propagated; it is inseparably linked to lysogenization; the limit of conversion efficiency is that of lysogenization and may be as high as 3 % of the initial cell population; every phage particle seems capable of causing conversion; and, hitherto, only the character of toxigenicity has been carried to the new host. In transduction, the nature of the characters carried by a phage is determined by the genome of the donor cells on which it has been grown; transduction can occur without lysogenization; the general efficiency of transduction is low, about 10^{-6} to 10^{-7} per character per particle; a large number of independent characters can be transduced; and the frequency of joint transduction is proportional to the linkage of the characters concerned as determined by sexual crosses.

A possible bridge linking the two systems is provided by the observations of high-frequency transduction of phage lysates of the heterogenotes of Morse (1954) and Morse *et al.* (1955). Here a single group of loci is transduced with an efficiency of from 10^{-1} to 1 per phage particle. The established proximity of the λ locus to the Gal loci probably accounts for this, so that the transduction is still dependent on the genome of the donor cell. It seems probable that in the *Corynebacterium diphtheriae–phage-β* system the genetic information determining toxigenicity is an intrinsic part of the phage architecture which will operate whenever the phage assumes the prophage state.

The recently demonstrated genetic potentialities of phages in relation to their host cells emphasizes the closeness of the active life of phages, in both the prophage and the vegetative state, to what Luria (1950) described as the bacterial 'genetic level'.

EXPERIMENTAL

The incidence of phages in sewage and faeces

In attempting to assess the possible magnitude of the ecological effects of phages on bacteria under natural conditions, it is useful to gain some idea of the distribution of phages able to exert such effects and of the concentrations in which they normally occur. Two traditional sources of phages are sewage and faeces, and we carried out a small investigation of these materials. Sixteen samples of sewage and seventy-eight of faeces were examined. The samples were tested on the following indicator strains: Vi-type A of *Salmonella typhi*; strain 0901 of *S. typhi*; phage type 1(1363) of *S. paratyphi* B; phage type 1(307) of *S. typhimurium*; and *S. gallinarum* strain 780. These strains were chosen because they have wide phage susceptibilities. The test plates were inspected for plaque formation after incubation for about 16 hr. Individual plaques were cut and suspended in 1 ml. of nutrient broth which was heated at 57° for 40 min. to kill the host cells. The phages were purified by further single-plaque selection. Attempts were made with each phage to lysogenize one of the indicator strains and to carry out transduction. Pathogenic bacteria isolated from the sewage or faeces samples were tested for their sensitivity to the phages isolated from the same samples. When the pathogens were lysogenic, their carried phages were compared with the phages originally isolated from the sewage or faeces. The maximum sensitivity of the method was about 100 phage particles/ml. for sewage, and about 1000 particles/ml. for faeces. Concentrations appreciably below these levels would escape detection.

Six phages were isolated from the sixteen samples of sewage, and six from the seventy-eight samples of faeces. One sample of sewage yielded two phages. The details of these phages are shown in Tables 1 and 2.

Table 1. *Phages isolated from sewage*

No. of phage	Approxi- mate titre/ml. in sewage	Indicator strains on which phage was isolated	Indicator strains lysed by phage grown	Pathogen isolated from sewage sample	Sensitivity of pathogen to phage	Temperate (*T*) or virulent (*V*)
1	10^2	*Salmonella typhi* 0901	*S. typhi* Vi-type A *S. typhi* O 901	Nil	.	*V*
2	10^2	*S. gallinarum* 780	*S. paratyphi* B 1363 *S. gallinarum* 780	Nil	.	*V*
3	10^2	*S. typhi* Vi-type A	*S. typhi* Vi-type A *S. typhi* O 901 *S. gallinarum* 780	*S. paratyphi* B phage type 1	—	*V*
4	10^2	*S. paratyphi* B 1363	*S. typhi* Vi-type A *S. typhi* O 901 *S. paratyphi* B 1363 *S. typhimurium* 307	Nil	.	*V*
5a	2×10^2	*S. typhi* 0901 *S. paratyphi* B 1363	*S. typhi* Vi-type A *S. typhi* O 901 *S. paratyphi* B 1336 *S. typhimurium* 307	Nil	.	*V*
5b	2×10^2	*S. typhimurium* 307	*S. typhi* Vi-type A *S. typhi* O 901 *S. paratyphi* B 1363 *S. typhimurium* 307 *S. gallinarum* 780	Nil	.	*V*

Phages were not present in higher titres than about 2×10^2 in positive sewage samples. This figure is similar to that obtained in sewage coliphage counts by Ware & Mellon (1956). On the other hand, while three out of six faeces phages had titres of the order of 10^3, one had a titre of 2×10^4, another 2×10^5, and yet another 10^6. It will be noticed that a pathogenic organism was isolated from five out of six specimens of faeces in which phage was found, and in four instances the organism was *Salmonella typhimurium*. However, of the seventy-two faecal samples negative for phage, thirteen yielded strains of *Shigella sonnei*, and other individual specimens *Salmonella typhimurium*, *S. typhi*, *S. enteritidis* and *S. heidelberg*. No pathogens were isolated from any of the sewage samples that were negative for phage.

It is interesting to note that all the phages isolated from sewage were virulent. Obviously, this does not indicate that only virulent phages are present in sewage. It may suggest, however, that the titres in which temperate phages occur are considerably lower than those of virulent phages. On the whole this would be expected, because the release of temperate phages from lysogenic cultures does not usually produce

Table 2. Phages isolated from faeces

No.	Approximate titre/ml. in faeces	Indicator strains on which phage was isolated	Indicator strains lysed by phage grown	Pathogens isolated from faeces sample	Sensitivity of pathogen to phage	Temperate (T) or virulent (V)	Lysogenicity of pathogen	Identity of phage in faeces with that from pathogen
1	10^3	S. typhimurium 307	S. typhimurium 307 S. paratyphi B1363 S. gallinarum 780	S. typhimurium phage type 2 c	−	T	+	+
2	10^3	S. gallinarum 780	S. paratyphi B1363 S. gallinarum 780	S. typhimurium unidentified phage type	−	T	+	+
3	2×10^5	S. typhi Vi-type A S. typhi O901	S. typhi Vi-type A S. typhi O901 S. gallinarum 780	Shigella sonnei	−	T	·	+
4	10^6	S. gallinarum 780	S. gallinarum 780	S. typhimurium phage type 1a	−	T		
5	2×10^4	S. typhi O901	S. typhi Vi-type A S. typhi O901 S. paratyphi B1363 S. typhimurium 307 S. gallinarum 780	Nil	·	V		
6	10^3	S. paratyphi B1363	S. paratyphi B1363 S. typhimurium 307 S. gallinarum 780	S. typhimurium phage type 1a	−	T	+	+

titres as high as those resulting from lytic multiplication of virulent phages. Moreover, the titres attained by many temperate phages, even under the most favourable conditions of multiplication in sensitive cells, are appreciably less than those characteristic of virulent phages.

It is reasonable to assume that the virulent phage titres found (c. 10^2) are maintained by multiplication on suitable hosts. As the concentration of salmonellas in sewage is usually low (less than 50/ml.), it seems probable that the natural hosts of the virulent phages found in sewage are other members of the Enterobacteriaceae which are present in greater abundance. For reasons which will be clear later, however, it is improbable that the particular host cells concerned are present in concentrations much higher than 10^5/ml. (The *Escherichia coli* counts on most of the sewage tested for phage content ranged from 2×10^3 to 3×10^5/ml., and at such cell concentrations the low-titre phages found would be unable to exert a selection pressure (see Fig. 1, below).)

We were unable to carry out transduction with any of the phages isolated from sewage.

All but one of the phages isolated from faeces were temperate; their titres ranged from 10^3 to 10^6/ml. In two instances the phage isolated seemed to be identical with that carried by the lysogenic strain of *Salmonella typhimurium* present in the same sample of faeces. The remaining temperate phages, however, were distinct from those carried by the respective pathogens.

From the phage titres observed it is apparent that the possibility of contact between bacteria and free phage particles in faeces is considerably higher than that in sewage. It must be pointed out that the faecal specimens came from cases of enteritis and were largely liquid. For this reason the phages would be dispersed throughout the material, and if their titres and those of sensitive cells were high enough, there would be reasonable probabilities of contact between the two agents. Evidence will be produced later to show that, if a selective action is to be exerted by phage at a titre of about 10^6/ml., the sensitive host must have a count of the same order. Moreover, the phage titre at which virtual elimination of sensitive cells may occur must be much higher still. Hitherto I have no indication of the maximum titres that may be attained by phage in the intestine. It is always possible, of course, that high focal concentrations may occur.

The fact that none of the faecal phages was active in transduction obviously does not preclude the possibility that phages present in faeces may be competent in this respect and, in fact, Jacob (1955) has shown that transducing phages may be found in faeces. However, bearing in mind the low efficiency of transduction (10^{-6} per character per particle) it is apparent that it could occur only with the utmost rarity, even in respect of single characters, in the range of phage titres commonly encountered in the intestine.

Growth of phages in sewage

Six samples of sewage were chosen at random, and to 5 ml. of each were added 500 particles of Vi-phage A and 500 cells of Vi-type A. The mixtures were incubated at 38·5° and at room temperature (18–20°). The Vi-phage titres obtained in the series incubated at 38·5° were as high as those normally resulting from growth in the medium used as a routine in our laboratory, that is, between 10^9 and 10^{10} particles/ml. These titres were maintained during incubation for 10 days at 38·5°. In addition to *Salmonella typhi*, *Escherichia coli* was present in abundance, together with a varied assortment of unidentified cocci, aerobic spore-bearing bacteria and other organisms, in all the samples of sewage used in this experiment.

In contrast to these results, no phage multiplication was observed in the mixtures of sewage, Vi-phage A and Vi-type A maintained at room temperature. As multiplication of the organism had occurred in these mixtures, the absence of phage reproduction was possibly due to lack of Vi antigen in the host cells; this antigen, which is necessary for the adsorption of Vi phages to *Salmonella typhi*, is inadequately developed at 18° (Nicolle, Jude & Diverneau, 1953). It is evident that suboptimal conditions for growth of the host cells may restrict phage multiplication in any environment, even when contacts between the virus and its host occur and, in spite of the fact that sewage appears to provide a good nutrient medium, other factors such as temperature, pH and so on may act as a brake on the rise of phage titres in sewage. Anything which restricts the phage titre limits the selective action of phage.

When phage A alone was maintained at room temperature in samples from the same bottles of sewage as those used in the foregoing experiments, its titre dropped by 75 to 90 % in 10 days. Phage A held under similar conditions in nutrient broth showed no detectable drop in titre. There is no reason to suppose that phage A is unique in this instability, and the concentrations of many phages in sewage may be restricted by such a process of attrition.

The selective action of bacteriophages in varying concentrations

Selection pressure may be exerted by virulent phages, and Hewitt (1953) has suggested that as the result of such selection, and of serial parallel mutations in bacteria and phage, populations of both organisms may finally emerge that differ widely from the parent strains from which they sprang. Before such an effect can be considered, however, we must examine the factors on which such population changes depend in a given environment suitable for the multiplication of both bacteria and phage. They are: the concentration of phage particles; the concentration of susceptible cells; the rate of mutation of cells to phage resistance; and the ability of the phage to mutate to attack cells resistant to the parent phage stock. The rate of mutation of bacteria to phage resistance naturally varies with different bacteria and phages. Luria & Delbrück (1943) found that *Escherichia coli* B mutated to resistance to phage T2 at a rate of about $2 \cdot 5 \times 10^{-8}$ per bacterium per division cycle. On the other hand, where phage sensitivity is dependent on the possession of an antigen that is lost rather frequently by mutation, the rate of mutation to phage resistance is high. The type strain of Vi-type A of *Salmonella typhi* mutates to the Vi-negative state at a rate of approximately $1 \cdot 0 \times 10^{-3}$, and this is therefore its rate of mutation to resistance to Vi phages.

The elimination of phage-sensitive cells is usually considered under conditions ideal for its occurrence: relatively few cells and high phage concentrations; but even under such conditions sensitive cells often unexpectedly escape phage destruction. In order to determine the initial levels of phage concentration necessary to destroy most sensitive cells in a culture we felt that it would be interesting to test the effect of varying phage concentrations on very small numbers of cells. Two phages were used: phage d1, a temperate phage; and a virulent phage attacking most salmonellas, which we will designate phage O. Vi-phage type A of *Salmonella typhi* was used as the host organism. Tubes were inoculated with a culture of the host organism diluted so as to give a mean content of less than one cell per tube. Varying concentrations of phage were added, the total volume being 1 ml., and the tubes were incubated at 37° for 48 hr. Control tubes without phage were inoculated from the same bacterial dilutions. Tables 3 and 4 show the results obtained.

There was a low probability that any tubes in these experiments contained more than two cells, and the probability of more than three cells per tube was negligible. Table 3 shows that, even with such small numbers of organisms, a sterilizing effect was not apparent until a phage concentration of 10^8 particles/ml. was used. Complete sterilization did not occur even at a phage concentration of 10^{10}, but, as d1 is a temperate phage, this may be attributed to immediate lysogenization of the cells, because they must have sustained rapid multiple contacts with phage particles. It is worth remembering that in phage concentrations of 10^6/ml. a given cell would not be expected to contact a phage particle more than once in about 10 hr. All cultures surviving attack by phage d1 in this series were, as could be anticipated, lysogenic.

Table 3. *Effect of phage d1 on small numbers of* Salmonella typhi *in multiple samples*

Exp. no.	Phage concentration/ml.	No. of tubes in each series	Mean no. of cells inoculated per tube	Fraction of tubes showing growth of organisms	
				Controls without phage	With phage
1	1.5×10^6	48	0.90	0.60	0.62
2	1.5×10^6	50	0.51	0.40	0.34
3	1.5×10^7	50	0.30	0.26	0.40
4	1.0×10^8	50	0.30	0.26	0.08
5	1.0×10^{10}	50	0.55	0.42	0.04

Table 4. *Effect of phage O on small numbers of* Salmonella typhi *in multiple samples*

Exp. no.	Phage concentration/ml.	No. of tubes in each series	Mean no. of cells inoculated per tube	Fraction of tubes showing growth of organisms	
				Controls without phage	With phage
1	1.0×10^4	100	0.35	0.28	0.31
2	1.0×10^5	100	0.35	0.28	0.31
3	1.0×10^6	100	0.12	0.08	0.14
4	1.0×10^7	100	0.12	0.08	0.01
5	1.0×10^8	50	0.65	0.48	0

Phage O is highly virulent and few resistant colonies appear when it is applied to a bacterial lawn on solid media. It can be seen from Table 4 that sterilization of what were almost certainly single-cell cultures did not occur until the initial phage concentration reached 10^7 particles/ml. The fertile tubes in experiments 1, 2, 3 and 4 of Table 4 were tested for phage content. They showed titres ranging from 1.0×10^{10} to 2×10^{11}/ml., representing lysis of between 10^8 and 10^9 bacteria. Sensitive cells were still present, apparently in a majority, in 12/31 fertile tubes in Exp. 1, 22/31 fertile tubes in Exp. 2, and in 8/14 tubes in Exp. 3.

These experiments show that, in order to exert a selection pressure sufficiently strong to eliminate a majority of sensitive cells so as to give a survival advantage to a phage-resistant mutant, high phage concentrations are necessary, and that, even under such conditions, total elimination of the phage-sensitive population is by no means certain, even in the static environment of a test-tube. In the natural environments of sewage, the animal intestine, or soil, population changes due to the mass elimination of sensitive bacteria by phage would seem unlikely.

An experiment was carried out to ascertain the concentration of organisms at which phage multiplication would commence in a culture grown from few organisms in a low concentration of phage. The starting concentrations were: 100 *Salmonella typhi* Vi-type A organisms/ml., and 100 Vi-phage A particles/ml. The total volume was 150 ml. Samples were taken hourly for the first 5 hr., and half-hourly thereafter. Phage titrations were carried out in agar layer plates (see Adams, 1950), and total viable organisms, that is, phage-sensitive plus phage-resistant cells, were estimated by surface counts on nutrient agar plates. Phage-resistant organisms were estimated by mixing 0·25 ml. amounts of the suspension with 10^9 particles of Vi-phage A/ml., incubating for 5 min. at 37°, mixing with molten agar at a final concentration of 0·7 % and pouring as agar layer plates. These plates were incubated for 48 hr. so as to allow full development of the resistant colonies. The results of this experiment are shown in Fig. 1.

The latent period of Vi-phage A is 35 min. and the mean burst size about 200 particles. The following conclusions can be drawn from Fig. 1:

(1) The first rise in phage titre was from 10^2 (the starting concentration) to 3×10^2/ml., equivalent to one burst/ml. If one extrapolates back 35 min. (i.e. the phage latent period) from the point at which the first rise in titre was registered, that is, to $3\frac{1}{2}$ hr., the concentration of cells at this time is seen to have reached about 3×10^4/ml. Thus, at such a cell concentration, single contacts with phage were occurring.

(2) The generation time of this strain of *Salmonella typhi* during logarithmic growth is about 30 min. In spite of the rising phage titre, insufficient phage contacts with cells could occur to affect the rate of bacterial growth until the cell and phage concentrations had exceeded 3×10^6/ml. At this point mass infection of the culture occurred, the cell counts dropped in the following $1\frac{1}{2}$ hr. to about $2·0 \times 10^4$/ml. and the phage titre rose to $1·5 \times 10^9$. This was, of course, in accordance with expectations, since equality of phage and cell titres at a sufficiently high level would ensure rapid contact between both agents with a detectable diminution in the concentration of sensitive cells. From then on the resistant cells became an important fraction of the population. It had been calculated from independent experiments that the rate of

mutation of the stock strain of Vi-type A to the Vi-negative state was approximately 10^{-3}, and the experiment represented in Fig. 1 shows that, until destruction of cells by phage began materially to reduce the sensitive cell population, the proportion of resistant mutants present was of about this order. After mass lysis had occurred, however, the counts of total and phage-resistant organisms became indistinguishable within the limits of experimental error, and it was clear that most of the

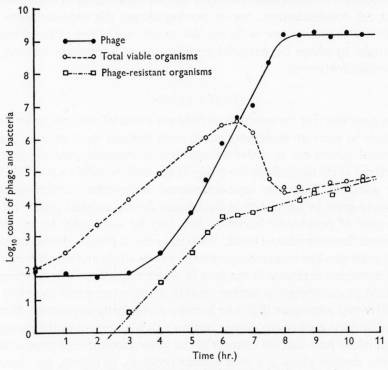

Fig. 1. Growth of Vi-phage A and Vi-type A of *Salmonella typhi* from small initial inocula.

colonies found were descended from resistant cells. The resistant cultures isolated during this experiment were Vi-negative and, although virulence tests in mice were not carried out, it can reasonably be assumed from previous experience that such organisms were of lower virulence than the parent stock.

For this virus-host cell system, then, a phage concentration exceeding 10^6 particles/ml. is necessary to exert a selective effect in the test-tube, and for the effect to make itself felt, a sufficiently high cell concentration is needed to permit multiple cell infection to raise the phage titre about 3 log units above this level. The detection of the population change is facilitated by the high rate of mutation of the host organism to phage resistance. It is apparent that, unless closed systems of a similar character are common in nature, the selection pressure exerted on bacteria by virulent phages is negligible. Such closed systems are found in cheese vats, a subject I have already discussed, and perhaps occasionally in the intestine. The walls of sewers, pockets in sewage systems, cesspools and so on may also lend themselves to the creation of the immobilized environment necessary for the building up of high phage-host cell concentrations, but in moving sewage the concentrations of both agents are too low to favour the occurrence of any of the changes wrought by phage on bacterial populations with anything but inconsiderable frequency.

DISCUSSION

It is clear that, for the selection of resistant bacterial mutants by virulent phages to exert an ecological effect, such mutants must possess some survival advantage in order to establish dominance over the parent bacterial stock away from the phage-laden environment responsible for the selection. They may have nutritional independence which enables them to grow in surroundings inadequate for the original strain; or, in the case of pathogenic bacteria, they may be more infective or more virulent for their natural hosts. Assuming that a phage-selected mutant of a pathogen has an advantage over its parent strain and that it becomes the dominant organism in the host in which the selection has occurred, it must be distributed to further hosts in which it can prove its ability to survive and propagate if it is to become ecologically important. Moreover, it must replace the parent strain to such an extent in the environment of the host that the chances of the latter encountering descendants of the mutant clone are of a similar order to, or exceed, the chances of meeting the parent strain. This establishment of environmental superiority must obviously take place in the absence of the selecting phage.

The one organism in which it is possible, because of the special environmental conditions, to observe selection pressure by phage is *Streptococcus lactis*. The importance of lysogenicity in this relationship has not yet been established and the troublesome phages seem to be virulent. Resistance to a number of viruses may be acquired by the lactic streptococcus by a series of mutational steps and the phage problem in this field may eventually be solved in this way. But I think that it will have to be done in the laboratory, where the organism can be brought into contact with a wide range of phages in a short time.

As I have pointed out earlier, it has been impossible to establish that phages control the course of epidemic diseases under either natural or artificial conditions. The difficulties of attaining sufficiently high phage titres in the animal body to ensure the elimination of the majority of cells of an invading pathogen or indeed to obtain any more than occasional contacts between organisms and phage, the potentially rapid production of phage-resistant variants—lysogenic or non-lysogenic—of virulence equal to that of the parent strain, and the speedy elaboration of phage-neutralizing antibodies by the animal, seem to offer unscalable obstacles to the cure of systemic bacterial diseases by phages.

The influence of phages on the rhizobium-leguminous plant relationship is hypothetical. If sufficiently high phage titres could be reached in soils, the sensitive rhizobium population might be materially diminished, in which case the observations of Kleczkowska (1950) concerning the impaired nitrogen fixation of some phage-resistant rhizobium strains might be important. The results of a widespread impairment of nitrogen fixation in leguminous plants would certainly have repercussions on agriculture in general, and hence on ourselves. However, it has not yet been proved that clover sickness in soil is due to the presence of phage, and here again we have to conclude that the influence of phage on the ecology of the rhizobia is probably not great.

With the diphtheria bacillus, there is no direct evidence that conversion of avirulent strains to virulence is a common occurrence in nature. The unique observation of Dudley (1923) that a virulent strain isolated from a case of diphtheria was, with the exception of its toxigenicity, identical with an avirulent strain which the patient had carried in his throat for the previous two months, came too early for us to assess its true significance. Perhaps this was an instance of phage conversion of a non-toxigenic strain to toxigenicity, and it is, of course, tempting to conclude that it was. But it may have been coincidence, and we cannot now decide one way or another. More observation is obviously called for in this field. In particular, it is important to know whether all toxigenic diphtheria strains carry toxin-determining phages, and whether phages from other bacterial species or genera can become adapted to the diphtheria bacillus and can possess the converting property. The observations of Howard & Jann (1954) concerning the inability of phages carried by other corynebacteria found in the throat to attack the diphtheria bacillus are not encouraging in this respect, but the subject is barely touched and there is room for much more exploration.

The possible importance of transduction lies in the fact that the addition of a particular character to the existing genome of an organism may enlarge, or add the final brick that completes, the complex structure we call virulence in a pathogen, or may provide a non-pathogenic organism with the means of replacing the parent stock in its normal environment. The observation of transduction requires special laboratory conditions: suitable donor cells; a high titre of a competent phage; suitable recipient cells; and a method of selection to demonstrate the transformed clones. Individual characters are transduced with an efficiency of 10^{-6} per particle. None of the phages isolated from sewage or faeces in the investigations described earlier possessed the ability to transduce, but there is no reason why transducing phages should not be found in sewage, and Jacob (1955) showed that one phage of twenty-three isolated from faeces could transduce characters in *Escherichia coli*. If, as the result of transduction, a cell acquires some characteristic which gives it a survival advantage over the parent stock, its establishment of such dominance demands fulfilment of the same conditions as those outlined for phage-resistant mutants at the beginning of this discussion.

We can accept the idea that transduction might bring about a change which confers an ecological advantage on a bacterial strain. However, it is evident that the possibilities of being present at the natural occurrence of any transduction are negligible. What evidence have we, then, apart from the laboratory indications of possibility, that it may take place in nature? First, we know that a small percentage of strains of Enterobacteriaceae are phage-infected on primary isolation from faeces, so that contact with phage undoubtedly occurs occasionally in the animal intestine. Secondly, observations on staphylococci and on *Salmonella paratyphi* B show that new lysogenizations occur in nature with a sufficiently high frequency to be detected on rare occasions. Smith (1948) found three phage types of *Staphylococcus* in different animals of a herd of cattle, and showed that, when two of these were grown together, the third type was produced. Each of the parent types was carrying one phage, but the derived type was doubly lysogenic, carrying the phages of both parents. My own observations (see Anderson & Williams, 1956) were of a similar nature. A culture isolated from a patient in an outbreak of paratyphoid B fever proved to be a mixture of two phage types, which we will call A and B, of which only A was the epidemic type. A phage was isolated from type B which converted type A into type B, and, as all other patients in the outbreak were excreting only type A, it was concluded that the type-converting phage had been encountered in the intestine of the patient in which the change had occurred. This is not an isolated instance, as the pheno-menon has been met with on three or four occasions in connexion with cultures of the paratyphoid B bacillus. However, its incidence is low, because only these few instances have been encountered in the examina-tion of over 10,000 cultures of the paratyphoid B bacillus.

In the examples just described the change of character examined (phage susceptibility pattern) occurs in 100 % of lysogenized cells. In this respect it resembles the toxigenic conversion of the diphtheria bacillus and the phage-controlled conversion of group E1 and E3 salmonellas to group E2 (Iseki & Sakai, 1953a, b; Uetake, Nakagawa & Akiba, 1955). The conversion of *Corynebacterium diphtheriae* to virulence in the human host may thus eventually be detected as the result of prolonged observation. But with transduction it is another matter. The typhoid and paratyphoid B bacilli have passed through innumerable intestines, sewage systems and waterways of all sorts for very many years. Yet the organisms isolated from cases of enteric fever continue to show the antigenic composition 9, 12, d:– or 4, 5, 12, b: 1, 2, and the biochemical properties characteristic of the serotypes concerned. Many of these strains are lysogenic, but this does not seem to have had any other effect than to protect them against the phages they carry and often against others. Unless their temperate phages are endogenous products of the bacterial cells, the lysogenic organisms must have come into contact with phages at some stage in their history, but no cultures isolated from cases of typhoid or paratyphoid fever show features suggesting that they have undergone transduction. This is only one example of the qualitative constancy of micro-organisms in their normal ecological relationships. Innumerable others exist, in both pathogenic and non-pathogenic bacteria.

In considering the evolution of bacteria we must take into account natural mutation, the establishment of survival advantages of mutants in particular hosts and environments, and the many other influences on microbial ecology dealt with in this Symposium. Direct selection and genetic transformation by phage cannot be ignored as possible sources of organismal change which may affect bacterial ecology. However, because of the apparent rarity with which the conditions necessary for the occurrence of these changes can be satisfied, it is impossible at present to argue that phages are ecologically important to bacteria, except perhaps over very long periods of time.

I am indebted to the Lea Conservancy Catchment Board and to Dr E. Windle Taylor of the Metropolitan Water Board for the supply of sewage samples; to Dr J. Kleczkowska for permission to use her unpublished observations on rhizobium phages; to Miss Anthea Fraser and Dr A. Bernstein for carrying out the experiment summarized in Fig. 1; and to Mr F. J. Flynn for valuable technical assistance.

REFERENCES

ADAMS, M. H. (1950). Bacterial viruses. In *Meth. med. Res.* **2**. Chicago Year Book Publishers.

ALMON, L. & WILSON, P. W. (1933). Bacteriophage in relation to nitrogen fixation in red clover. *Arch. Mikrobiol.* **4**, 209.

ANDERSON, E. B. & MEANWELL, L. J. (1945). The problem of bacteriophage in cheese making. *J. Dairy Res.* **13**, 58.

ANDERSON, E. S. & WILLIAMS, R. E. O. (1956). Bacteriophage typing of enteric pathogens and staphylococci and its use in epidemiology. *J. clin. Path.* **9**, 94.

ARCHAMBAULT, P. R. (1948). Evolution d'un traitement de la typhoide par les bactériophages antityphiques Vi. *Sem. Hôp. Paris*, **24**, 3077.

ASHESHOV, I. N. (1933). *Rep. sci. adv. Bd Indian Res. Fd Ass.* 1932-3, p. 38. Simla: Government of India Press.

ASHESHOV, I. N., ASHESHOV, I., KHAN, S. & LAHIRI, M. N. (1930). Bacteriophage inquiry: Report on work during period from 1st January to 1st September 1929. *Indian J. Med. Res.* **17**, 971.

ASHESHOV, I. N., ASHESHOV, I., KHAN, S., LAHIRI, M. N. & CHATTERJEE, S. K. (1933). Studies on cholera bacteriophage. *Indian J. Med. Res.* **20**, 1101.

ASHESHOV, I. N., KHAN, S. & LAHIRI, M. N. (1931). The treatment of cholera with bacteriophage. *Indian med. Gaz.* **66**, 179.

ASHESHOV, I. N., WILSON, J. & TOPLEY, W. W. C. (1937). The effect of an anti-Vi bacteriophage on typhoid infection in mice. *Lancet*, **1**, 319.

BABEL, F. J. (1946a). Studies on the resistance of various cheese cultures to the action of bacteriophage. *J. Dairy Sci.* **29**, 496.

BABEL, F. J. (1946b). Factors influencing acid production by cheese cultures. II. Influence of bacteriophage on acid production in the manufacture of cheddar and cottage cheese. *J. Dairy Sci.* **29**, 597.

BARKSDALE, W. L. & PAPPENHEIMER, A. M. Jr. (1954). Phage-host relationship in non-toxigenic and toxigenic diphtheria bacilli. *J. Bact.* **67**, 220.

BARON, L. S., FORMAL, S. B. & SPILMAN, W. (1953). Use of Vi phage lysates in genetic transfer. *Proc. Soc. exp. Biol., N.Y.*, **83**, 292.

BARON, L. S., FORMAL, S. B. & SPILMAN, W. (1955). Vi phage-host interaction in *Salmonella typhosa. J. Bact.* **69**, 177.

BERTANI, G. (1951). Studies of lysogenesis. I. The mode of phage liberation by lysogenic *Escherichia coli. J. Bact.* **62**, 293.

CRAIGIE, J. & YEN, C. H. (1938). The demonstration of types of *B. typhosus* by means of preparations of type II Vi-phage. *Canad. publ. Hlth J.* **29**, 448, 484.

DEMOLON, A. & DUNEZ, A. (1933). Bactériophage et fatigue du sol cultivé en luzerne. *C.R. Acad. Sci., Paris*, **197**, 1344.

DEMOLON, A. & DUNEZ, A. (1935). Recherches sur le rôle du bactériophage dans le fatigue des luzernières. *Ann. agron., Paris*, **5**, 89.

DESRANLEAU, J. M. (1948). The treatment of typhoid fever by the use of Vi antityphoid bacteriophages. *Canad. publ. Hlth J.* **39**, 317.

DESRANLEAU, J. M. (1949). Progress in the treatment of typhoid fever with Vi bacteriophages. *Canad. publ. Hlth J.* **40**, 473.

D'HERELLE, F. (1926). *The Bacteriophage and its behaviour.* English translation (G. H. Smith). London: Baillière, Tindall and Cox.

DUDLEY, S. F. (1923). The Schick test, diphtheria and scarlet fever. *Spec. Rep. Ser. med. Res. Coun., Lond.,* **75**, 29. London: H.M. Stationery Office.

EDWARDS, P. R., DAVIS, B. R. & CHERRY, W. B. (1955). Transfer of antigen by phage lysates with particular reference to the *l, w* antigens of *Salmonella. J. Bact.* **70**, 279.

FISK, R. T. (1938). Protective action of typhoid phage on experimental typhoid infection in mice. *Proc. Soc. exp. Biol., N.Y.,* **38**, 659.

FORD, H. F. & BABEL, F. J. (1950). Effect of incubation temperatures on the retention of bacteriophage by a culture of *Streptococcus lactis. J. Dairy Sci.* **33**, 466.

FREEMAN, V. J. (1951). Studies on the virulence of bacteriophage-infected strains of *Corynebacterium diphtheriae. J. Bact.* **61**, 675.

FREEMAN, V. J. & MORSE, V. (1952). Further observations on the change to virulence of bacteriophage-infected avirulent strains of *Corynebacterium diphtheriae. J. Bact.* **63**, 407.

GROMAN, N. B. (1953*a*). Evidence for the induced nature of the change from non-toxigenicity to toxigenicity in *Corynebacterium diphtheriae* as a result of exposure to specific bacteriophage. *J. Bact.* **66**, 184.

GROMAN, N. B. (1953*b*). The relation of bacteriophage to the change of *Corynebacterium diphtheriae* from avirulence to virulence. *Science,* **117**, 297.

GROMAN, N. B. (1955). Evidence for the active role of bacteriophage in the conversion of non-toxigenic *Corynebacterium diphtheriae* to toxin production. *J. Bact.* **69**, 9.

GROMAN, N. B. & EATON, M. (1955). Genetic factors in *Corynebacterium diphtheriae* conversion. *J. Bact.* **70**, 637.

GROMAN, N. B. & LOCKART, R. Z. (1953). A study of the application of standard phage techniques to the host-phage system of *Corynebacterium diphtheriae. J. Bact.* **66**, 178.

HEWITT, L. F. (1952). Diphtheria bacteriophages and their relation to the development of bacterial variants. *J. gen. Microbiol.* **7**, 362.

HEWITT, L. F. (1953). Influence of bacteriophage on bacterial variation and evolution. In *Adaptation in Micro-organisms. Third Symp. Soc. gen. Microbiol.* p. 276.

HEWITT, L. F. (1954*a*). Autoadaptation of bacterial viruses and its effect on bacterial variation and evolution. *J. gen. Microbiol.* **11**, 261.

HEWITT, L. F. (1954*b*). Mechanism of virulence transfer by bacterial viruses. *J. gen. Microbiol.* **11**, 272.

HEWITT, L. F. (1954*c*). The effect of certain antibiotics and other chemotherapeutic agents on lysogenicity and virulence transfer in *Corynebacterium diphtheriae. J. gen. Microbiol.* **11**, 288.

HOWARD, D. H. & JANN, G. J. (1954). The isolation and characterization of bacteriophage active against the diphtheria-like *Corynebacteria. J. Bact.* **68**, 316.

HUNTER, G. J. E. (1944). The influence of bacteriophage on the cheese-making process. *J. Dairy Res.* **13**, 294.

HUNTER, G. J. E. (1947). Phage-resistant and phage-carrying strains of streptococci. *J. Hyg., Camb.,* **45**, 307.

HUNTER, G. J. E. & WHITEHEAD, H. R. (1949). Phage-carrying cultures as cheese starters. *J. Dairy Res.* **16**, 368.

ISEKI, S. & SAKAI, T. (1953*a*). Artificial transformation of O antigens in *Salmonella* E group. I. Transformation by antiserum and bacterial autolysate. *Proc. Jap. Acad. Sci.* **29**, 121.

ISEKI, S. & SAKAI, T. (1953*b*). Artificial transformation of O antigens in *Salmonella* E group. II. Antigen-transforming factor in bacilli of subgroup E2. *Proc. Jap. Acad. Sci.* **29**, 127.

JACOB, F. (1955). Transduction of lysogeny in *Escherichia coli*. *Virology*, **1**, 207.

JACOB, F., LWOFF, A., SIMINOVITCH, L. & WOLLMAN, E. (1953). Définition de quelques termes relatifs à la lysogénie. *Ann. Inst. Pasteur*, **84**, 222.

JOHNS, C. K. (1942). Further studies on bacteriophage in relation to cheddar cheese making. *J. Dairy Res.* **13**, 119.

KAUFFMANN, F. (1953). On the transduction of serological properties in the *Salmonella* group. *Acta path. microbiol. scand.* **33**, 409.

KLECZKOWSKA, J. (1950). A study of phage-resistant mutants of *Rhizobium trifolii*. *J. gen. Microbiol.* **4**, 298.

KNOUF, E. G., WARD, W. E., REICHLE, P. A., BOWER, A. G. & HAMILTON, P. M. (1946). Treatment of typhoid fever with type specific bacteriophage. *J. Amer. med. Ass.* **132**, 134.

LAIRD, D. G. (1932). Bacteriophage and the root nodule bacteria. *Arch. Mikrobiol.* **3**, 160.

LEDERBERG, J. & EDWARDS, P. R. (1953). Serotypic recombination in *Salmonella*. *J. Bact.* **71**, 232.

LENNOX, E. S. (1955). Transduction of linked genetic characters of the host by bacteriophage P1. *Virology*, **1**, 190.

LURIA, S. E. (1950). Bacteriophage: an essay on virus reproduction. *Science*, **111**, 507.

LURIA, S. E., & DELBRÜCK, M. (1943). Mutations of bacteria from virus sensitivity to virus resistance. *Genetics*, **28**, 491.

MARSHALL, K. C. (1956). A lysogenic strain of *Rhizobium trifolii*. *Nature, Lond.*, **177**, 92.

MORISON, J. (1932). *Bacteriophage in the Treatment and Prevention of Cholera*. London: H. K. Lewis.

MORSE, M. L. (1954). Transduction of certain loci in *Escherichia coli* K-12. *Genetics*, **39**, 984.

MORSE, M. L., LEDERBERG, E. M. & LEDERBERG, J. (1955). Transduction in *Escherichia coli* K-12. *Genetics*, **41**, 142.

NICHOLS, A. A. & INESON, P. J. (1947). Cheese starter recovery after attack by bacteriophage (strain dominance in multiple-strain starters). *J. Dairy Res.* **15**, 99.

NICHOLS, A. A. & WOLF, J. Z. (1946). Observations on cheese starters with reference to bacteriophage and the phage-organism relationships of strains isolated. *J. Dairy Res.* **14**, 81.

NICOLLE, P., JUDE, A. & DIVERNEAU, G. (1953). Antigènes entravant l'action de certains bactériophages. *Ann. Inst. Pasteur*, **84**, 27.

OKELL, C. C. (1929). The relationship of virulent to avirulent diphtheria bacilli. *J. Hyg., Camb.*, **29**, 309.

OVERCAST, W. W., NELSON, F. E. & PARMELEE, C. E. (1951). Influence of pH on proliferation of lactic streptococcus bacteriophage. *J. Bact.* **61**, 87.

PARSONS, E. I. & FROBISHER, M. Jr. (1951). Effect of bacteriophage on virulence of *Corynebacterium diphtheriae*. *Proc. Soc. exp. Biol., N.Y.*, **78**, 746.

SMITH, H. W. (1948). Investigations on the typing of staphylococci by means of bacteriophage. *J. Hyg., Camb.*, **46**, 82.

STARK, P. & SHERMAN, J. M. (1935). Concerning the habitat of *Streptococcus lactis*. *J. Bact.* **30**, 639.

STOCKER, B. A. D., ZINDER, N. D. & LEDERBERG, J. (1953). Transduction of flagellar characters in *Salmonella*. *J. gen. Microbiol.* **9**, 410.

TAYLOR, J. (1930). Bacteriophage in cholera and dysentery. *Rep. sci. adv. Bd Indian Res. Fd Ass.* 1928–9, p. 28. Delhi: Government of India Press.

TOPLEY, W. W. C., WILSON, J. & LEWIS, E. R. (1925). The role of the Twort–D'Herelle phenomenon in epidemics of mouse-typhoid. *J. Hyg., Camb.*, **24**, 17.

UETAKE, H., NAKAGAWA, T. & AKIBA, T. (1955). The relationship of bacteriophage to antigenic changes in group E salmonellas. *J. Bact.* **69**, 571.

VANDECAVEYE, S. C. & KATZNELSON, H. (1936). Bacteriophage as related to the root nodule bacteria of alfalfa. *J. Bact.* **31**, 465.

WAHL, R. & TERRADE, A. (1950). Multiplication des bactériophages et des bactéries chez les souris infectées par *Salmonella enteritidis* var. Danysz. *Ann. Inst. Pasteur*, **79**, 878.

WARE, G. C. & MELLON, M. A. (1956). Some observations on the coli/coliphage relationship in sewage. *J. Hyg., Camb.*, **54**, 99.

WHITEHEAD, H. R. & HUNTER, G. J. E. (1941). Starter cultures for cheese manufacture. Further attempts to eliminate failures due to bacteriophage. *J. Dairy Res.* **12**, 63.

WHITEHEAD, H. R. & HUNTER, G. J. E. (1946). Bacteriophage infection in cheese manufacture. *J. Dairy Res.* **14**, 64.

WHITEHEAD, H. R. & HUNTER, G. J. E. (1947). Bacteriophage in cheese manufacture. Contamination from farm equipment. *J. Dairy Res.* **15**, 112.

WOLF, J. Z., NICHOLS, A. A. & INESON, P. J. (1946). Mists containing hypochlorite in the destruction of air-borne bacteriophages attacking lactic streptococci. *J. Dairy Res.* **14**, 291.

YEN, C. H. (1949). Further studies on the protective action of Vi-phages in experimental typhoid infection in mice. *Proc. IVth int. Cong. Microbiol.*, Copenhagen, p. 363.

YEN, C. H. & CHANG, K. P. S. (1941). Protective values of various types of Vi-phage on experimental typhoid infection in mice. *Proc. Soc. exp. Biol., N.Y.*, **48**, 243.

ZINDER, N. D. (1955). Bacterial transduction. Symposium on genetic recombination. *J. cell. comp. Physiol.* **45**, Supplement 2, p. 23.

ZINDER, N. D. & LEDERBERG, J. (1952). Genetic exchange in *Salmonella*. *J. Bact.* **64**, 679.

THE PREDACIOUS FUNGI AND THEIR PLACE IN MICROBIAL ECOLOGY

C. L. DUDDINGTON

Biological Laboratories, The Polytechnic, Regent Street, London

The predacious fungi form a well-marked ecological group, united by their habit of capturing and consuming microscopic animals. Taxonomically, they fall into two main series: the Zoopagales, a phycomycetous group belonging to the Zygomycetes, and the predacious Hyphomycetes, a rather diverse collection of form genera all included in the Moniliales. These two predacious series are roughly equal in size, and nearly all known predacious species can be placed in one group or the other.

The animals preyed upon by these fungi are mostly Rhizopoda and nematode worms, and among the former various species of terricolous amoebae are the commonest victims, though some species of Zoopagales and a few predacious Hyphomycetes attack testaceous rhizopods such as *Arcella* and *Difflugia*. A few predacious fungi attack rotifers, and one species, *Arthrobotrys entomopaga* (Drechsler, 1944), captures springtails. The Zoopagales, which are morphologically simple and lack specialized organs of capture, prey mainly on slow-moving protozoa, while the predacious Hyphomycetes, with their often complex structural adaptations to the predacious habit, are principally concerned with the capture of nematodes.

Two forms of predacious activity may be recognized. The endozoic predacious fungi, such as *Endocochlus* and *Cochlonema* among the Zoopagales, and *Harposporium*, *Acrostalagmus* and other genera of predacious Hyphomycetes, pass the whole of their vegetative phase within the bodies of their hosts, which they attack by means of spores that are usually sticky. These spores stick to the integument of the victim on contact, their germ tubes penetrating into the host and giving rise to a mycelium within it. These endozoic forms may be regarded as being predacious during their reproductive phase. The active predators, on the other hand, capture living animals on their mycelia, absorbing their contents by means of haustoria or trophic hyphae that penetrate the tissues of the host. The mycelial Zoopagales and the nematode-trapping Hyphomycetes come into this category. The distinction between the two types is not quite absolute, however, as some species of *Nemat-*

octonus among the predacious Hyphomycetes, and *Bdellospora helicoides* (Drechsler, 1935a) among the Zoopagales, are intermediate in habit.

The endozoic habit in the Zoopagales is well shown in *Cochlonema verrucosum* (Drechsler, 1935a), a fungus that is not uncommon in leaf mould and other decaying vegetable matter. The small, cigar-shaped spores of this fungus are ingested by *Amoeba sphaeronucleus* Greef. Inside the animal, the spore puts out a germ tube that swells at the end to form a small sphere of protoplasm; this lengthens, bends sharply in the middle, and finally grows into a thallus that is coiled into a spiral of about one and a half turns. The growth of the fungus takes place at the expense of the endoplasm of the amoeba, which is eventually killed. From the thallus fertile hyphae grow out through the remains of the ectoplasm of the animal and rise vertically into the air, becoming constricted at regular intervals along their length to form chains of fusiform spores. The spore chains are easily disrupted, so that the spores become scattered over the substratum, where they are readily picked up by passing amoebae; they are produced in large numbers, so that the fungus is effectively dispersed.

In addition to the copious production of asexual spores, *Cochlonema verrucosum* reproduces sexually by the conjugation of two similar gametangia. These are formed on slender branches that emerge from the carcass of the host; at the ends of the branches gametangia are cut off by septa. The pair of conjugating gametangia fuse at their tips, and as a result of the fusion a spherical, thick-walled zygospore is formed. The wall of the enveloping zygosporangium is ornamented with rounded, warty swellings, as is usual in the Zoopagales. The zygospores are presumably resting structures, but as their germination has not yet been observed it is impossible to say to what extent they are important in the maintenance of the species.

Fifteen species of *Cochlonema* have been described from England and America (Drechsler, 1935a, 1937a, 1939a, b, 1941a, 1942a, 1945, 1946b; Duddington, 1940, 1951a). All attack Rhizopoda and are found in leaf mould, rotting vegetation and similar habitats.

The four species of *Endocochlus* (Drechsler, 1935a, 1936, 1949a) have so far been recorded only from America. They resemble *Cochlonema* in vegetative structure and are found in similar habitats; they differ in that their conidia are formed laterally on prostrate fertile hyphae instead of in aerial chains.

The genus *Euryancale* has two species, both endoparasitic in nematodes (Drechsler, 1939b, 1955); both have so far been found only in America. The monotypic *Aplectosoma microsporum*, with its curious cushion-shaped thallus in amoebae and its chains of fusiform spores, has been recorded once only (Drechsler, 1951).

The gap between the endoparasitic Zoopagales and the actively predacious members of the order is to some extent bridged by the curious American species *Bdellospora helicoides* (Drechsler, 1935a). This fungus is ectoparasitic on amoebae. The spores of *Bdellospora* are fusiform and produced in aerial chains as in *Cochlonema*. The spores readily adhere to the ectoplasm of an amoeba that accidentally comes into contact with them. From the spore a germ tube penetrates into the endoplasm of the animal and there forms a system of dichotomously branched haustoria, which absorb nourishment from the host and pass it back to the spore; this increases in size, forming a lemon-shaped thallus which is carried about by the amoeba as it moves. When exhaustion of the endoplasm has led to the death of the host the fungus produces chains of aerial conidia, thus spreading the infection through the population of amoebae.

The remainder of the Zoopagales are active predators, capturing their prey by means of their vegetative mycelia. The animals captured are mostly Protozoa, but a few of the more robust species are able to capture nematode worms. The mycelium of these fungi consists of non-septate hyphae which are usually very delicate, measuring only $1-2\mu$ in diameter. The branched mycelium covers a wide area, and the hyphae appear to be sticky, so that when a potential victim comes into contact with the mycelium it is held as a fly is caught on fly-paper. Capture of prey is followed by the growth of haustoria from the fungus into the animal; these gradually absorb the contents of the victim. If the latter is an amoeba, it takes some time for death to supervene. As the endoplasm of the amoeba is progressively absorbed, the contractile vacuole gradually ceases to function. The streamings of the endoplasm slow down and finally cease, the animal assuming a rounded shape with no pseudopodia apparent. After the death of the animal the remainder of the endoplasm is absorbed by the fungus, leaving only the shrivelled remains of the ectoplasm still attached to the mycelium.

A well-developed mycelium of one of these predators can destroy amoebae in very large numbers, at least in Petri-dish cultures. How far observations in culture are representative of what happens in nature we cannot say, but where such a fungus is growing, say, on the surface of a decaying leaf or twig—a common habitat for these fungi—it is likely that conditions would be equally favourable for its development.

As already noted, a few species of Zoopagales are able to capture nematode worms—no mean feat, when we consider the strength and activity of these animals. In the nematode-capturing species the hyphae are more robust, a diameter of 4–5 μ being usual. Here again the mycelium is sticky, and it has been shown by Comandon & de Fonbrune (1938) that a sticky fluid is secreted when an eelworm touches the mycelium, and that the secretion of this fluid is accompanied by great protoplasmic activity.

When caught by one of these fungi, such as *Stylopage hadra* (Drechsler, 1935c), a nematode struggles violently for a time, dragging the mycelium from side to side in its efforts to get away. At this stage the sticky fluid secreted by the fungus can be clearly seen. After an hour or so the movements of the animal become gradually weaker, until finally it is motionless and, apparently, dead. The body of the animal is then invaded by trophic hyphae that grow into it from the mycelium at the point at which the animal is held; these trophic hyphae grow and spread throughout the carcass of the animal, absorbing its contents. At length only the empty integument of the nematode is left, still attached to the mycelium.

Stylopage hadra is exceptional among the Zoopagales in that when a nematode has been captured a bulbous structure grows out from the hypha of the fungus at the point at which the animal is held. This appears to act as an appressorium, for it is from the bulb that the trophic hyphae penetrate the body of the animal. Such a structure is unique in the Zoopagales; the other nematode-capturing species do not show it, nor is it found in the species that capture amoebae. The presence of an appressorium may be connected with the large size of the eelworms captured by *S. hadra*, but the closely related *S. grandis* (Duddington, 1955c), which is equally ambitious, shows no sign of it.

The mycelial Zoopagales reproduce asexually by means of conidia, and the genera are distinguished from one another by their mode of spore formation. In *Zoopage* (Drechsler, 1935a) the spores are fusiform and catenulate as in *Cochlonema*; in *Stylopage* (Drechsler, 1935b) they are borne singly, two or more at intervals, or in groups, on long erect aerial conidiophores; in *Acaulopage* (Drechsler, 1935b) they are formed singly on short sterigmatic branches of the mycelium. The conidia of most species of *Acaulopage* are provided with empty appendages of various forms; the possible ecological significance of these will be discussed later. The genus *Cystopage* (Drechsler, 1941a) is unusual in that it reproduces solely by means of lateral or intercalary chlamydospores.

Sexual reproduction is known in many of the Zoopagales, though not in all. Where it occurs it is of the zygomycetous type, conjugation of two similar or somewhat dissimilar gametangia resulting in the formation of a thick-walled resting zygospore ornamented externally with bullate or dentate protuberances. The zygospores of the Zoopagales are very characteristic and are easily recognized under the microscope, a feature that is often useful in detecting the presence of these fungi in plate cultures (Duddington, 1955b).

An interesting feature of those members of the Zoopagales that prey on Protozoa is their host-specificity. Nearly all species have been described as strictly confined to a single species of prey, though there are one or two instances (Drechsler, 1947a, b, 1948) where the same fungus captures two different amoebae. It must be remembered, however, that the Zoopagales have so far only been observed in laboratory cultures, and it is possible that under natural conditions they might be more versatile.

With the possible exception of three recently discovered species (Drechsler, 1955) that have not been shown definitely to be predacious, the Zoopagales appear to be obligate predators. There are no records of their having been grown in pure culture away from their animal prey. Indeed, there is evidence that, in some species at least, the spores will not germinate in the absence of suitable animals (Duddington, 1955d).

The predacious Hyphomycetes, like the Zoopagales, may be divided into two groups in respect of their host-parasite relations: the endozoic and the nematode-trapping forms. The former are, like the Zoopagales, obligate parasites. The mycelium, which consists of septate hyphae, is formed within the body of the host animal, which is nearly always a nematode worm. Only the fertile hyphae bearing the spores are aerial. The spores are generally small and very numerous, and infection of the host is almost invariably by means of a spore that sticks to the exterior of the animal, though in *Harposporium bysmatosporium* (Drechsler, 1946d) infection of the nematode host is by a spore ingested orally.

Probably the commonest, as well as the best known, of the endozoic predacious Hyphomycetes is *Harposporium anguillulae* (Lohde, 1874; Karling, 1938). The spores of this fungus are small and sickle-shaped; they stick to the integument of a nematode on contact, penetrate it by means of a fine germ tube, and form a mycelium of branched, septate hyphae within the animal. The mycelium grows at the expense of the body contents of the host, which is eventually killed. From the carcass of the animal short aerial fertile hyphae emerge, bearing globular phialides on which groups of the tiny sickle-shaped spores are carried. Spore production is profuse, so that the infection is readily spread.

Several other species of *Harposporium* have been described (Dixon, 1952; Drechsler, 1941b, 1946d, 1950b; Shepherd, 1955b); they are all parasitic in nematodes.

Acrostalagmus obovatus (Drechsler, 1941b) resembles *Harposporium* in its vegetative structure, but differs in its spore production. The spores are very small, ovoid structures, formed in clusters on flask-shaped phialides borne at intervals on rather long aerial fertile hyphae that emerge from the carcass of the nematode host. As in *Harposporium*, infection of the host is brought about by means of an adhesive spore. Three other species of *Acrostalagmus* attack nematodes, and one, *A. tagenophorus* (Drechsler, 1942b), is parasitic in rotifers. *Verticillium sphaerosporum* (Goodey, 1951) and *Cephalosporium balanoides* (Drechsler, 1941b), both attacking nematodes, show strong resemblances to *Acrostalagmus*.

The genus *Nematoctonus* stands apart from the rest of the predacious Hyphomycetes in that its mycelium and fertile hyphae bear well-marked clamp connexions. This suggests that *Nematoctonus* is an imperfect member of the Basidiomycetes, though its relationships are quite obscure. There are six recorded species, all endozoic in nematodes in America (Drechsler, 1941b, 1943, 1946a, 1949b) and Britain (Duddington, 1951a, 1954). The species of *Nematoctonus* differ from other endozoic Hyphomycetes in the relatively large size of their spores. These are formed on aerial fertile hyphae that emerge from the carcass of the host in the normal way; they are ovoid or club-shaped, and in some species the spores bear appendages that enable them to stick to nematodes.

The endozoic Hyphomycetes that attack nematodes show a certain degree of host-specificity in that the range of nematodes that can be attacked by a given species appears to be limited; the host-specificity is not, however, as strict as it is in the Zoopagales.

The best known of the predacious fungi are the nematode-trapping Hyphomycetes, and it is among them that morphological adaptations to the predacious life reach their peak. These fungi are provided with nematode traps by which eelworms are captured with great ease and efficiency, and in many instances the traps show an astonishing degree of morphological and physiological specialization.

Easily the commonest of these fungi is *Arthrobotrys oligospora*, first described as a saprophyte by Fresenius (1852) and later shown to be predacious by Zopf (1888) and Drechsler (1937b). The mycelium consists of septate hyphae, which are usually about 5μ in diameter. Short lateral branches grow out and curl round into semicircular loops, their tips anastomosing with the subtending hypha or with other similar loops. From the primary loops others arise, so that complex three-dimensional networks are formed, in which the individual loops tend to be orientated at right angles to one another, rather like the semicircular canals in the mammalian ear. These systems of networks are arranged at intervals along the hyphae of the mycelium, and they provide a large surface on which eelworms may be caught.

The nematodes are captured by adhesion, as in the mycelial Zoopagales. The networks secrete an intensely sticky fluid, so that nematodes are held on casual contact and are unable to get away, despite their violent struggles. The sticky fluid secreted by the networks is easily visible under the microscope; it appears to be of about the viscosity of treacle, and according to Comandon & de Fonbrune (1938) it is, under normally moist conditions, adhesive only for nematodes.

A captured nematode usually struggles for about 2 hr., towards the end of which time its movements become more and more sluggish until it is motionless and, apparently, dead. When the animal has become moribund its cuticle is penetrated by a very fine outgrowth from the fungus; this swells inside the eelworm to form a bulbous structure, the infection bulb, from which trophic hyphae grow out and fill the carcass of the animal, absorbing its contents. The formation of the infection bulb has been described in detail by Shepherd (1955a).

The adhesive network is the commonest type of eelworm trap found in the predacious Hyphomycetes and, judging from the extent of the slaughter seen in laboratory cultures, it is probably the most efficient. Such reticulate species as *Arthrobotrys oligospora*, *A. robusta* (Duddington, 1951d), *Dactylaria thaumasia* (Drechsler, 1937b), *D. scaphoides* (Peach, 1952), and *Trichothecium flagrans* (Duddington, 1949) can effectively exterminate the nematodes in a plate culture in a few days. Other reticulate species are but little behind them in the gusto with which they massacre their prey.

In *Dactylella cionopaga* (Drechsler, 1950a; Duddington, 1950a) the eelworm traps are simpler. Short adhesive branches, one, two, or three cells long, grow out at right angles to the mycelium, and nematodes are captured by adhesion. As the mycelium ages the adhesive branches tend to elongate and proliferate to form simple networks, but these never approach the complexity of those found in the true reticulate species. A similar kind of arrangement is found in *D. lobata* (Duddington, 1951c).

Allied to the adhesive process is the stalked adhesive knob, such as is found in *Dactylella ellipsospora* (Grove, 1886; Drechsler, 1937b; Duddington, 1950a). The mycelium of this very common fungus is provided with small subspherical knobs, about 10μ or rather less in diameter, attached to the hyphae by short two-celled stalks. The knobs are sticky, and they capture eelworms by adhesion in the same way as the networks of the reticulate species. The stalks of the knobs usually stand perpendicularly to the surface on which the fungus is growing, so that the knobs are placed in a good position for the ensnarement of nematodes; the distance between adjacent knobs is such that a captured nematode, during its struggles, will often touch one or even two other knobs, thus becoming doubly or trebly held.

All the nematode traps so far discussed depend on the secretion of a sticky fluid for their operation. Some species of predacious Hyphomycetes depend upon mechanical traps rather than sticky ones, and these are of two kinds: the non-constricting ring and the constricting ring. The former consists of a ring formed by three curved cells, attached to the mycelium of the fungus by a short stalk. The ring is of such a diameter that an eelworm accidentally pushing its head into the opening becomes wedged as it tries to force its way through, and is unable to withdraw. After the death of the captive, trophic hyphae grow from the ring cells into its body and absorb its contents. There appears to be no sticky secretion involved in this mechanism; the eelworms are held purely by their being jammed into the rings.

The stalks that attach the non-constricting rings to the mycelium are usually rather slender, and it quite frequently happens that a violently struggling captive manages to tear the ring from its moorings and thus get away, still encircled. This may happen several times to the same eelworm, so that in cultures nematodes may be seen moving about with several detached rings about their bodies. Their freedom is usually brief, however, for a detached ring will eventually kill its wearer, and when this happens a new mycelium grows out from the remains of the animal. Thus, the non-constricting rings may serve as means of dispersal as well as organs of capture. Many fungi with non-constricting rings are also provided with stalked adhesive knobs; this is the case with the very well-known *Dactylaria candida* (Drechsler, 1937*b*; Peach, 1954).

The most remarkable of the structures developed by the predacious Hyphomycetes for the capture of nematodes is the constricting ring. Like the non-constricting kind, these rings consist of three curved cells which are joined to the parent mycelium by a short, stout stalk, usually of two cells. If an eelworm passes its head into one of these rings the three cells suddenly and rapidly swell to about three times their former volume, so that the opening in the ring is virtually obliterated and the nematode is tightly held with its body crushed where the ring has closed around it. The stimulus that brings the mechanism into operation appears to be friction or pressure on the inner faces of the ring cells

(Comandon & de Fonbrune, 1938). The reaction is very rapid; after a lag phase of a few seconds, the actual swelling is accomplished in about one-tenth of a second. How the remarkable swelling is brought about is quite unknown; Rees (personal communication) has found that the reaction of the rings of *Dactylella doedycoides* (Drechsler, 1940*a*) to acetylcholine suggests a possible comparison with animal muscle, but this awaits confirmation.

Nematodes captured by constricting rings seldom, if ever, succeed in tearing the rings adrift from the mycelium. This may be partly due to the robust structure of the short stalk, but the damage inflicted on the eelworm by the savage constriction that it suffers may well be an important factor in preventing escape. As the rings are placed fairly close together on the mycelium, it is not at all unusual for a captive, in struggling to get away, to flick its tail into another ring and thus be held at both ends.

When a nematode has been captured by a constricting ring it struggles violently for a time, but soon becomes quiescent. Trophic hyphae then grow into its body from the ring cells; these absorb the body contents of the animal and pass the material back, via the ring, to the mycelium.

The constricting ring trap is not uncommon. The best-known species with this kind of trap is *Dactylella bembicodes* (Drechsler, 1937*b*); others frequently met with are *Dactylella doedycoides* (Drechsler, 1940*a*), *Dactylaria brochopaga* (Drechsler, 1937*b*; Peach, 1954), *D. gracilis* (Duddington, 1951*a*), and *Arthrobotrys dactyloides* (Drechsler, 1937*b*; Duddington, 1954). It is interesting that, while the non-constricting ring is often accompanied by the stalked knob, this is not true of the constricting ring.

When the fungus is growing on a flat surface the rings are usually orientated in a plane perpendicular to that surface, like rabbit snares. In this way they are well placed to ensnare nematodes.

While nematodes are by far the most important prey of the predacious Hyphomycetes, there are a few members of this group that capture Protozoa. Thus, *Dactylella tylopaga* (Drechsler, 1935*d*) catches *Amoeba verrucosa*, and *Dactylella passalopaga* preys on *Geococcus vulgaris* and *Euglypha levis* (Drechsler, 1936). *Pedilospora dactylopaga* (Drechsler, 1934) captures testaceous rhizopods, and *Tridentaria carnivora* (Drechsler, 1937*c*) attacks *Difflugia constricta*.

The Zoopagales and the predacious Hyphomycetes between them account for nearly all known predacious fungi, but a few species outside these groups are also worthy of mention. *Protascus subuliformis* (Dangeard, 1906; Duddington, 1946, 1950*b*, 1955*d*; Juniper, 1954*a*;

Karling, 1942; Maire, 1915) and *Myzocytium vermicolum* (Zopf, 1884; Dangeard, 1906; Duddington, 1955*d*; Karling, 1942) are endozoic members of the Lagenidiales that are parasitic in nematodes; they form thalli inside their hosts, and when mature the entire thallus becomes a sporangium, its contents dividing to form spores. Both these fungi, which appear to be closely related, are probably best placed in the phycomycetous group Lagenidiales, and it is interesting that *Protascus* produces only non-motile spores, instead of the motile zoospores that are characteristic of the order. Most of the Lagenidiales are parasitic in algae, and it is possible that the non-motile spores of *Protascus* are adapted to attack nematodes, which themselves are highly motile; for such prey a motile spore might not be an advantage. Two other similar fungi, *Haptoglossa heterospora* (Drechsler, 1940*b*) and *Gonimochaete horridula* (Drechsler, 1946*c*), also form non-motile spores, and the zoospores of *Myzocytium vermicolum*, which are usually biflagellate, are sometimes provided with adhesive lobes instead of flagella. Some members of the Lagenidiales that attack rotifers have been described from Brazil (Karling, 1944).

By far the best known of the rotifer-attacking fungi is *Zoophagus insidians* (Sommerstorff, 1911; Arnaudow, 1921, 1923; Barnes & Melville, 1932; Giklhorn, 1922; Mirande, 1920; Prowse, 1954; Sparrow, 1929, 1932, 1933, 1936, 1943; Valkanov, 1932). The mycelium of this fungus bears peg-like branches which appear to be sticky, and on which rotifers are caught. More recently a second species, *Z. tentaculum* (Karling, 1936), has been described. *Sommerstorffia spinosa* (Arnaudow, 1923), a phycomycete that captures rotifers by means of specially modified tips of mycelial branches, is superficially not unlike *Zoophagus insidians*, though it is unlikely that the two are related. A few other zoophagous Phycomycetes have been described from time to time.

Very little is known about the habitat relations of the predacious fungi. This is partly because the subject has received little attention, and partly because the present lack of an adequate quantitative sampling technique for these fungi makes it difficult to draw hard and fast conclusions from what little information we have. Most of the work that has so far been done on the predacious fungi has been morphological or physiological, with consequent neglect of their ecology. This is a pity, for, apart from its scientific interest, a study of the ecology of predacious fungi might have important economic implications in connexion with the control of eelworms that damage crops.

The principal hosts of predacious fungi, Rhizopoda and nematode worms, are to be found almost everywhere where there is rotting organic material and sufficient moisture, and the same could be said of the predacious fungi. They have been observed in the soil, in rotting vegetation of many kinds, in the dung of animals, in decaying wood, in moss cushions, and in water. A predacious phycomycete, *Pythium anguillulae*, has even been found attacking the vinegar eelworm in vats of vinegar (Sadebeck, 1887). Where free-living eelworms are being kept in laboratory cultures, it is often difficult to exclude predators. The distribution of predacious fungi is world-wide, and several species are known to occur in at least three continents. Some species, such as *Arthrobotrys oligospora*, are extremely common. It is almost impossible to examine adequately a specimen of vegetable compost or farmyard dung without finding one or more species of predacious fungi.

A great deal of the pioneer work of Drechsler on predacious fungi was concerned with leaf mould as a source, and from the long list of species that he has described there is no doubt of their frequency in this habitat. Leaf mould is usually rich in Protozoa and free-living nematodes; it tends to retain moisture—an important point where predacious fungi are concerned—and the micro-climate on the floor of a forest is more sheltered than that of open ground. I have found leaf mould a good source of predacious fungi, especially of the Zoopagales.

Rotting wood is an excellent source of predacious fungi, both Zoopagales and predacious Hyphomycetes. In particular, pieces of bark from tree stumps with the phloem in a liquid state of decay harbour a great variety of predacious fungi; this is no doubt connected with the large numbers of Protozoa and free-living nematodes found in such a habitat. There is no definite evidence that predacious fungi are able to hydrolyse cellulose, but as far as I am aware this point has never been specially investigated.

Vegetable compost is usually well supplied with predacious fungi, but the numbers vary with the nature and age of the material, and with its degree of decomposition. A new compost heap is usually poor or lacking in predacious species; as the heap ages and the plant material becomes more fully decomposed the predacious fungi begin to colonize it, usually reaching their maximum development at a stage when the decomposition is fairly well advanced, but before the original form of the plant material has been completely lost. It is unsafe to generalize here, however, as compost is a very variable material. I have known some composts—though not many—that were apparently free from predacious fungi. Some species of predacious fungi appear to have a particular affinity for compost; *Trichothecium flagrans* (Duddington, 1949) is a case in point.

Apart from compost heaps, partly decayed plant remains anywhere are liable to contain predacious fungi, and are often surprisingly rich in them. A useful method of obtaining predacious fungi from soil is to lay some pieces of cabbage leaf on the surface of the ground, covered by glass plates or flat stones, until decomposition is proceeding nicely. On making cultures from the portions of leaf, predacious fungi will usually be found.

The predacious fungus flora of moss cushions is surprisingly rich, especially in the layers near to the soil. The fungi do not appear to attack the moss plants in any way, but live on the nematodes and Protozoa that are present; Overgaard (Nielsen) (1948) has shown that these animals are abundant in moss cushions. As an example of the varied flora of this habitat, the gleanings from a small mixed collection of bryophytes from the side of a lane near Hatch Bridge, Devon, may be quoted (Duddington, 1951 b). The collection contained six different species of mosses, and yielded the following eight predacious fungi: *Acaulopage ischnospora* Drechsl., *Cochlonema* sp., *Stylopage hadra* Drechsl., *Arthrobotrys oligospora* Fres., *Dactylella bembicodes* Drechsl., *Harposporium anguillulae* Lohde, *H. oxycoracum* Drechsl, and *Nematoctonus tylosporus* Drechsl. A sample of the moss *Bryum argenteum* from between paving stones in a street near Kingston-on-Thames contained *Dactylella ellipsospora* (Preuss) Grove, *Dactylaria psychrophila* Drechsl. and *Harposporium anguillulae*, all attacking nematodes, and an unidentified member of the Zoopagales capturing amoebae.

Dung as a habitat for predacious fungi has been little investigated, but recent work (Duddington, 1953; Juniper, 1953, 1954a, b; Peach & Juniper, 1955) has shown that the dung flora is a rich one; this is hardly surprising when we consider the numbers and variety of Protozoa and nematodes that inhabit dung. The occurrence of predacious fungi in dung may have important economic implications in connexion with the biological control of plant pathogenic nematodes (Duddington, 1956, 1957).

The study of predacious fungi occurring in the soil is difficult but fascinating. A recent survey (Duddington, 1954) has shown that there are many common soil species in this country, and the unpublished work of Shepherd in Denmark has demonstrated that they are equally common in Danish soils. A striking feature of the soil flora is the very widespread occurrence of *Arthrobotrys oligospora*. A survey of nematode-attacking fungi in agricultural soils in Britain yielded twenty-one records of *A. oligospora* from forty-nine soil samples (Duddington, 1954). Almost as frequent was a member of the Zoopagales that could not be identified as it formed no spores; this fungus was recorded eighteen times from the same forty-nine collections. The next in order of frequency was *Harposporium anguillulae* with six records, followed by *Acrostalagmus obovatus* with five records.

It is a little surprising, when we consider the richness of the soil predacious fungus flora, that they do not play a larger part in published lists of soil fungi. This may be partly due to their failure to show themselves in cultures unless suitable prey is available; for obvious reasons, soil mycologists do not encourage nematodes and Protozoa to wander unchecked over their isolation plates. Deprived of animal victims, the predacious fungi are unable to compete with more vigorously growing moulds. The low pH commonly used for soil isolation media is also unsuitable for the growth of most predacious fungi.

Water as a habitat for the predacious fungi has been investigated by Peach (1948, 1950, 1952, 1954), who has recorded a number of predators, both Zoopagales and Hyphomycetes, from aquatic habitats. Among the Zoopagales, Peach has found that species of *Acaulopage* with empty appendages attached to their spores are particularly common on organic debris in water, and this gives rise to the suggestion that the appendages may assist dispersal by giving the spores added buoyancy. There is an interesting parallel here with the curious non-predacious aquatic Hyphomycetes recorded by Ingold (1942, 1943a, b, 1944, 1952, 1956), with their beautifully complex spores.

It is interesting that the predacious species recorded by Peach were all apparently terrestrial fungi that were growing in an aquatic habitat. Examples of the predacious habit among such aquatic groups as the Saprolegniales are extremely rare. Judging by the frequency with which the Zoopagales and the predacious Hyphomycetes occur in water it does not seem as if aquatic life offers any insuperable difficulty for the predacious habit. Possibly the more uniform conditions in water compared with those on land fail to provide the stimulus to evolution needed for the development of predacious adaptations. Further work on aquatic predacious fungi is badly needed.

The factors that govern the distribution of predacious fungi in nature, apart from the presence or absence of their animal prey, are unknown. Some species, such as *Arthrobotrys oligospora*, are very widespread, while others appear to be severely restricted. *Stylopage haploe* is established in abundance in Guiting Wood, Gloucestershire (Duddington, 1940, 1955a), but apart from this it appears to be an uncommon species in Britain. *Arthrobotrys musiformis* has been recorded from three woods, fairly close together, in Warwickshire (Duddington, 1950a,

1951 *b*), but from nowhere else in this country; this species has also been found in Denmark by Shepherd (personal communication). *Dactylaria scaphoides* has been seen once only (Peach, 1952), yet this is a vigorous and hardy species and soil inoculation experiments have shown that it is a good colonizer. Much more work will have to be done before the known distribution of predacious fungi falls into any coherent pattern.

The temperature requirements of predacious fungi have not been studied, but a few observations are available. Drechsler (1946 *b*) finds that *Cochlonema agamum* attacks amoebae with vigour at 23°, but that when the temperature is reduced to 15° the amoebae seem able to recover from attack and inhibit the growth of the fungus. *Dactylella gephyropaga* captures nematodes actively at 25–30°, while at this temperature *D. cionopaga* is almost inactive; at 15–18° the position is reversed (Drechsler, 1950 *a*). This behaviour appears to be correlated with the more northern distribution of *D. cionopaga* in America compared with *D. gephyropaga*, and it is interesting that *D. cionopaga* is a common fungus in Britain, while *D. gephyropaga* has not so far been recorded over here. Drechsler (1948) points out that cool, humid weather seems to favour the development of predacious fungi in laboratory cultures.

The effect of predacious fungi on the natural micro-fauna is an interesting subject, about which we know very little. Since they are so common in nature, they must play an important part in the microbial ecosystem as natural enemies of Protozoa and nematodes. Unfortunately, most of our knowledge of their habits has been derived from the study of laboratory cultures, where conditions for both predators and prey are highly artificial. Generalizations about ecology based purely on laboratory observations are highly dangerous, and must be checked against observations from nature before they can be considered valid. For the predacious fungi, this remains to be done.

The Zoopagales, both endozoic and mycelial species, can be highly destructive of Protozoa in agar cultures under the right conditions. The mycelial forms usually show their greatest predacious activity while the mycelium is still young, the later stages in their growth being given over mainly to reproduction. Their continued activity as predators depends, therefore, upon their surroundings remaining moist enough for mycelial growth; as the cultures begin to dry up the mycelium dies off and fewer animals are caught, and this curtailment of activity is heightened by the fact that under desiccation the amoebae that they are destroying tend to encyst and thus escape capture. It is reasonable to suppose that a drying up of the substratum will affect them in a similar way in nature, and this may partly account for their abundance in such habitats as leaf mould and moss cushions, and their relative scarcity in the soil where periodical drying up is likely to be more severe.

We do not know to what extent the Zoopagales are effective in limiting the numbers of Protozoa under natural conditions, as quantitative studies are entirely lacking.

We are in no better case with the endozoic Hyphomycetes than we are with the Zoopagales. We know that they are very numerous, and that they can be highly destructive to nematodes in agar cultures. How nearly these cultures reflect what is happening in nature we have at present no idea. Such common and destructive species as *Harposporium anguillulae* must be a serious hazard to free-living nematodes, at least locally, but we have no quantitative information available to tell us just how important they are in the natural ecosystem. Such information would be most valuable from the economic and from the scientific points of view.

With the nematode-trapping Hyphomycetes we are slightly better off, as the results of experiments on the biological control of plant-pathogenic nematodes have given us a certain amount of information. The fact that these fungi are able, under appropriate conditions, to curtail the activity of such plant pests as the pineapple root-knot eelworm (Linford & Yapp, 1939; Linford, Yapp & Oliveira, 1938) and the potato root eelworm (Duddington, 1956, 1957) indicates that their potentialities as eelworm destroyers in the soil are high.

The nematode-trapping Hyphomycetes, unlike the endozoic Hyphomycetes and the Zoopagales, are able to live and thrive in pure culture as saprophytes. These fungi show a remarkable dual activity. In pure cultures they grow vigorously and sporulate abundantly, but usually no eelworm traps are formed. The addition of nematodes to cultures of the fungi usually stimulates them to form traps and some of the nematodes are captured, but it is often found that predacious activity under these conditions is slight. If, on the other hand, a *small* piece of fungus culture is added to a thriving culture of eelworms, the fungus indulges in a diabolical orgy of eelworm destruction that may exterminate the nematodes on an agar plate. Only after the fungus is gorged with prey does sporulation occur with any abundance.

It seems, therefore, that the nematode-trapping Hyphomycetes are balanced between two opposing phases of activity: saprophytic and predacious. This balance can be affected by the presence or absence of nematode prey. In what state do they exist under natural conditions?

We do not know, but it is likely that they are profoundly affected by the number of nematodes present in the environment. Linford (1937) showed that the addition of green plant material to the soil produced a rapid increase in the numbers of free-living nematodes, and this was immediately followed by a great increase in the activity of predacious fungi in the soil. This observation has been confirmed by recent work on cereal root eelworm in this country (Duddington, 1956, 1957). It is likely that the eelworm-trapping Hyphomycetes exist in nature in a state of dynamic equilibrium with their prey, and that the equilibrium will shift this way or that according to the changing numbers of eelworms present in the environment at any given time. Attempts to use the predacious Hyphomycetes for the biological control of nematodes depend largely on the possibility of adjusting this equilibrium in the direction of decreased saprophytic and enhanced predacious activity.

The predacious fungi offer great opportunities to the ecologist. The most pressing need at the moment is for the development of quantitative methods of investigating these fungi under natural conditions, for without such methods we shall not get very far. The techniques of statistical ecology could help us a great deal here. The work is likely to be arduous, and it may be a long time before concrete results are obtained; but in the long run the reward will be worth the labour.

REFERENCES

ARNAUDOW, N. (1921). Zur Morphologie und Biologie von *Zoophagus insidians* Sommerstorff. *Jber. Univ. Sofia*, **15–16**, 1.

ARNAUDOW, N. (1923). Ein neuer Rädertiere(Rotatoria)fangender Pilz (*Sommerstorffia spinosa*, nov.gen., nov.sp.). *Flora*, **116**, 109.

BARNES, B. & MELVILLE, R. (1932). Notes on British aquatic fungi. *Trans. Brit. mycol. Soc.* **17**, 82.

COMANDON, J. & FONBRUNE, P. DE (1938). Recherches expérimentales sur les champignons prédateurs du sol. *C.R. Soc. Biol., Paris*, **129**, 619.

DANGEARD, P. A. (1906). Recherches sur le développement du périthèce chez les Ascomycètes. Ière partie. Les ancêtres des champignons supérieurs. Chap. 5. Les Hemiasci. *Botaniste*, **9**, 256.

DIXON, S. M. (1952). Predacious fungi from rotten wood. *Trans. Brit. mycol. Soc.* **35**, 144.

DRECHSLER, C. (1934). *Pedilospora dactylopaga* n.sp., a fungus capturing and destroying testaceous rhizopods. *J. Wash. Acad. Sci.* **24**, 395.

DRECHSLER, C. (1935a). Some conidial Phycomycetes destructive to terricolous amoebae. *Mycologia*, **27**, 6.

DRECHSLER, C. (1935b). Some non-catenulate conidial Phycomycetes preying on terrestrial amoebae. *Mycologia*, **27**, 176.

DRECHSLER, C. (1935c). A new species of conidial Phycomycete preying on nematodes. *Mycologia*, **27**, 206.

DRECHSLER, C. (1935d). A new mucedinaceous fungus capturing and consuming *Amoeba verrucosa*. *Mycologia*, **27**, 256.

DRECHSLER, C. (1936). A *Fusarium*-like species of *Dactylella* capturing and consuming testaceous rhizopods. *J. Wash. Acad. Sci.* **26**, 397.

DRECHSLER, C. (1937a). New Zoopagaceae destructive to soil rhizopods. *Mycologia*, **29**, 229.

DRECHSLER, C. (1937b). Some Hyphomycetes that prey on free-living terricolous nematodes. *Mycologia*, **29**, 447.

DRECHSLER, C. (1937c). A new species of *Tridentaria* preying on *Difflugia constricta*. *J. Wash. Acad. Sci.* **27**, 391.

DRECHSLER, C. (1939a). A few new Zoopagaceae destructive to large soil rhizopods. *Mycologia*, **31**, 128.

DRECHSLER, C. (1939b). Five new Zoopagaceae destructive to rhizopods and nematodes. *Mycologia*, **31**, 388.

DRECHSLER, C. (1940a). Three new Hyphomycetes predacious on terricolous nematodes. *Mycologia*, **32**, 448.

DRECHSLER, C. (1940b). Three fungi destructive to free-living terricolous nematodes. *J. Wash. Acad. Sci.* **30**, 240.

DRECHSLER, C. (1941a). Four Phycomycetes destructive to nematodes and rhizopods. *Mycologia*, **33**, 248.

DRECHSLER, C. (1941b). Some Hyphomycetes parasitic on free-living terricolous nematodes. *Phytopathology*, **31**, 773.

DRECHSLER, C. (1942a). New species of *Acaulopage* and *Cochlonema* destructive to soil amoebae. *Mycologia*, **34**, 274.

DRECHSLER, C. (1942b). Two zoophagous species of *Acrostalagmus* with multicellular *Desmidiospora*-like chlamydospores. *J. Wash. Acad. Sci.* **32**, 243.

DRECHSLER, C. (1943). Two new basidiomycetous fungi parasitic on nematodes. *J. Wash. Acad. Sci.* **33**, 183.

DRECHSLER, C. (1944). A species of *Arthrobotrys* that captures springtails. *Mycologia*, **36**, 382.

DRECHSLER, C. (1945). Several additional Phycomycetes subsisting on nematodes and amoebae. *Mycologia*, **37**, 1.

DRECHSLER, C. (1946a). A clamp-bearing fungus parasitic and predacious on nematodes. *Mycologia*, **38**, 1.

DRECHSLER, C. (1946b). Three new Zoopagaceae subsisting on soil amoebae. *Mycologia*, **38**, 120.

DRECHSLER, C. (1946c). A nematode-destroying phycomycete forming immotile spores in aerial evacuation tubes. *Bull. Torrey bot. Cl.* **73**, 1.

DRECHSLER, C. (1946d). A species of *Harposporium* invading its nematode host from the stoma. *Bull. Torrey bot. Cl.* **73**, 557.

DRECHSLER, C. (1947a). Three zoopagaceous fungi that capture and consume soil-inhabiting rhizopods. *Mycologia*, **39**, 253.

DRECHSLER, C. (1947b). Three new species of Zoopagaceae predacious on terricolous rhizopods. *Mycologia*, **39**, 379.

DRECHSLER, C. (1948). Three Zoopagaceae that subsist by capturing soil amoebae. *Mycologia*, **40**, 85.

DRECHSLER, C. (1949a). An *Endocochlus* having binary helicoid thalli of left-handed rotation. *Mycologia*, **41**, 229.

DRECHSLER, C. (1949b). A nematode-capturing fungus with anastomosing clamp-bearing hyphae. *Mycologia*, **41**, 369.

DRECHSLER, C. (1950a). Several species of *Dactylella* and *Dactylaria* that capture free-living nematodes. *Mycologia*, **42**, 1.

DRECHSLER, C. (1950*b*). *A Harposporium* infecting eelworms by means of externally-adhering, awl-shaped conidia. *J. Wash. Acad. Sci.* **40**, 405.

DRECHSLER, C. (1951). Various zoopagaceous fungi subsisting on protozoans and eelworms. *Mycologia*, **43**, 161.

DRECHSLER, C. (1955). Additional species of Zoopagaceae subsisting on rhizopods and eelworms. *Mycologia*, **47**, 364.

DUDDINGTON, C. L. (1940). Predacious fungi from Cotswold leaf-mould. *Nature, Lond.*, **145**, 150.

DUDDINGTON, C. L. (1946). Predacious fungi in Britain. *Trans. Brit. mycol. Soc.* **29**, 170.

DUDDINGTON, C. L. (1949). A new predacious species of *Trichothecium*. *Trans. Brit. mycol. Soc.* **32**, 284.

DUDDINGTON, C. L. (1950*a*). Further records of British predacious fungi. *Trans. Brit. mycol. Soc.* **33**, 209.

DUDDINGTON, C. L. (1950*b*). Predacious fungi. *J. Quekett micr. Cl.*, Ser. 4, **3**, 67.

DUDDINGTON, C. L. (1951*a*). Further records of British predacious fungi. II. *Trans. Brit. mycol. Soc.* **34**, 194.

DUDDINGTON, C. L. (1951*b*). The ecology of predacious fungi. I. Preliminary survey. *Trans. Brit. mycol. Soc.* **34**, 322.

DUDDINGTON, C. L. (1951*c*). *Dactylella lobata*, predacious on nematodes. *Trans. Brit. mycol. Soc.* **34**, 489.

DUDDINGTON, C. L. (1951*d*). Two new predacious Hyphomycetes. *Trans. Brit. mycol. Soc.* **34**, 598.

DUDDINGTON, C. L. (1953). A new species of *Stylopage* capturing amoebae in dung. *Ann. Bot., Lond.*, **17**, 127.

DUDDINGTON, C. L. (1954). Nematode-destroying fungi in agricultural soils. *Nature, Lond.*, **173**, 500.

DUDDINGTON, C. L. (1955*a*). Some observations on the Zoopagaceae. *J. Quekett micr. Cl.* ser. 4, **4**, 160.

DUDDINGTON, C. L. (1955*b*). Notes on the technique of handling predacious fungi. *Trans. Brit. mycol. Soc.* **38**, 97.

DUDDINGTON, C. L. (1955*c*). A new species of *Stylopage* capturing nematodes. *Mycologia*, **47**, 245.

DUDDINGTON, C. L. (1955*d*). Fungi that attack microscopic animals. *Bot. Rev.* **21**, 377.

DUDDINGTON, C. L. (1956). The predacious fungi: Zoopagales and Moniliales. *Biol. Rev.* **31**, 152.

DUDDINGTON, C. L. (1957). *The Friendly Fungi*. London: Faber and Faber.

FRESENIUS, G. (1852). *Beiträge zur Mykologie*, Heft 1–2.

GIKLHORN, J. (1922). Studien an *Zoophagus insidians* Som., einen Tierefangenden Pilz. *Glasn. Soc. Sci. Nat. Croate*, **34**, 198.

GOODEY, J. B. (1951). A new species of hyphomycete attacking the stem eelworm *Ditylenchus dipsaci*. *Trans. Brit. mycol. Soc.* **34**, 270.

GROVE, W. B. (1886). New or noteworthy fungi. Part 2. *J. Bot., Lond.*, **24**, 197.

INGOLD, C. T. (1942). Aquatic Hyphomycetes of decaying alder leaves. *Trans. Brit. mycol. Soc.* **25**, 339.

INGOLD, C. T. (1943*a*). Further observations on aquatic Hyphomycetes of decaying leaves. *Trans. Brit. mycol. Soc.* **26**, 104.

INGOLD, C. T. (1943*b*). *Tricelophorus monosporus* n.gen., n.sp., an aquatic hyphomycete. *Trans. Brit. mycol. Soc.* **26**, 148.

INGOLD, C. T. (1944). Some new aquatic Hyphomycetes. *Trans. Brit. mycol. Soc.* **27**, 35.

INGOLD, C. T. (1952). *Actinospora megalospora* n.sp., an aquatic hyphomycete. *Trans. Brit. mycol. Soc.* **35**, 66.

INGOLD, C. T. (1956). Stream spora in Nigeria. *Trans. Brit. mycol. Soc.* **39**, 108.

JUNIPER, A. J. (1953). Some predacious fungi occurring in dung. *Trans. Brit. mycol. Soc.* **36**, 356.

JUNIPER, A. J. (1954*a*). Some predacious fungi occurring in dung. II. *Trans. Brit. mycol. Soc.* **37**, 171.

JUNIPER, A. J. (1954*b*). *Dactylaria pyriformis* sp.nov. *Trans. Brit. mycol. Soc.* **37**, 437.

KARLING, J. S. (1936). A new predacious fungus. *Mycologia*, **28**, 307.

KARLING, J. S. (1938). *Harposporium anguillulae*. *Mycologia*, **30**, 512.

KARLING, J. S. (1942). *Simple Holocarpic Biflagellate Phycomycetes*. New York: published by the author.

KARLING, J. S. (1944). New lagenidiaceous parasites of rotifers from Brazil. *Lloydia*, **7**, 328.

LINFORD, M. B. (1937). Stimulated activity of natural enemies of nematodes. *Science*, **85**, 123.

LINFORD, M. B. & YAPP, F. (1939). Root-knot nematode injury restricted by a fungus. *Phytopathology*, **29**, 596.

LINFORD, M. B., YAPP, F. & OLIVEIRA, J. M. (1938). Reduction of soil populations of root-knot nematode during decomposition of organic matter. *Soil Sci.* **45**, 127.

LOHDE, G. (1874). Einige neue parasitische Pilze. *Tageblatt der 47. Versammlung deutscher Naturforscher und Aerzte in Breslau*, pp. 203.

MAIRE, R. (1915). Remarques sur le *Protascus subuliformis* à propos de la communication de M. E. Maupas. *Bull. Soc. Hist. nat. Afr. N.* **7**, 50.

MIRANDE, R. (1920). *Zoophagus insidians* Sommerstorff, capteur de rotifers vivants. *Bull. Soc. mycol. Fr.* **36**, 47.

OVERGAARD (NIELSEN), C. (1948). Studies in the soil Microfauna. *Publications de la Société des Sciences et des Lettres d'Aarhus*, **2**, 1.

PEACH, M. (1948). An aquatic predacious fungus, *Acaulopage dichotoma*, in Britain. *Nature, Lond.*, **162**, 148.

PEACH, M. (1950). Aquatic predacious fungi. *Trans. Brit. mycol. Soc.* **33**, 148.

PEACH, M. (1952). Aquatic predacious fungi. II. *Trans. Brit. mycol. Soc.* **35**, 19.

PEACH, M. (1954). Aquatic predacious fungi. III. *Trans. Brit. mycol. Soc.* **37**, 240.

PEACH, M. & JUNIPER, A. J. (1955). *Stylopage araea* Drechsler var. *magna* var.nov. *Trans. Brit. mycol. Soc.* **38**, 431.

PROWSE, G. A. (1954). *Sommerstorffia spinosa* and *Zoophagus insidians* predacious on rotifers, and *Rozellopsis inflata* the endoparasite of *Zoophagus*. *Trans. Brit. mycol. Soc.* **37**, 134.

SADEBECK, R. E. B. (1887). Ueber *Pythium anguillulae aceti* nov.sp. *Bot. Zbl.* **29**, 318.

SHEPHERD, A. M. (1955*a*). Formation of the infection bulb in *Arthrobotrys oligospora* Fresenius. *Nature, Lond.*, **175**, 475.

SHEPHERD, A. M. (1955*b*). *Harposporium crassum*, sp.nov. *Trans. Brit. mycol. Soc.* **38**, 47.

SOMMERSTORFF, H. (1911). Ein tierefangender Pilz (*Zoophagus insidians*, nov.gen., nov.sp.). *Öst. bot. Z.* **61**, 361.

SPARROW, F. K. (1929). A note on the occurrence of two rotifer-capturing Phycomycetes. *Mycologia*, **21**, 90.

SPARROW, F. K. (1932). Observations on the aquatic fungi of Cold Spring Harbor. *Mycologia*, **24**, 268.

SPARROW, F. K. (1933). Inoperculate chytridiaceous organisms collected in the vicinity of Ithaca, N.Y., with notes on other aquatic fungi. *Mycologia*, **25**, 513.

SPARROW, F. K. (1936). A contribution to our knowledge of the aquatic Phycomycetes of Great Britain. *J. Linn. Soc. (Bot.)*, **50**, 417.

SPARROW, F. K. (1943). *Aquatic Phycomycetes.* Michigan: University of Michigan Press.

VALKANOV, A. (1932). Nachtrag zu meiner Arbeit über rotatorienbefallende Pilze. *Arch. Protistenk.* **78**, 485.

ZOPF, W. (1884). Zur Kenntnis der Phycomyceten. I. Zur Morphologie und Biologie des Ancylisteen und Chytridiaceen. *Nova Acta Leop. Carol.* **47**, 143.

ZOPF, W. (1888). Zur Kenntnis der Infections-Krankheiten niederer Thiere und Pflanzen. *Nova Acta Leop. Carol.* **52**, 314.

ECOLOGICAL FACTORS AND THE
SURVIVAL OF FUNGI

LILIAN E. HAWKER

Department of Botany, University of Bristol

The fungal thallus or vegetative body, known as the mycelium, usually consists of thin-walled, often colourless, filaments or hyphae, which may be aseptate, in the Phycomycetes, or septate, in the Higher Fungi. Both types of filament are normally vacuolate except at the growing points. Such a system presents a relatively large surface area to the influence of external factors. While this is a distinct advantage in permitting the rapid assimilation of food under favourable conditions, it must increase the liability to injury by adverse factors of all kinds. The survival of such a structure as the mycelium depends upon the maintenance of a high degree of humidity in the atmosphere or of water content of the substrate, of a favourable temperature and a continuous supply of suitable food at a favourable pH. Excess light may injure delicate or colourless hyphae. Mechanical damage is a further hazard, particularly with aseptate hyphae. Very few natural habitats provide favourable conditions for more than a short period. Even such an unusually constant environment as that of a fresh-water lake or the sea varies in available food supply and, to a certain extent, in temperature and illumination, while smaller volumes of water frequently dry up or are liable to flooding. It is seldom, therefore, that the mycelium is long-lived under natural conditions, since it has little power of resistance to adverse changes in the environment. When a filamentous fungus is grown under conditions of limited food supply, as in a culture medium in a Petri dish, the older parts of the hyphae regularly become empty and dead and are sealed off by the cross-walls while their contents are translocated to the growing hyphal tips by streaming of the cytoplasm. Thus the individual cells normally die as a result of local exhaustion of food supply, while the younger parts of the hyphae continue to extend outwards over unused parts of the substrate. Even this continuous flow of cell contents into the surviving younger parts of the mycelium is insufficient to ensure the survival of the colony once the food supply is completely exhausted or when other factors, such as temperature, availability of water or competition of other organisms become limiting. However, the mycelium of certain fungi is, to some extent, able to resist adverse circumstances by alteration of the nature of the vegetative cells or of some of them, or by very rapid linear growth. More frequently survival of temporary unfavourable conditions is achieved by the formation of resistant structures of various types. Rapid migration to new habitats, by efficient spore dispersal or other means, enables the species to escape from permanent adverse changes in the original habitat. Other species survive by tolerance of suboptimal conditions and the ability to grow in border-line habitats.

Different parts of the life cycle of fungi usually need different sets of conditions. Therefore for survival of the fungus it is necessary that the environment should vary in a particular way at a particular time to allow for the completion of the life cycle.

Fungi can seldom be identified with certainty in the vegetative condition. The complete study of the fungus flora of a particular habitat is thus both difficult and laborious and often impossible. The many lists of fungi found in different habitats seldom or never give a complete picture of the population. Even lists of the larger and more conspicuous fungi are incomplete, since the fruit bodies of these fungi may not be produced every year, even though the mycelium is alive in the soil. Such knowledge as we possess of the factors inducing the formation of fruit bodies of the larger fungi in the natural habitat are based on observations over a long period rather than on experiment (Wilkins & Patrick, 1940; Wilkins & Harris, 1946; Grainger, 1946; Hawker, 1954). Attempts at a more exact estimation of the nature and quantity of the fungus flora of a natural habitat, such as woodland soil, by the plate method also fail to give a complete picture, since many fungi known to be present fail to grow on the isolation plates or are swamped by more rapidly growing species. Nevertheless, studies of this type, such as those of Warcup (1951 a, b), provide valuable information even though this is incomplete.

Recently a number of studies have been made of more restricted habitats and have yielded information of particular ecological groups of fungi, such as those growing on submerged leaves and stems in fresh water (Ingold, 1942, 1954a, 1955; Glen-Bott, 1955), on submerged wood in the sea (Wilson, 1954) or epiphytically on various living leaves (Last, 1955). Similarly, a very real contribution to our knowledge of fungal ecology has been made by studies of a particular group of fungi in a restricted habitat, such as Canter's studies on the chytrids parasitizing the phytoplankton of British lakes (Canter, 1950, 1951, 1954; Canter & Lund, 1948, 1953), the work of Drechsler (1941) in America and of Duddington (1955) in England, about which we have heard in an earlier paper in this Symposium, on the fungi predacious on small soil animals, or Webster's (1951, 1952, 1955) study of the Ascomycetes to be found on grass haulms.

The study of plant diseases often includes a study of the ecology of particular fungal species, as with Garrett's (1936–48) comprehensive study of *Ophiobolus graminis*. Such studies have contributed much to our knowledge of the relation between ecological factors and the survival of fungi under natural conditions. Plant pathologists, too, have been the first to recognize the importance of what may be termed the 'microclimate', that is, the climate of small isolated spaces, such as those sheltered from wind or rain by large or closely growing leaves.

Pure-culture experiments on the effects of environmental factors on the growth of particular species (summarized by Lilly & Barnett, 1951; Hawker, 1950, 1956) have told us much. Such a method of attack is essential to the elucidation of the influence of environment on growth and survival of fungi in the natural state and is particularly valuable when taken in conjunction with the data of field observations. The work of Melin (1948) and his school on the mycorrhizal and litter fungi of Swedish forests is a notable example of such an approach.

Field observations over a reasonably long period combined with pure-culture studies can give much information, but for the proper understanding of the effects of environmental changes on growth and survival of fungi it is essential that methods should be worked out for the experimental analysis of the same effects in the field. Few such attempts have so far been made.

SURVIVAL OF THE INDIVIDUAL

In order to survive the fungus must be equipped to escape or to endure temporarily adverse conditions, such as shortage of food, drought, extremes of temperature and the competition of other organisms

Survival through alteration of the nature of vegetative cells

It has long been known that vegetative cells of certain fungi may alter in shape, wall structure and cell contents as a result of exposure to abnormal conditions. Thus Bail (1857) and Pasteur (1876) showed that if fungi, such as species of *Mucor* or *Aspergillus*, were grown in submerged culture under conditions of poor aeration, a yeast-like habit developed with changes in the shape of the individual cells. Mycelial cells of many fungi become swollen and distorted when grown under acid conditions, as with *Sordaria fimicola* (Lilly & Barnett, 1951).

A morphological change from elongated cylindrical cells to globose swollen yeast-like cells (oidia) is seen when some fungi, such as species of *Mucor*, *Penicillium* or *Endomyces*, are grown in a concentrated sugar solution. Modified cells of this type present a reduced area of surface per unit of volume to the surrounding medium, and this in itself may reduce the harmful effect of unfavourable solutions. The cell contents usually become denser and the vacuoles may disappear, thus reducing the harmful effects of differences in osmotic pressure between cell sap and a concentrated external solution.

In response to unfavourable conditions some fungi show modification of a proportion of the cells of the mycelium to give thick-walled resting cells with dense, usually oily, contents—the 'dauerzellen' of the yeasts or the chlamydospores of such filamentous fungi as *Mucor racemosus* or *Fusarium* spp., etc. Little is known of the exact conditions leading to the formation of these forms (Hawker, 1956), but it is generally thought that they develop in response to various adverse conditions, and at least one example (Venkat Ram, 1952) is reported of the formation of such chlamydospores in a species of *Fusarium* in response to the presence of a bacterium producing an antibiotic substance.

Survival of mycelial cells is seen in the dormant mycelium of certain plant pathogens at particular stages of the host life cycle, as with that of the typical loose smuts of cereals which overwinter in infected grain. Here the mycelium escapes the adverse effects of winter conditions and is sheltered within the host.

The production of special resting bodies

The most frequent method by which the individual, or part of it, survives temporary adverse conditions is by the production of special resistant bodies protected by a thick wall. The simplest types of these are the mycelial chlamydospores already referred to, but spores, fruiting bodies, and aggregates of hyphae such as sclerotia and rhizomorphs, all play a part in the survival of various fungi.

Sclerotia and rhizomorphs

While individual hyphae are seldom able to survive adverse conditions, aggregates of hyphae may do so more readily. The ability of many plant parasites to produce sclerotia on the surface of the host or in the soil is correlated with their ability to survive. The factors influencing the survival of sclerotia of the cotton root-rot fungus (*Phymatotrichum omnivorum*) have been investigated in detail (King, Loomis, & Hope,

1931; King & Eaton, 1934; Taubenhaus & Ezekiel, 1936; Ezekiel 1945). Sclerotia of different species are formed in various ways (Townsend & Willetts, 1954) and differ in details of construction, but nearly all of them are surrounded by a layer of thick-walled, usually pigmented, closely interwoven hyphae forming a pseudosclerenchyma. The central hyphae are usually more like the ordinary mycelial ones in general morphology but often contain denser cytoplasm with reserve foods, commonly glycogen or oily substances. The formation of sclerotia on the external parts of the host plant, as with the sclerotia of *Rhizoctonia solani* on potato tubers, those of *Sclerotinia gladioli* on gladiolus haulms or of *Botrytis* spp. on stems and bulbs of various host plants, suggests response to increasingly dry conditions as the host plant dies or becomes dormant. Many sclerotia, however, occur inside the host, as with *Sclerotinia tuberosa* in the rhizomes of *Anemone nemorosa* or *Sclerotinia curreyana* in the haulms of *Juncus communis*, or partially embedded in the host tissue, as with the sclerotia of the ergot (*Claviceps purpureum*) which replaces the grain of rye and other grasses. Here the sclerotia are not exposed to excess desiccation, and Garrett (1956) points out that conditions of extreme desiccation are seldom found in the soil where sclerotia of many fungi develop. Nevertheless, the superior power of survival in air-dried soil of the sclerotium-producing damping-off fungus *Rhizoctonia solani* compared with the non-sclerotial *Pythium* spp. has been attributed to the ability of the sclerotia to withstand desiccation (Deshpande, 1940). Garrett (1956), however, is inclined to believe that the primary function of sclerotia is the increased 'inoculum potential' represented by such an aggregate of hyphae containing stored food substances. This is supported by the fact that many sclerotia later bear the fruiting bodies of the fungus (e.g. *Claviceps purpureum*, *Sclerotinia* spp.) for the formation of which a reserve of food is essential. The sclerotia of the cotton root-rot fungus, *Phymatotrichum omnivorum*, constitute a reservoir of semi-dormant infectious material in the soil where a diseased cotton crop has been grown. Control measures have been designed to free the soil from infection by inducing the germination of the resistant sclerotia to produce the more vulnerable mycelium (Mitchell, Hooton & Clark, 1941; Rogers, 1942).

Garrett (1956) considers that sclerotia and rhizomorphs are homologous structures and that the protection afforded to each by thick-walled outer layers does not imply that their primary function is survival of desiccation, but is merely supplementary to their function as reserves of food with sclerotia, or as pathways for translocation of foodstuff from an established to a young mycelium with rhizomorphs. Nevertheless, both structures may survive a degree of drying too severe for the vegetative absorbing hyphae and may give rise to a fresh crop of the latter on the return of wetter conditions. While Garrett is undoubtedly correct in stressing the importance of these organs as reserves of food, they may perhaps be regarded as an example of economy of effort in their ability to aid survival, not only by the provision of such food reserves but also through their resistance to drought.

Resistant spores

Fungi produce a variety of types of spore. The asexual spores, zoo-spores or non-motile sporangiospores in the Lower Fungi, conidia of many Higher Fungi or uredospores of the Rusts, are primarily organs of dispersal and serve to spread the fungus rapidly over a suitable substrate when other environmental conditions are favourable. Their ability to survive unfavourable conditions is limited, but they are often rather better equipped for such survival than is the mycelium. Even the naked zoospores of the water moulds are able to encyst and rapidly develop a protective, often thick, wall under certain conditions. The conidia of the Higher Fungi usually have denser cytoplasmic contents than have the hyphae, and vacuoles are usually absent. This confers a degree of resistance to desiccation and to the effects of high concentrations of food substances. Pigmentation of many conidia is also denser than that of the parent hyphae and confers an increased power of resistance to intense light. The uredospores of most rusts not only possess orange, brown or red pigments which confer resistance to ultra-violet light of the upper atmosphere, but are often relatively thick-walled and thus also resistant to desiccation to some extent. It is this combination of pigmentation and wall thickness that permits these spores to travel long distances in the upper air without loss of viability and thus enables the cereal rusts, and probably also other less economically important rusts, to spread in the direction of the prevailing winds over large areas of country. Not even the uredospores of the rusts, however, can be described as resting spores, since they remain viable for a relatively short time during which they germinate immediately on the occurrence of favourable conditions. They are unable to survive the extreme cold and long winters of the wheat belt of the Northern Hemisphere. True resting spores are thick-walled and contain dense, often oily, cytoplasm. They are often incapable of germination when first formed and must undergo a period of 'after-ripening' before germination can occur under even the most favourable conditions. An example is the oospore of *Phytophthora cactorum* (Blackwell, 1943). Among the Phycomycetes, resting spores are generally the immediate result of a sexual process, as with the oospores of the Oomycetes or the zygospores of the Zygomycetes. In the Higher Fungi the sexual process, which is often reduced to a pairing and subsequent fusion of nuclei, results in the formation of the characteristic ascospores or basidiospores. These may be resistant in some species. The ascospores of *Byssochlamys fulva* are unusually resistant to heat (Olliver & Smith, 1933) and at least some of them can survive temperatures normally used in fruit canning, so that this fungus constituted a serious problem in the canning industry until it was found that only a small further increase in temperature was sufficient to destroy even the most resistant individual spores (Hull, 1939). Warcup (1951*b*) uses partial sterilization of the soil by steam as a selective method for isolating certain Ascomycetes, such as *Aspergillus fischeri*, *Sordaria fimicola*, *Penicillium luteum* and *P. baarnense*, resistant ascospores of which survive the steam treatment. The spores of the coprophilous Ascomycetes, and of coprophilous fungi in general, are usually highly resistant to the relatively high temperatures and the enzymic effect of the intestinal juices encountered during passage through the animal gut. They are often purple or black in colour, have dense contents and thick, often sculptured walls and are, in some species, incapable of germination under experimental conditions until after treatment with acids, digestive enzymes or relatively high temperatures. The ascospores of the truffles and of the ecologically similar *Elaphomyces*, which are thick-walled and deeply sculptured, are so excessively resistant to external changes that, like the zygospores of the superficially similar *Endogone*, they have never been germinated in artificial culture (Hawker, 1954, 1955; Godfrey, 1957). Basidiospores are seldom particularly resistant, with the exception of those of the hypogeous Gasteromycetes, or false truffles, which occupy a similar ecological niche to that of *Endogone*, *Elaphomyces* and the true truffles. These often have thick sculptured walls and again have not so far been induced to germinate in artificial culture. The selective ecological factors which have induced the development of such extremely resistant spores have apparently also greatly reduced the usefulness of these as a means of spread and dispersal of these fungi. Many members of the rusts and smuts produce resting spores (teleutospores and smut or brand spores respectively) prior to nuclear fusion which takes place in the young spores before maturity. With a few exceptions these do not germinate immediately. Many of them, as those of the cereal rusts, are highly resistant to cold.

Formation of spores inside protective fruit bodies

The spores of most of the Higher Fungi are not particularly resistant but are protected from adverse conditions by being enclosed in a protective fruit body, which may be thick-walled and is often closed until maturity. Such a fruit body may itself be regarded as an efficient resistant body and, in many examples, as a resting body. A good example of this is the cleistocarp of the powdery mildews (Erysiphaceae) which is formed in summer or autumn and seldom sheds its ascospores until spring. During the resting period the peridium is impermeable to water, and it is through the rapid intake of water in spring and the consequent swelling of the contents of the fruit body that the peridium cracks and allows the discharge of the ascospores. The fruit bodies of many other plant parasites (e.g. the perithecia of the apple and pear scab fungi, *Venturia inaequalis* and *V. pyrina*, and the apothecia of *Lophodermium* spp. on leaves of conifers or of the tar-spot fungus, *Rhytisma acerinum* on sycamore) are formed in the leaves of the host in summer and overwinter in the dead leaves, remaining dormant until spring when they dehisce to allow the discharge of the ascospores. These spores have been protected by the walls of the fruit bodies during the winter. Even such soft fleshy fruit bodies as those of most mushrooms and toadstools afford some protection from desiccation to the developing basidiospores. In the hemiangiocarpic forms this protection continues until the spores are reaching maturity. The completely angiocarpic Gasteromycetes give even more protection so that the spores are not exposed until they are completely mature. Friedrich (1936) observed that certain Agarics produced fruit bodies even in an exceptionally dry year and suggested (1940) that hairs, scales or mucilage on the surface of the pileus might reduce water loss from transpiration. Many of the fruit bodies of the Agarics and other larger fungi are xeromorphic and are able to recover from a considerable amount of drying. Fruit bodies of *Daldinia concentrica* have been shown to continue active discharge of spores for a long period after being severed from the mycelium and being subjected to the dry air of the laboratory (Ingold, 1946). Isolated sporophores of *Fomes fomentarius* or *Ganoderma applanatum* cease to shed their spores after a few days (Ingold, 1954b) but may continue to shed them for long periods under dry conditions when still attached to the tree or to a large branch (Ingold, 1954b; Buchwald, 1938). Such leathery Agarics as species of *Marasmius* or *Schizophyllum commune* are well known to have the power of recovery from seemingly complete desiccation. The actual spores of these species, however, may not be more resistant to desiccation than are those of fleshy species, but the fruit body survives as a whole. It is not known whether the spores already formed within such a resistant fruit body survive or whether new ones are produced when the fruit body is rewetted.

SURVIVAL OF THE SPECIES

The survival of the species, as opposed to that of the individual, has been achieved not only by the formation of such resistant bodies as those described above, which serve to tide the individual over a limited period of unsuitable conditions, but also by escape from a habitat which has become permanently unsuitable and by the development of strains capable of themselves modifying the environment in the direction of greater suitability.

Survival through escape from an unsuitable habitat

When a habitat has become permanently unsuitable for the growth of a particular species, through exhaustion of food supply, occupation by a more successful species or some other change, it is obvious that the formation of passive resistant structures will only aid survival for a short time and will not solve the problem unless the habitat changes again. Survival can only be assured by migration to a new habitat.

Rapid growth of mycelium

The simplest method of achieving such migration is by rapid linear growth of the mycelium. Many highly successful species, notably species of *Mucor* and allied genera, owe their success to such a high growth rate. *Mucor* is limited in its ability to break down complex food substances and to utilize various nitrogenous compounds. It is unable to break down lignin or cellulose, although it readily utilizes the products of their hydrolysis by other organisms. It is dependent on ammonium salts or organic nitrogen for its source of nitrogen and is unable to use nitrate nitrogen. In spite of these disadvantages it maintains its position as a common soil saprophyte by its ability to grow rapidly after exhaustion of local supplies of food and thus to reach new supplies made available by the decomposition of complex plant remains by other members of the soil microflora. Many other soil saprophytes, such as species of *Sordaria*, *Chaetomium* and such specialized ones as *Pyronema confluens*, which characteristically colonizes burnt ground, together with facultative parasites of the *Pythium* type also possess this advantage of rapid mycelial growth.

Rapid formation and efficient dispersal of spores

Some species of soil fungi which are at least as successful as *Mucor* as soil saprophytes have a relatively slow rate of growth, e.g. species of *Aspergillus* and *Penicillium*. This is compensated by the rapid formation of very large numbers of spores. This in itself would not overcome the disadvantage of a permanent adverse change in the environment were it not for the ease with which these spores are dispersed so that they readily reach the surrounding areas, with the chance that some at least may fall on a suitable substrate where other conditions are also favourable to germination and the establishment of the fungus.

Escape from an unfavourable environment by the formation and dispersal of spores is a more efficient method than the most rapid mycelial growth. Thus we find that fungi inhabiting an ecological niche, which by its nature is favourable to them for only limited periods, are usually those with an efficient mechanism of spore discharge and dispersal. A striking example of this is the coprophilous fungus flora. Dung of various animals shows a succession of characteristic fungi. First the newly shed dung becomes covered with the coarse mycelium of species of *Mucor* and related forms, often including the parasitic *Chaetocladium* and *Piptocephalis*. Some of these may actually have been shed with the dung, others are airborne colonizers. They all produce large numbers of light airborne spores which are formed rapidly with relatively low expenditure of material and which disperse the fungus widely before the rapidly growing but ephemeral mycelium dies down. Next there is usually a crop of true coprophilous fungi, beginning with the mucoraceous *Pilobolus* followed by various members of the Sordariaceae and such Discomycetes as species of *Ascobolus*, *Humaria* and *Lachnea*. These are all phototropic at some stage of their development and possess explosive mechanisms which discharge the spores violently. The organs which are sensitive to direction of light vary in the different groups (the sporangiophore with *Pilobolus*, the necks of the perithecia with the species of *Sordaria* and the tips of the asci with the Discomycetes), but the net result is the same with all of them, namely, that the spores are shot away from the stale and now unsuitable dung balls in the direction of the greatest light intensity, which is also that most likely to be free of obstruction. Certain Agarics, notably species of *Coprinus*, are usually the last species to produce their fruit bodies on the old dung. Buller (1924) gives a detailed account of the development of these and of the environmental conditions that control their development and the dispersal of their spores. Both

Buller and Ingold (1953) have shown the perfect correlation between environment and the mechanism of spore dispersal among these coprophilous forms. The spores alight on the surrounding grass where they are eaten by herbivorous animals, which in their wanderings provide further opportunities for the dispersal of the fungi. If the species of animal is suitable the spores either germinate during passage through the gut or are shed with the dung and germinate later. Here we have a perfect example of a balanced reaction to a specialized habitat, induced by and controlled by the factors making up that habitat. Efficient dispersal is essential to survival on such an ephemeral substrate. The biological implications of spore dispersal have recently been considered in detail by Ingold (1953) and it is unnecessary to consider them further here.

The science of aerobiology is of comparatively recent development both here and in America, but it has already transformed our ideas on the subject of the microflora of the air. Gregory (1945) has shown that 'eddy diffusion', that is, quite small and intermittent movements of air, is sufficient to maintain such light objects as fungal spores in an airborne condition for long periods. The airborne spore is thus one solution to the problem of survival of the species by dispersal of spores. The well-known story of the northward migration of the black stem rust of wheat, *Puccinia graminis*, in North America by wind-blown clouds of uredospores need not be repeated in detail here, but is a striking example of wind dispersal. Nevertheless, wind dispersal is wasteful, since only a small proportion of such wind-borne spores alight on a suitable substrate under conditions permitting germination and the establishment of a mycelium. While the amount of food material, including vitamins and other complex substances, wasted in a single unsuccessful spore is negligible, the total lost when a large number of spores fail to become established is considerable. A few fungi are dispersed by insects, e.g. the stinkhorn (*Phallus impudicus*) and related forms, the Dutch elm disease fungus (*Ceratostomella ulmi*), ergot of rye and other grasses (*Claviceps purpurea*), and some members of the Fungi Imperfecti and Ascomycetes which produce slimy spores. This is likely to be a more efficient mechanism of dispersal than wind dispersal. It is of interest that most of the species which have evolved a method of dispersal by insects are of an advanced type.

Dispersal of spores of aquatic fungi is closely correlated with the environment. The primitive forms, which have almost certainly had no terrestrial phase in their evolutionary history, produce motile zoospores by which they are dispersed, but a large and heterogeneous group of marine and fresh-water Higher Fungi (Ascomycetes and Hyphomycetes), which have probably returned to an aquatic mode of life after having been terrestrial at some stage in their evolution, have lost and not regained the ability to produce zoospores. These fungi are nearly all characterized by the possession of filamentous spores or of spores with branched, curved or mucilaginous appendages, so that they readily become attached to objects in the water. It is obvious that spores of this type would have a survival value in such a habitat. There is no evidence that the production of such spores is actually induced by a submerged existence. In fact spores of *Ramularia vallisambrosae*, the cause of white mould of narcissus leaves, are actually shorter and broader when formed under conditions of high humidity than in drier conditions (Gregory, 1939).

Advantage of rapid germination

The rapid production of spores and the development of efficient dispersal methods will not ensure survival unless the spores are able to germinate rapidly and to produce a colony when they reach a suitable new habitat. Park (1955) showed that fungal spores decompose rapidly when placed on the surface of soil but that this decomposition is reduced if natural plant materials are present in the soil. Some fungi then successfully colonize the soil and survive competition from other soil oganisms. Thus rapid germination is another character of successful saprophytic species, such as *Mucor, Penicillium, Aspergillus*, and many successful plant parasites, such as *Fusarium* or *Botrytis*. Rapid germination of rust uredospores is said to allow the entry of the parasite into the host before the film of dew dries on the leaves. Rapid penetration of the host is obviously of survival value, for once established inside the plant the fungus is relatively insulated from the effects of external conditions.

Ability to colonize unusual or border-line habitats

Thus rapid growth, profuse sporulation, efficient dispersal of spores or of other propagating units, and the ability to colonize new substrates rapidly, permit a fungus to exploit favourable habitats and to survive by migration when conditions are no longer favourable. The formation of resting spores, or other resistant structures, enables a fungus to survive temporary adverse conditions without migration. In some instances the resistant structures are themselves dispersed, thus combining the advantages of both methods of survival.

Many fungi, however, possess few if any of these advantages and yet manage to survive by their ability to colonize border-line habitats, unsuitable for the growth of the majority of micro-organisms, or by their ability to modify the environment so as to make it unsuitable for the growth of other species, as by the production of antibiotic substances, or by changes in the acidity of the substrate.

Bisby, Timonin & James (1935) claimed that fungi taken from deeper layers of Manitoba soils were more capable of behaving as facultative anaerobes than were those isolated from the surface layers. Burges & Fenton (1953) grouped the fungi isolated by them from East Anglian soils in three groups: (1) those abundant in the surface layers or litter but only occasionally found at a greater depth than 5 cm., (2) those abundant in the lower layers but absent or uncommon in the surface layers and (3) a small group present throughout the soil profile. They examined representative species for tolerance of carbon dioxide concentration and found that those in group (2) were the most and those in group (1) the least resistant. They concluded that groups (2) and (3) were able to grow at greater depths than group (1) through tolerance of carbon dioxide concentration rather than through ability to grow in the absence of oxygen. This is an example of ability to colonize a habitat unfavourable to most fungi which, no doubt, allows group (2) to escape from competition from group (1) species. It must be assumed that the wider range of group (3) is due to tolerance of both competition and excess carbon dioxide.

The recolonization of soil after sterilization by various methods also illustrates the advantage to particular species of the initial start gained by tolerance of fungicidal residues. Thus when soil is sterilized by the application of formalin (Warcup, 1951c; Evans, 1955) the dominant recolonizing fungus is *Trichoderma viride*. This fungus also recolonizes soil sterilized by a low dosage of carbon disulphide, but with higher dosages the soil is recolonized by slower growing but more resistant species, such as *Penicillium luteum* and *Aspergillus fischeri* (Warcup, 1951c). Closely packed steam-sterilized soil, in which there are no fungicidal residues, is usually recolonized by fast-growing Phycomycetes (Evans, 1955), although *Trichoderma* is again dominant with more loosely packed steam-sterilized soil. Warcup also (1951d) suggests that certain Ascomycetes survive more readily than some other fungi in the mycelial zones of fairy rings caused by certain Basidiomycetes because they are relatively resistant to antibiotic substances produced by the basidiomycetous mycelium. Thus we have here several examples of survival through ability to inhabit border-line habitats.

Attempts to explain specificity of parasites which are often able to grow only on one species or even one variety of host plant, have revealed that conditions of pH, food supply, etc., within the host seldom coincide with those optimal for the particular fungus concerned (Brown, 1955). The latter is able to survive in the host by its tolerance of conditions which are near the limit of its range but which at the same time exclude competitors. In fact conditions optimal for fungi are surprisingly uniform, and it is endurance of, or toleration of, suboptimal or even extreme conditions that determine the ability of a particular species to colonize a border-line habitat. Fungi parasitizing acid fruits, for example, are tolerant of acidity, and their optimum growth may occur at a slightly more acid reaction than is optimal for most fungi, but they do not usually grow best at the low pH of the fruit juices. Certain animal pathogens show dimorphism in that they produce mycelial growth on culture media but only yeast-like cells in the host, indicating that the conditions within the host are not the most suitable for the growth of such fungi. Again, while many species of *Penicillium* and *Aspergillus* or of yeasts or yeast-like fungi are able to grow on jam or other sugary substrates, they do so through their high sugar tolerance and not because such conditions are optimal for them. Growth of species of *Chaetomium* and *Sordaria* in manure or compost heaps depends upon their ability to grow at high temperatures, but the optimal temperature for their growth may be not much higher than that for other fungi.

The predacious fungi described by Duddington in an earlier contribution to this Symposium (p. 218) are a notable example of an ecological group which cannot compete saprophytically with other soil moulds but which are able to survive by the ability to attack and consume small soil animals, a habitat the exploitation of which is not possible to the majority of more vigorously growing soil fungi. Drechsler (1941) has described how, in a plate of medium inoculated with a small quantity of decayed leaf litter from the surface of a woodland soil, crops of common soil moulds grow and subsequently die down. By this time large numbers of nematodes are present and the typical predacious fungi develop. Until the initial food supply is exhausted these predacious fungi are not able to compete with the other soil fungi and they do not therefore appear during the initial period of maximum growth of the latter. During this period they survive, probably as spores; and are later able to develop through exploiting a source of food supply, the living nematodes, which is not available to the vigorous saprophytic moulds.

Similarly some fungi, such as species of *Blastocladia* (Emerson & Cantino, 1948) or *Helicodendron* (Glen-Bott, 1955), survive by their ability to grow on rotting submerged organic material under conditions of low oxygen content. The more actively growing fungus flora of leaves and other organic remains competes successfully with these partial anaerobes in aerated water but is inhibited by low oxygen content. The fact that *Helicodendron* produces spores only under aerobic conditions indicates that the almost completely anaerobic conditions of the normal habitat of this fungus are by no means optimal for it. Many such examples could be cited. Much could no doubt be learnt from the study of the 'subsistance level' at which the various members in the succession series on any changing habitat, such as the dung already mentioned, fallen branches or cut stumps of trees, compost heaps, etc., can exist. The slow-growing mycelium of the litter fungi (Melin, 1948), i.e. Basidiomycetes growing on leaf and other remains in woods, competes successfully with quick-growing sugar fungi (Garrett, 1956) through its ability to break down cellulose or lignin, but on a culture plate containing sugar such fungi are seldom isolated.

Ability to alter the environment in a direction unfavourable to other organisms

Many fungi are able to survive competition in habitats which are not originally border-line ones, not through superior vigour but through their power of producing antibiotic substances which check or prevent the development of competitors. This is exemplified by many soil Actinomycetes, which are not usually rapid growers but which are known to produce a variety of antibiotic substances which inhibit the growth of both fungi and bacteria. The effect of antibiotics on growth of fungi has already been dealt with in this Symposium by Brian (p. 168) and need not be further expanded here. There are other ways in which a fungus may modify an environment in a direction unsuitable for other organisms, such as alteration in acidity, alteration or utilization of food, etc. Little exact work has been done on this aspect.

Variability

Survival, either through the ability to tolerate extreme conditions or through the power of producing antibiotics, depends ultimately on the enzyme apparatus of the fungus. Thus the possession of unusual enzyme systems or the ability to produce adaptive enzymes in response to changes in the chemical nature of the substrate is of first importance to survival among active competitors. Obviously those fungi initially well equipped or those with a tendency to the production of mutations of physiological characters are much more likely to survive. Thus variability is itself a means of survival when the variants are selected by external conditions. Most of the lower fungi and many of the higher ones are in the haploid state during most of their life cycle, so that mutations, even if not more frequent, have a better chance of showing up than in a diploid organism. The frequency of such mutations is itself a means of the survival of a species.

SELECTIVE INFLUENCE OF THE ENVIRONMENT

The part played by the environment in determining the growth form of the individual, and the form and physiology of species of fungi, through selection of mutant strains cannot be over emphasized.

The same environmental and ecological factors which are resisted by resting bodies of various types actually induce the formation of these bodies in many instances. Thus many plant parasites which produce large quantities of asexual spores of low resistance to adverse conditions during the summer, cease to do so with the onset of winter and produce more resistant types of spore instead. This may be due to the fall in temperature or to changes in the composition of the host plant itself, but few or no exact data are available on this subject. A reduction in food supply is a well-known factor inducing spore production and particularly production of the sexual or perfect types of spore, which are often either themselves resistant or are produced in resistant fruit bodies, as already pointed out. The problems connected with the mechanism by which changes in environment induce the change leading from the vegetative to the reproductive phase are too complex to be considered within the space allotted to this article, and I have recently discussed them elsewhere (Hawker, 1956, 1957). While much is known of the effect of various factors on the formation of various types of resting body, the mechanism by which such factors act is largely unexplored. Both an acceleration of the rate of metabolism and an alteration in its pathway probably play a part. Thus the formation of perithecia of certain Pyrenomycetes results from any changes tending to increase the rate of respiration (Hawker, 1950). Conjugation in certain species of the Mucorales can be similarly increased and accelerated. Raper (1952) showed that the formation of antheridia and oogonia leading to the production of oospores in dioecious strains of certain water moulds is controlled by a series of specific sex hormones formed in orderly sequence, and that environmental factors acting on the production of these may influence the formation of sex organs and thus of the resistant oospores. Cantino (1951, 1952, 1953, 1954, 1956) in a series of studies showed that the formation of resting sporangia (which may best be

interpreted as resting gametangia) in certain members of the Blasto-
cladiales depends on the actual pathway of metabolism. If this is
altered, as by the presence or absence of bicarbonate in the medium,
changes in the enzyme systems are produced and morphogenesis is
influenced in the direction of either the formation of or the inhibition of
such resting bodies.

The process of natural selection has therefore in all probability worked
by favouring those fungi which, in response to adverse conditions of
a type commonly met with, produce structures capable of resisting
them.

It has been pointed out above that certain fungi growing in a discontinuous habitat are able to pass from an area exhausted of food to
another, as yet unexhausted, by means of rapid mycelial growth. Pure
culture studies show that the rate of linear growth of such a fungus is
greater on a poor medium than on a rich one. On water agar, fungi
such as *Pyronema confluens, Sordaria* sp., or *Mucor* fill a plate in a few
days but the hyphae are sparsely branched and widely spaced and are
adpressed to the surface of the medium, no conspicuous aerial tufts being
formed. This type of growth is usually termed 'starvation growth'. Often
as with *Sordaria* (*Melanospora*) *destruens* the growth varies strikingly with
the concentration of sugar in the medium (Hawker, 1950), but although
the total amount of growth, as measured by dry weight, is greatest
at relatively high sugar concentrations, the rate of spread across the
plate is greater at relatively low ones. Thus the value of the intrinsically
high rate of growth is enhanced by just those conditions of poor nutrition where a rapid linear advance is most advantageous. The growth of
some species of *Sordaria* and other fungi on an agar plate takes place in
successive waves. This can best be explained as the result of the depletion
of nutrients immediately in advance of the hyphae, leading to rapid
growth across such a depleted part of the plate. A reduction in rate of
linear growth with an increased production of aerial hyphae follows when
an undepleted area is reached. Such a response to local variations in food
supply obviously has survival value in a habitat, such as soil, where
suitable organic food is likely to be distributed unequally. Small pieces
of dead plant and animal material are rich sources of food for micro-
organisms, but their distribution in the soil is by no means uniform. The
ability to produce much-branched hyphae with little or no linear spread
on such local concentrations of suitable food, thus exploiting them to
the full, combined with the ability to produce long, unbranched, rapidly
growing hyphae bridging the gap between one source of food and another,
is of great value to the fungus and enables it to survive in soils where the

areas of food supply are scattered. The period of active feeding on a localized food area is one of consolidation during which energy is obtained to permit the growth of the fungus from the 'food base' (Garrett, 1956) out into the surrounding 'starvation' areas. When the food thus obtained is entirely exhausted, growth will obviously cease unless a new food area has been reached.

The moulding effect of the environment on fungi, through the selection of characters with survival value, can be well seen in the parasites of plants and particularly with such obligate parasites as the rusts or with the various forms of mycorrhizal fungi, but this aspect has already been dealt with by another contributor. The moulding effect is also seen in the numerous examples of parallel development among the members of an ecological group consisting of unrelated fungi. I have already mentioned one such group, namely, the coprophilous fungi, where Phycomycetes (*Pilobolus*), Pyrenomycetes (*Sordaria*) and Discomycetes (*Ascobolus*) show parallel development leading to orientation of the spore-bearing organs, through response to directional light, and an explosive discharge of the spores. Similarly, among hypogeous fungi (i.e. those forming fruit bodies beneath the surface of the soil) there is a superficial morphological resemblance among Phycomycetes (*Endogone*), Ascomycetes (Elaphomycetaceae and Tuberales) and Basidiomycetes (Hymenogastrales in the larger sense). All these produce spherical or irregularly globose fruit bodies containing masses of thick-walled spores which are thought to be dispersed through being eaten by animals. The methods by which these superficially similar fruit bodies develop, however, are widely different (Hawker, 1954) in the different groups. The similarity of form is almost certainly the result of the selection of mutants able to live in such a specialized habitat. Many similar examples of parallel development could be cited.

Thus the problem of the distribution and succession of fungi in the natural habitat, which is seldom constant for more than a brief interval, is also the problem of the survival of different individuals and different species under changing conditions. A knowledge of the methods by which fungi survive under adverse conditions is essential to the interpretation of the distribution of species in time and space. Pure-culture work has already provided much information of this type, but the application of this to experiments in the field should be the next step in the study of fungal ecology.

REFERENCES

BAIL, T. (1857). *Flora*, **40**, 417, 433. Reference in Foster, J. W. (1949). *Chemical Activities of Fungi*. New York.

BISBY, G. R., TIMONIN, M. I. & JAMES, N. (1935). Fungi isolated from soil profiles in Manitoba. *Canad. J. Res.* C, **13**, 47.

BLACKWELL, E. (1943). The life-history of *Phytophthora cactorum* (Leb. and Cohn) Schroet. *Trans. Brit. mycol. Soc.* **26**, 71.

BROWN, W. (1955). On the physiology of parasitism in plants. *Ann. appl. Biol.* **43**, 325.

BUCHWALD, N. F. (1938). Om Spareproduktionens Størvelse hos Tøndefsvampen. *Friesia*, **2**, 42.

BULLER, A. H. R. (1924). *Researches in Fungi*, vol. 3. London.

BURGES, A. & FENTON, E. (1953). The effect of carbon dioxide on the growth of certain soil fungi. *Trans. Brit. mycol. Soc.* **36**, 104.

CANTER, H. M. (1950). Fungal parasites of the phytoplankton. I. *Ann. Bot., Lond.*, N.S., **14**, 129.

CANTER, H. M. (1951). Fungal parasites of the phytoplankton. II. *Ann. Bot., Lond.*, N.S., **15**, 129.

CANTER, H. M. (1954). Fungal parasites of the phytoplankton. III. *Trans. Brit. mycol. Soc.* **37**, 111.

CANTER, H. M. & LUND, J. W. G. (1948). Studies on plankton parasites. I. Fluctuations in the numbers of *Asterionella formosa* Hass., in relation to fungal epidemics. *New Phytol.* **47**, 238.

CANTER, H. M. & LUND, J. W. G. (1953). Studies on plankton parasites. II. The parasitism of diatoms with special reference to lakes in the English Lake District. *Trans. Brit. mycol. Soc.* **36**, 13.

CANTINO, E. C. (1951). Metabolism and morphogenesis in a new *Blastocladiella*. *Leeuenhoek J. Microbiol. Serol.* **17**, 59.

CANTINO, E. C. (1952). The biochemical nature of morphogenetic patterns in *Blastocladiella*. *Amer. Nat.* **86**, 399.

CANTINO, E. C. (1953). The role of metabolism and α-ketoglutarate oxidase in the growth and differentiation of the aquatic phycomycete *Blastocladiella emersonii*. *Trans. N.Y. Acad. Sci.* Series II, **15**, 159.

CANTINO, E. C. (1954). The role of metabolism in the morphological differentiation of the water fungus *Blastocladiella emersonii*. Preliminary programme, Internat. Bot. Congr., Paris.

CANTINO, E. C. (1956). The relation between cellular metabolism and morphogenesis in *Blastocladiella*. *Mycologia*, **48**, 225.

DESHPANDE, R. S. (1940). A study of conditions which influence the persistence of certain phycomycetous parasites in soils, together with an account of fungicidal control measures. Thesis, Univ. London.

DRECHSLER, C. (1941). Predacious Fungi. *Biol. Rev.* **16**, 265.

DUDDINGTON, C. L. (1955). Fungi that attack microscopic animals. *Bot. Rev.* **21**, 377.

EMERSON, R. & CANTINO, E. C. (1948). The isolation, growth and metabolism of *Blastocladia* in pure culture. *Amer. J. Bot.* **35**, 157.

EVANS, E. (1955). Survival and recolonization by fungi in soil treated with formalin or carbon disulphide. *Trans. Brit. mycol. Soc.* **38**, 335.

EZEKIEL, W. N. (1945). Effect of low temperatures on survival of *Phymatotrichum omnivorum*. *Phytopathology*, **35**, 296.

FRIEDRICH, K. (1936). Zur Ökologie der Höheren Pilze. *Ber. dtsch. bot. Ges.* **54**, 388.

FRIEDRICH, K. (1940). Untersuchungen zur Ökologie der Höheren Pilze. *Pflanzen-forschung*, 22, hsg. von R. Kolkwitz, p. 22. Jena: G. Fischer.

GARRETT, S. D. (1936, 1937, 1938, 1939, 1940, 1941, 1944a, 1944b, 1948). Soil conditions and the take-all disease of wheat. I–IX. *Ann. appl. Biol.* 23, 667; 24, 747; 25, 742; 26, 47; 27, 199; 28, 14; 28, 325; 31, 186; 35, 14.

GARRETT, S. D. (1956). *Biology of Root-infecting Fungi*. Cambridge.

GLEN-BOTT, JANET I. (1955). On *Helicodendron tubulosum* and some similar species. *Trans. Brit. mycol. Soc.* 38, 17.

GODFREY, ROSEMARY M. (1957). Studies on British species of *Endogone*. 3. Germination of spores. *Trans. Brit. mycol. Soc.* (in the Press).

GRAINGER, J. (1946). Ecology of the larger fungi. *Trans. Brit. mycol. Soc.* 29, 52.

GREGORY, P. H. (1939). The life-history of *Ramularia vallisumbrosae* Cav. on narcissus. *Trans. Brit. mycol. Soc.* 23, 24.

GREGORY, P. H. (1945). The dispersion of air-borne spores. *Trans. Brit. mycol. Soc.* 28, 26.

HAWKER, LILIAN E. (1950). *Physiology of Fungi*. London.

HAWKER, LILIAN E. (1954). British hypogeous fungi. *Phil. Trans.* B, 237, 429.

HAWKER, LILIAN E. (1955). Hypogeous fungi. *Biol. Rev.* 30, 127.

HAWKER, LILIAN E. (1956). Presidential Address: Experimental control of form and phase in fungi. *Trans. Brit. mycol. Soc.* 39, 1.

HAWKER, LILIAN E. (1957). *The Physiology of Reproduction in Fungi*. Cambridge.

HULL, R. (1939). Study of *Byssochlamys fulva* and control measures in processed fruits. *Ann. appl. Biol.* 26, 800.

INGOLD, C. T. (1942). Aquatic Hyphomycetes of decaying alder leaves. *Trans. Brit. mycol. Soc.* 25, 339.

INGOLD, C. T. (1946). Spore discharge in *Daldinia concentrica*. *Trans. Brit. mycol. Soc.* 29, 43.

INGOLD, C. T. (1953). *Dispersal in Fungi*. Oxford.

INGOLD, C. T. (1954a). Aquatic Ascomycetes: discomycetes from lakes. *Trans. Brit. mycol. Soc.* 37, 1.

INGOLD, C. T. (1954b). Presidential Address: Fungi and water. *Trans. Brit. mycol. Soc.* 37, 97.

INGOLD, C. T. (1955). Aquatic Ascomycetes: further species from the English Lake District. *Trans. Brit. mycol. Soc.* 38, 157.

KING, C. J. & EATON, E. D. (1934). Influence of soil moisture on the longevity of cotton root rot sclerotia. *J. agric. Res.* 49, 793.

KING, C. J., LOOMIS, H. F. & HOPE, C. (1931). Studies on sclerotia and mycelial strands of the cotton root rot fungus. *J. agric. Res.* 42, 827.

LAST, F. T. (1955). Seasonal incidence of *Sporobolomyces* on cereal leaves. *Trans. Brit. mycol. Soc.* 38, 221.

LILLY, V. C. & BARNETT, H. L. (1951). *Physiology of the Fungi*. New York.

MELIN, E. (1948). Recent advances in the study of tree mycorrhiza. *Trans. Brit. mycol. Soc.* 30, 92.

MITCHELL, R. B., HOOTON, D. R. & CLARK, F. E. (1941). Soil bacterological studies on the control of *Phymatotrichum* root rot of cotton. *J. agric. Res.* 63, 535.

OLLIVER, M. & SMITH, G. (1933). *Byssochlamys fulva* sp.nov. *J. Bot., Lond.*, 71, 196.

PARK, D. (1955). Experimental studies on the ecology of fungi in soil. *Trans. Brit. mycol. Soc.* 38, 130.

PASTEUR, L. (1876). *Études sur la bière*. Paris.

RAPER, J. R. (1952). Chemical regulation of sexual processes in the Thallophytes. *Bot. Rev.* 18, 447.

ROGERS, C. H. (1942). Cotton root rot studies with special reference to sclerotia, cover crops, rotations, tillage, seeding rates, soil fungicides and effects on seed quality. *Bull. Tex. agric. Exp. Sta.* no. 614.

TAUBENHAUS, J. J. & EZEKIEL, W. N. (1936). Longevities of sclerotia of *Phymatotrichum omnivorum* in moist soil in the laboratory. *Amer. J. Bot.* **23**, 10.

TOWNSEND, B. B. & WILLETTS, H. J. (1954). The development of sclerotia of certain fungi. *Trans. Brit. mycol. Soc.* **37**, 213.

VENKAT RAM, C. S. (1952). Soil bacteria and chlamydospore formation in *Fusarium solani. Nature, Lond.,* **170**, 889.

WARCUP, J. H. (1951a). The ecology of soil fungi. *Trans. Brit. mycol. Soc.* **35**, 248.

WARCUP, J. H. (1951b). Soil-steaming: a selective method for the isolation of Ascomycetes from soil. *Trans. Brit. mycol. Soc.* **34**, 515.

WARCUP, J. H. (1951c). Effect of partial sterilization by steam or formalin on the fungus flora of an old forest nursery soil. *Trans. Brit. mycol. Soc.* **34**, 519.

WARCUP, J. H. (1951d). Studies in the growth of Basidiomycetes in soil. *Ann. Bot., Lond.,* N.S., **15**, 305.

WEBSTER, J. (1951). Graminicolous Pyrenomycetes. I, II and III. *Trans. Brit. mycol. Soc.* **34**, 304.

WEBSTER, J. (1952). Graminicolous Pyrenomycetes. IV. *Trans. Brit. mycol. Soc.* **35**, 208.

WEBSTER, J. (1955). Graminicolous Pyrenomycetes. V. *Trans. Brit. mycol. Soc.* **38**, 347.

WILKINS, W. H. & HARRIS, G. C. M. (1946). The ecology of the larger fungi. V. *Ann. appl. Biol.* **33**, 179.

WILKINS, W. H. & PATRICK, S. H. M. (1940). The ecology of the larger fungi. *Ann. appl. Biol.* **27**, 15.

WILSON, IRENE M. (1954). *Ceriosporopsis halima* Lindner and *Ceriosporopsis cambrensis* sp.nov.: two marine Pyrenomycetes on wood. *Trans. Brit. mycol. Soc.* **37**, 272.

SOME FACTORS IN THE LIFE OF FREE-LIVING PROTOZOA

J. A. KITCHING

Department of Zoology, University of Bristol

INTRODUCTION

Protozoa, like other organisms, play their part in ecological systems. Occasionally this is a major one, as on certain wood piles in the Bristol Docks, which are covered, just below water level, with a carpet-like growth of green algae and certain peritrich ciliates. In this case the peritrichs provide a home for various other organisms, including both protozoa and metazoa, and food for some of them. Food for the peritrichs, in the form of bacteria, is probably unlimited, and the spread of peritrichs is probably determined only by the space available to them at the appropriate level. In other cases, some of which will be mentioned, protozoa play a relatively less important part in the ecological structure, although sometimes the vastly greater extent and concern to man of the habitat in question may lend them a great practical interest. In any case, the approach should be a general rather than a purely protozoological one.

In ecological studies it is reasonable that field surveys should establish certain basic information about the environmental conditions and the chief species present, that laboratory experiments should determine under exact conditions the reactions of these species, that further field surveys, carried out with a knowledge of what to look for, should then provide a deeper understanding of the ecological situation, and so on. At present we are only in a rather early stage of this oscillating process. It is the purpose of this paper to draw attention to some laboratory observations which may give guidance in future field work, and also, by a consideration of the effects of certain environmental factors on protozoa, to illustrate the very great complexity and difficulty of the problems involved. An empirical approach is likely to prove sterile; a full knowledge is needed of the physiological effects of the various factors which characterize the environment.

Habitats

Free-living protozoa occupy four important levels in food cycles. (*a*) The plant flagellates are mainly photosynthetic primary producers, even though some require auxiliary growth factors; they provide food for micropredators and filter feeders. (*b*) Many rhizopods (e.g. soil amoebae) and many ciliates are micropredators, feeding upon bacteria. (*c*) Other rhizopods and ciliates are predators at a higher level, feeding on other protozoa or on minute metazoa, such as rotifers. (*d*) A number of flagellates and ciliates are saprozoic, that is, they are nourished by dissolved organic matter.

Without attempting any comprehensive review, it will be convenient to refer very briefly to the obvious major habitats for protozoa, namely, ponds and streams, lakes, the sea, the soil and sewage. Of these, ponds and streams are economically of rather little importance, but they are accessible to academic institutions, and they yield a number of types which are convenient for culture in the laboratory; for these reasons by far the most work has been done on pond protozoa. It is unfortunate that owing to the academic estrangement of bacteriology from zoology most of the surveys of protozoa in small bodies of fresh water have included various easily measured physical or chemical features of the environment, such as temperature, pH or oxygen content, but not the bacteria used for food by most of the ciliates, nor the substrates upon which these bacteria are living. The investigation of Hobson's Brook by Gray (1951, 1952) is a notable exception.

A most valuable survey has also been made of the peritrich ciliates both on natural substrates and on microscope slides suspended at various depths in a pool in the Botanic Gardens at Bonn (Hammann, 1952). The seasonal fluctuations in population density and in the occurrence of conjugation of a number of peritrich ciliates have been considered in relation to various environmental factors, and once again the importance is emphasized of an abundance of bacterial food for the growth of ciliate populations. Extensive lists of protozoa collected from various types of aquatic habitats have been published by Hausmann (1917), Noland (1925) and Lackey (1938).

The plankton of the sea and of lakes has attracted much attention because of the vital part it plays in the general economy of these waters, and its fluctuations have been studied in relation to the physical and chemical conditions (reviewed for the sea by Harvey, 1955). It includes many protozoa, but their importance in the economy may be rather limited in comparison with other more abundant organisms such as diatoms. For instance, Cushing (1955) has summarized the very scanty existing knowledge of the population density of microflagellates around the British Isles and has concluded that they play rather little part in the food cycle associated with the production of herring. The systematics of the microflagellates are becoming more accessible thanks to electron microscopy (Parke, Manton, & Clarke, 1955), but the collection and separation of these organisms from sea water presents difficulties (Ballantine, 1953). A number of phytoflagellates are heterotrophic, requiring certain specific growth factors such as cobalamin (Provasoli & Pintner, 1953; Hutner & Provasoli, 1955; Droop, 1955), and the investigation of these requirements in relation to conditions in the sea is likely to prove interesting (Lucas, 1955). Extensive surveys have been made of seasonal fluctuations in dinoflagellate populations both in the sea (Lebour, 1916; Allen, 1928, 1940; Lackey, 1936; Whedon, 1939; Bandel, 1940) and in fresh water (Czernin-Chudenitz, 1955). Field observations have been supplemented by important laboratory studies of the conditions necessary for the growth of cultures (Barker, 1935; Braarud & Pappas, 1951; Braarud & Rossavik, 1951). Besides the normal seasonal fluctuations, certain dinoflagellates are liable to occasional very local, very great and apparently very sudden increases in population, leading to 'red water' seen for instance off the Californian coast (Allen, 1942, 1943). Nordli (1953) has attributed outbursts of *Ceratium* spp. off the Norwegian coast to a favourable combination of low salinity and high temperature, assisted in the Oslo fiord by an abundance of nutrient salts arising from sewage. These outbursts set an interesting problem in the control of population density. In addition, they are notorious because they may render mussels poisonous, and because sometimes (depending on the species) an exotoxin is produced which may kill fish and other animals (Ballantine, 1955).

The soil protozoa have been investigated with special reference to the effects which they may have on fertility, and in this work the Department of Soil Microbiology at Rothamsted has played a leading part. The very arduous investigation of fluctuations in numbers of bacteria and soil amoebae by Cutler, Crump & Sandon (1923) revealed that a high population density of active soil amoebae was correlated with a low population density of bacteria, but the considerable unexplained fluctuations which occurred from day to day in numbers both of amoebae and of bacteria show that much more remains to be discovered. The control of soil bacteria by amoebae was also demonstrated experimentally (Cutler, 1923). This investigation led to important laboratory studies of the systematics of the soil amoebae, of growth of amoebae on

different types of soil bacteria, and of the conditions leading to excystment (reviewed by Thornton & Crump, 1952; see also Franz, 1951;
Singh, 1955).

Special studies have been made of certain other restricted habitats
such as sphagnum bogs (Paulson, 1953; Grospietch, 1954) and sand
beaches (Fauré-Fremiet, 1950a, 1951; Pennak, 1951). The microclimate
and population levels of a fresh-water beach are discussed briefly by
Pennak, while Fauré-Fremiet has drawn attention to the thread-like or
ribbon-like shape and thigmotactic behaviour (that is, tending to remain
in contact with solid objects) of species found in the interstices of the
finer marine sands. The protozoan fauna of sewage has been studied
with special reference to the species associated with different methods
of sewage disposal and to the flocculation of bacteria (Barker, 1946,
with references; Sugden & Lloyd, 1950).

PATTERNS OF BIOLOGICAL RESPONSE
Growth of a culture

The application of bacteriological techniques to the culture of protozoa
has led to the establishment of pure bacteria-free ('axenic') cultures of
a number of saprozoic or phototrophic species, and this in turn has
given rise to very extensive nutritional investigations (reviewed by
Kidder, 1947; Hutner & Provasoli, 1955; Wagtendonk, 1955a). Another
development of particular ecological interest has been the establishment
of two-membered cultures (Kidder, 1951), in which an autotrophic or
saprozoic organism (whether protozoon or bacterium) forms the food
for a predacious protozoon. Work of this kind has already provided
useful information about the growth of populations and the factors
which affect growth, and might form the basis for a study of the structure
of ecological systems.

The growth of a population of the ciliate *Tetrahymena pyriformis* in
axenic culture is shown in Fig. 1 (Phelps, 1935). It comprises an exponential phase, a phase of decreasing growth rate, a stationary maximum
phase, and a slow death phase; this last is not shown in the figure. There
is also an initial lag phase if the original inoculation is made with
organisms from an old culture. Evidently in this case the lag is due to
a persistence of some condition induced during the decline or arrest of
growth after the end of the exponential phase. This confirms earlier work
with non-sterile cultures on other protozoa. For instance, the lag phase
was eliminated in *Paramecium aurelia* by means of transfers from young
cultures (Greenleaf, 1926), and no lag phase was found in the ciliates

Didinium nasutum or *Stylonychia pustulata* (Beers, 1933). Considerable attention has been given to the theory that protozoa discharge a growth-promoting substance into the medium ('allelocatalysis'), but this has not been substantiated.

The exponential phase is eminently suitable for the study of the effects of various environmental conditions upon growth. Various examples will be mentioned in connexion with temperature and salinity.

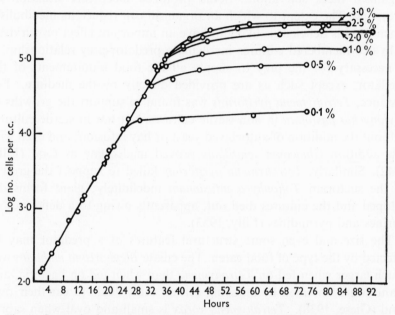

Fig. 1. Composite figure showing growth of population of *Tetrahymena pyriformis* in different concentrations of Difco yeast extract. (From Phelps, 1936.)

In axenic cultures of *Tetrahymena (Glaucoma) pyriformis* (= *T. geleii*) the population density at which the exponential phase gives way to the phase of decreasing growth rate and to the stationary maximum was higher the greater was the concentration of food initially present in the medium (Fig. 1) (Phelps, 1936; Rottier, 1936, for *Polytoma uvella*). Evidently in this case the exponential phase is brought to a close by deficiency of food rather than by the accumulation of excretory products. This does not necessarily mean that there is a shortage of food in general. The rate of growth of the population, and the continuation of the exponential phase, may be limited by the deficiency of a single component such as thiamine (Hall & Schottenfeld, 1941). There are some thirty components, including ten amino acids and ten food factors or vitamins, essential for the growth of *T. pyriformis*. At the beginning of the stationary maximum for *T. pyriformis* the number of dividing individuals falls off sharply. This implies that deaths also must be few, if the population remains approximately constant (Ormsbee, 1942). (This confirms the earlier observation of Harding (1937*b*) that *Tetrahymena* may be starved for at least a month without any deaths occurring.) With metabolism depressed (Baker & Baumberger, 1941; Hutchens, 1941; Pace & Lyman, 1947) and division suspended, the organism faces starvation. Some protozoa meet this situation by encysting. The extent to which an organism can reduce its metabolism when food is deficient is likely to have an important effect on survival.

In two-membered cultures involving a predator-prey relationship, it is necessary for the prey to supply all the food requirements of the predator, except such as are provided directly by the medium. For instance, *Tetrahymena pyriformis* was found to support the growths of *Stylonychia pustulata* in non-sterile cultures, but not in sterile cultures without the addition of autoclaved yeast or hay infusion; and even with this addition *Glaucoma scintillans* proved inadequate as food (Lilly, 1942). Similarly, *Tetrahymena pyriformis* failed to support the growth of the suctorian *Tokophyra infusionum* indefinitely; giant forms developed and the cultures died out, apparently owing to a deficiency of purines and pyrmidines (Lilly, 1953).

The size and even some structural features of a predator may be affected by the type of food eaten. The ciliate *Blepharisma undulans* was much larger when fed on *Tetrahymena* than when fed on bacteria, and giants were obtained by inducing certain individuals to eat their own kind (Giese, 1938). *Tetrahymena vorax* is small and oval when saprozoic, but becomes elongated and provided with a 'tail' when fed on bacteria, and grows very large and develops a special preparatory vacuole for the accommodation of prey when predacious on various other ciliates (Kidder, Lilly & Claff, 1940). When *Tetrahymena* sp. was fed on *Pseudomonas fluorescens*, the size of the *Tetrahymena* was found to increase with increasing concentration of the *Pseudomonas* over the whole range studied (up to 7 million per cu.mm.); and the growth rate of the population increased at concentrations up to about 600,000 per cu.mm., but then became independent of food concentration (Fig. 2) (Harding, 1937*a*).

It is not surprising that a given predator will multiply at different rates on different foods. *Colpidium colpoda* was found to have significantly different population growth rates when fed with various different bacteria (Burbanck, 1942; Burbanck & Gilpin, 1946), and soil amoebae and a soil flagellate, *Cercomonas crassicauda*, multiply at different rates on different strains of bacteria (Singh, 1942). Certain bacteria (e.g. *Serratia marcescens*) produce exotoxins which in culture protect them and neighbouring bacteria from soil amoebae, but not from the flagellate *Cercomonas crassicauda* (Singh, 1942). When the ciliate *Colpoda* was fed on various kinds of chromogenic bacteria, some (*Pseudomonas* 3 spp., *Staphylococcus aureus*, *Flavobacterium* 2 spp. etc.) supported growth, though usually at a reduced rate; one (*Flavo-*

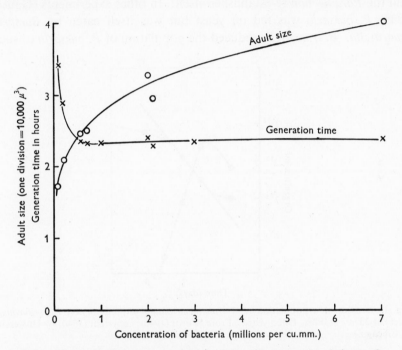

Fig. 2. The size and rate of reproduction of *Tetrahymena* sp. in relation to the concentration of bacteria. (From Harding, 1937*a*.)

bacterium sp.) gave no growth at all and the *Colpoda* encysted, as though starved; and yet others (*Chromobacterium violaceum* and *Serratia marcescens*) proved toxic (Kidder & Stuart, 1939*a*). It is not known to what extent protozoa can choose between different species of bacteria as food. *Paramecium caudatum* was found by Grittner (1951) to eat *Proteus* sp. in preference to *Bacillus subtilis*, even though the *Proteus* proved toxic; the selection was quite probably by size. There is no doubt that many protozoa have powers of selection, but it is not clear to what extent these rely on chemical rather than physical differences, nor even whether there is any useful selection between different species of bacteria (reviewed by Kitching, 1956*b*).

Populations of predator and prey

Various studies have been made of populations of predator and prey. Gause (1934), using non-sterile cultures of *Bacillus subtilis*, *Paramecium caudatum* and *Dinidium nasutum*, found that the *Didinium* eventually exterminated the *Paramecium*; but if he provided sediment, in which some of the *Paramecium* remained unmolested, the *Didinium* starved and the *Paramecium* re-established itself. In other experiments (Gause, 1935) *P. bursaria* was fed on yeast but was itself eaten by *Bursaria truncatella*. *B. truncatella* reduced the population of *P. bursaria* to such

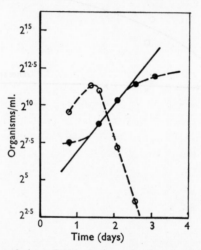

Fig. 3. Growth of a population of *Tetrahymena patula* ● (predator) on *T. pyriformis* ○ (prey) at 25° C. in 0·2% Difco yeast. (From Brown (1940); copyright (1940) by University of Chicago.)

a low level that *B. truncatella* died out owing to starvation, and *P. bursaria* then increased again in numbers. Bacteria-free two-membered cultures of *Peranema trum* (predator) and *Euglena gracilis* (Dewey & Kidder, 1940) ended in the extermination of the prey. The same was sometimes true of bacteria-free cultures of *Tetrahymena* (*Leucophrys*) *patula* (predator) and *T. pyriformis* (Fig. 3), but in other cases the increase in numbers of the predator was checked by some unexplained factor associated with population density, and the numbers of *T. pyriformis* became stabilized or showed some recovery (Brown, 1940).

In general, experiments of this sort deviate in certain important respects from conditions usually offered by nature. In the experiments, a homogeneous microhabitat is usually provided, the initial concentration of food is usually very high, and there is usually no slow or steady addition of nutrient materials, bacteria or other basic foods. Some prey may survive if the conditions are heterogeneous, as happens in nature. The same is also to be expected if the basic food supply is very limited in relation to the volume of the water mass. Then the predator will never attain a high density of population, and may fail to establish contact with all the prey organisms before it starves. *Didinium* might then encyst and perhaps excyst later, under suitable circumstances, when the prey population had risen again. Thus there would be cyclical outbursts of predation such as Gause expected but failed to achieve.

Competition

Competition in cultures was also studied by Gause (1935). The procedure in certain of his experiments was to place twenty individuals of a species into 5 ml. of balanced salt solution containing a standard inoculum of *Pseudomonas pyocyaneus*. Every day 0·5 ml. was removed for a count of the population, and the remaining 4·5 ml. were centrifuged to separate the protozoa, decanted and replaced with another 5 ml. of medium containing bacteria. (A complete washing of the population was also carried out every 2 days.) Under these conditions a population increased exponentially at first but finally reached a plateau, where it remained steady. Thus the daily supply of food was just sufficient under these conditions to maintain a given biomass, having regard to the need for the daily replacement of one-tenth of the population. It was found that both for *Paramecium aurelia* and *P. caudatum* the equilibrium biomass was almost doubled when the daily rate of supply of food was doubled. However, *P. aurelia* grew faster and attained a greater biomass under these particular experimental conditions. When the two species were grown together, the rate of increase of each was depressed, but *P. aurelia* eventually prevailed; the population of *P. caudatum* passed through a maximum and declined (Fig. 4). In competition, *P. aurelia* apparently made better use of the growth potential offered by the daily removal of one-tenth of the culture. However, *P. caudatum* prevailed over *P. aurelia* in other experiments in which yeast was given as food and the culture medium and other experimental conditions were different (Gause, Nastukova & Alpatov, 1934). The daily removal of an aliquot of the culture represents, in simplified form, the deaths by predation and the other density-dependent losses which occur continually in nature; clearly the effects of all environmental conditions, both biotic and otherwise, on the population growth rate of a species must be of profound ecological importance.

All these experiments represent a situation very much simpler than that of a mixed culture of protozoa, as for instance in a hay infusion. In experiments in which a number of hay infusions, set up in a standard way, were inoculated with a fixed amount of a mixture of various protozoa and bacteria, the protozoa at the surface appeared and reached

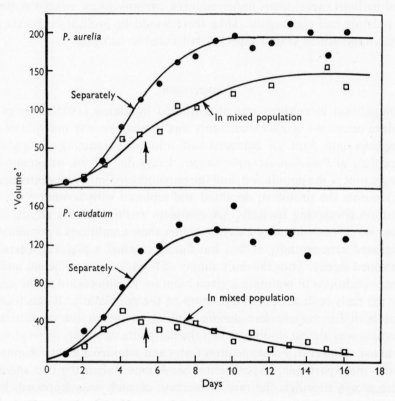

Fig. 4. The growth of the biomass of *Paramecium caudatum* and *P. aurelia* cultivated separately and in mixed population under certain cultured conditions. (From Gause, 1934.)

their maximum density of population in a definite order (Woodruff, 1912; Eddy, 1928). Hay infusions undergo progressive changes in pH and in fauna (Bodine, 1921; Pruthi, 1927; Hetherington, 1933). The bacteria, and to some extent no doubt the protozoa, modify not merely pH but many other conditions and so help to produce an ecological sequence. The hay infusion, in turn, is simpler than the pond or lake, which are more diverse in the types of habitat which they contain and more subject to climatic and associated changes.

Cysts

Some protozoa are able to escape from the slow death phase by encysting. *Didinium nasutum* can continue to feed and multiply by fission over very many generations if enough food is available, but if the supply of food is limited it shows an increasing tendency to encyst (Beers, 1926). *Colpoda duodenaria* encysts either in the general absence of food (Kidder & Stuart, 1939*b*) or if one or more specified growth factors are deficient (Garnjobst, 1947). Encystment in these cases is a response to starvation, and enables the organism, no doubt by a reduction of its metabolic rate, to survive without feeding for very long periods. *Didinium nasutum* is known to have survived in the encysted state, wet, for up to 10 years, although the proportion of cysts which hatched after that time was small (Beers, 1937). In some cases encystment has been attributed to various other adverse conditons, such as an accumulation of excretory products or a lack of oxygen (literature summarized by Wagtendonk, 1955*b*). Encystment involves a reversal and redirection of morphogenesis. Membranellae, cilia, pharynx and other organelles are resorbed, and the various layers of the cyst wall are secreted. It seems possible that starvation or certain other unfavourable external conditions lead to a metabolic depression which in turn prevents the kinetosomes from exercising their full potentialities or maintaining their metabolic fields of influence.

Some protozoa produce cysts which can survive drying, and these cysts may remain dormant for long periods and be distributed by wind or otherwise in the dry condition. It is well known that in widely different groups of the animal kingdom, including rotifers, tardigrades and chironomids, certain species can survive prolonged desiccation. In such cases the dried organisms can survive much more rigorous conditions than the active stages. Dried cysts of *Colpoda duodenaria* have survived exposure to 105° C. for 3 hr. and to liquid air for over 12 hr. (Taylor & Strickland, 1936). According to Wagtendonk (1955*b*) dried cysts of *C. duodenaria* have also survived for over 7 years in a vacuum of 10^{-6} mm. Hg. Respiration at this pressure must have been negligible, and such cysts must be regarded as in a state of suspended animation, as would be expected from their dry condition. This would account for their immunity from the destructive metabolic disturbances which would otherwise be expected at high temperatures. At the lower end of the temperature range they are protected from damage due to internal freezing because they contain very little water. It seems that, having achieved the power to endure desiccation, they have incidentally acquired with it a resistance to conditions far more rigorous than any which they would encounter naturally. Thus in addition to affording an alternative to starvation, encystment plays an important part during drought in protecting those protozoa which inhabit the soil (Fellers & Allison, 1920) or small ponds and puddles liable to dry up.

Excystment of the saprozoic ciliate *Colpoda duodenaria* is readily produced by the addition of certain plant or animal extracts to the medium; hay infusion or yeast extract are commonly used. Hay infusions contain a number of substances capable of inducing a certain proportion of cysts to hatch, especially various metabolically important organic acids, and it appears that this action is due to a mixture of such substances (Haagen-Smit & Thimann, 1938). It is also interesting that potassium ions promote excystment in certain suitable mixtures (Strickland & Haagen-Smit, 1947, 1948) in view of the association of potassium accumulation with metabolic activity. It is clear that excystment must be initiated by conditions capable of re-establishing the metabolic activity and intracellular metabolic differentiation of the organism, and therefore it is not surprising that a variety of apparently unrelated conditions may lead to it. In practice the conditions which are effective are usually of a kind which would normally be favourable for the active stage of the organism—the presence of nutrient solutes, of certain bacteria (Crump, 1950, for soil amoebae), or of fresh medium free from the accumulated effects of use (Bridgman, 1948). For further progress an understanding is needed of the biochemistry of the activation to excyst.

SOME EFFECTS OF THE INANIMATE ENVIRONMENT

The shifting dynamic balance of species, which is the outcome of growth, multiplication, predation, competition, encystment, death and so on, is sensitive to a variety of conditions imposed by the climate and other geographical features. These factors are independent (with minor exceptions) of the population density of the species in question, and include temperature, salinity, ionic composition of the medium, carbon dioxide concentration and pH, oxygen concentration, illumination, tidal conditions and many others. Their action will be illustrated by reference to a few. Sometimes one of these conditions becomes extreme, as in a spell of cold or dry weather, and many individuals of a species are annihilated. More often, perhaps, they act less violently but just as surely, by raising or depressing the growth rate.

Temperature

Laboratory studies of the thermal range for survival as tested by brief exposures probably have a rather limited ecological significance, as conditions of temperature tend in nature to persist over many hours or days. Important information is also to be obtained from a study of the effects of temperature on the growth rate of the population. There is usually a very pronounced maximum which is usually rather near the upper limit of the range over which division is possible (Fig. 5) (Mitchell, 1929; Barker, 1935; Smith, 1940; Phelps, 1946; Schoenborn, 1947; Stout, 1955). It would be interesting to supplement this information

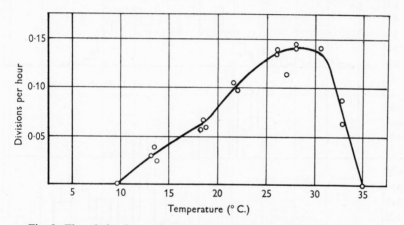

Fig. 5. The relation between temperature and the frequency of division in
Chilomonas paramecium. (From Smith, 1940.)

with a detailed study of the effects of temperature on the nutritional physiology, on the efficiency of growth in relation to food supply, and on the ability to survive when the food supply is limited. In some cases the optimal temperature for the growth of a population may also be affected by nutritional conditions. In *Euglena gracilis* grown in the dark the maximum growth rate of a population is at 10° in a hydrolysed casein medium, and is in any case very low; but when the medium is reinforced by the addition of acetate, the growth rate is greatly increased and the maximum is shifted to 23° (Jahn, 1935). The ability of *Chilomonas paramecium* to survive and multiply at high temperature is reduced by previous prolonged exposure to low temperature (Smith, 1940). There are also reports implying the selection of strains of protozoa having an increased tolerance of high temperatures, but our present knowledge of this subject is unsatisfactory.

Seasonal fluctuations in density of population have been observed for
a number of protozoa in all kinds of habitats. They are well illustrated
by a detailed investigation of a garden pond at Philadelphia carried out
by Wang (1928) (Fig. 6). He concluded that a number of species are
thermophilic and others psychrophilic, and in this respect there was
satisfactory agreement with earlier reports. In Noland's (1925) two-
year study of various types of fresh-water habitats, certain ciliates,

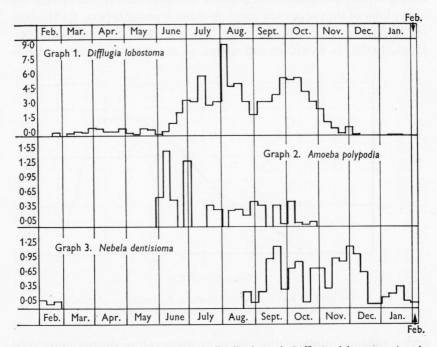

Fig. 6. Diagrams showing the seasonal distribution of *Difflugia lobostoma*, *Amoeba
polypodia*, and *Nebela dentistoma*. Ordinates indicate the number of animals per ml.
(From Wang, 1928.)

including *Halteria grandinella* and *Coleps hirtus*, were most abundant
in the field at higher temperatures and appeared in cultures of material
brought in from a cold pond when these were incubated at 20–22°, but
not in similar cultures kept at 4–5·5°. These two species, as pointed out
by Noland, were regarded by Birge and Juday as most abundant in
August and September, but apparently disappeared during the winter
months. This is also supported by Wang's observations. On the other
hand, Noland found that *Trochila palustris* was most abundant in
collections from very cold water (4–5·7°) but was absent from water over
15·5°. If allowed to warm up in the laboratory it burst. The season of

greatest abundance of a number of protozoa in various Austrian lakes, and the associated water temperatures, are given by Findenegg (1943).

However, a correlation with seasonal fluctuations of temperature in the field does not necessarily mean that temperature is influencing the species in question directly; it may act through the food or enemies of the species under consideration. The number of ciliates in Hobson's Brook was at a minimum in July when the number of dipterous larvae was greatest (Gray, 1952), and a negative correlation was also claimed between the numbers of protozoa in the film of sewage bacteria beds and the numbers of emerging flies (Barker, 1946). Moreover, other factors besides temperature may vary seasonally. For instance, in Hobson's Brook the spring outburst of the diatom *Melosira varians* was accompanied by an abundance of diatom-eating ciliates (*Condylostoma* sp. in 1947, *Loxodes* sp., *Loxophyllum* sp. and *Stylonychia* sp. in 1948) (Gray, 1952); it may be supposed that in this case illumination was also concerned. The spring and autumn population maxima of various peritrich ciliates in a pond was ascribed by Hammann (1952) to a combination of favourable temperature with abundance of bacterial food. It would be interesting in such cases to study the effects of combinations of conditions in the laboratory.

Geographical distribution may also suggest an effect of temperature. For instance, there are distinct tropical and circumpolar species of Foraminifera (Cushman, 1950), and the analysis of the fauna of Foraminifera from deep-sea cores should provide valuable information about past climates (Wiseman & Ovey, 1950). Some species of the dinoflagellate *Ceratium* are confined to tropical seas, others are circumpolar, and yet others are cosmopolitan (Graham, 1941). Nevertheless, other characteristics of the water vary besides temperature, and it is difficult to exclude these as possible causes (Graham & Bronikovsky, 1944). However, in spite of these various difficulties in the interpretation of field data, there can be no doubt that temperature plays a direct and very important part in the limitation of many species of protozoa. Laboratory experiments are needed to confirm individual cases.

Salinity

Salinity is a complex factor. The contrast between fresh water, brackish water and sea water involves a change in the osmotic pressure and in the concentrations of various ions in the medium. The protozoa are outstanding among the various phyla of the animal kingdom for the way in which, in all their classes and often within the same genus, they are equally at home in the sea and in fresh water. Moreover, in many cases a single species can endure a very wide range of salinities, and individuals of a species can endure wide fluctuations. This is true in spite of their very large relative surface area and of their frequently naked condition.

Changes of salinity impose an immediate osmotic problem, and there is an immediate swelling or shrinkage, controlled to some extent by a compensatory adjustment in the rate of output of the contractile vacuole (Kitching, 1956a). Sooner or later, however, after a change of salinity, the body returns to something approaching its original size, no doubt owing to a leakage of salts in or out. Once the immediate osmotic danger has been passed, the problem becomes one of ionic concentrations, both external and internal. A small fresh-water amoeba, *Amoeba lacerata*, has been cultured in concentrations of sea water ranging up to 125 % (where 100 % represents ordinary sea water) (Hopkins, 1946), and a small marine amoeba, *Flabellula mira*, has been cultured in concentrations of sea water from 20 to 150 % (Butts, 1935). Earlier work is summarized by Finley (1930), who has published lists showing the limits of salinity to which a number of protozoa can be transferred directly or by slow acclimatization. In most cases the endurance is considerably greater if transfer is gradual (Finley, 1930; see also Loefer, 1939). For instance, *Paramecium caudatum* is stated by Finley to survive 103 % sea water by gradual acclimatization but only 20 % by direct transfer. On the other hand, Frisch (1940) failed to acclimatize *P. caudatum* to concentrations of sea water higher than 52 %. The population growth rate of two marine dinoflagellates was found by Braarud (1951) to remain near its peak level over a very wide range of salinity. *Ceratium* spp. off the coast of Norway favour moderate salinity (Nordli, 1953). In contrast to these cases, some protozoa do not tolerate any appreciable salinity; the flagellate *Cryptomonas ovata* var. *palustris* is prevented from growing by concentrations of sodium chloride as low as 30 mg./100 ml. (Provasoli & Pintner, 1953). In assessing the significance of laboratory experiments in relation to field conditions, the experiments of Hardin (1942, 1944) on the flagellate *Oikomonas termo* are especially interesting. Under bacteria-free conditions this organism could not be cultured in a nutrient medium containing more than 45 % sea water, but in the presence of bacteria could be cultured in a medium containing up to 100 % sea water. (The provision of bacterial food also enabled *Oikomonas* to grow in alkaline media or in media without added calcium, but the original paper should be consulted for other important details.)

The part played by salinity in the physiology of the organism is not yet understood. Sodium is by far the most plentiful cation in sea water, and the leakage which occurs after transfer from one salinity to another could hardly result in a significant readjustment of body volume back towards the normal unless sodium chloride were concerned. On the other hand, experience with metazoan cells has emphasized in them the physiological importance of a low intracellular concentration of sodium, brought about by the 'sodium pump', and recent work by Carter (1957) on the fresh-water ciliate *Spirostomum ambiguum* has demonstrated that ionic regulation in this organism follows the same general pattern of an actively maintained high internal potassium and low sodium concentration. It remains to be discovered to what extent brackish water and marine protozoa regulate their internal ionic concentrations. Nevertheless, it seems likely that differences in the ability to tolerate a high internal sodium chloride concentration play an important part in determining tolerance of salinity. The normal rate of movement of small marine amoebae was found by Pantin (1926) to depend on the presence of Na^+, K^+, Ca^{2+} and Mg^{2+} in the correct ratios, as found in sea water, each ion contributing something towards the full activity of the organism, but Ca^{2+} playing an essential part in antagonizing Na^+. A very similar result was obtained with *Flabellula mira* (Butts, 1935), which can be grown in a wide range of mixtures of isotonic salt solutions provided that sodium chloride and calcium chloride are present in a suitable ratio of concentrations; the highest rate of growth of the population was in a mixture resembling sea water.

Oxygen

The tension of oxygen in the environment is recognized as an important factor in the life of protozoa, although it is often difficult to evaluate its influence on particular species in nature. It is to be expected that very often organisms will be able to obtain all the oxygen they need at very low external oxygen tensions, unless the body surface is unusually impermeable. At any rate it has been shown that certain species can make use of oxygen at rather low tensions. For instance, *Paramecium caudatum* which has been brought to a halt in the complete absence of oxygen is able to resume swimming, rather slowly, on admission of oxygen at a tension of about $\frac{1}{2}$ mm Hg (Kitching, 1939); and the flagellate *Chilomonas paramecium* will grow well in cultures at the same oxygen tension (Pace & Ireland, 1945). It is reported that with decreasing concentration of oxygen, the oxygen consumption of *Tetrahymena pyriformis* begins to fall off at $2\frac{1}{2}$ mm Hg (Baker & Baumberger, 1941). In describing an environment as anoxic, it is very necessary to be sure that the actual oxygen tension is so low that it would be of no use to protozoa, and in experiments on anaerobiosis it is advisable that it should be so small as to be meaningless. Unfortunately, the unmodified Winkler reaction commonly used for the determination of dissolved oxygen in the field is liable to give too low an estimate in the presence of reducing substances (Alsterberg, 1926), and experiments in the laboratory are often carried out without a completely convincing demonstration of the absolute elimination of oxygen.

There are three important physiological mechanisms which may contribute to survival at low tensions of oxygen: derivation of energy from metabolic processes not using oxygen, survival with a reduced or suppressed metabolism and the use of oxygen at very low tensions. It is convenient first to consider environments or experiments involving complete anaerobiosis because this must necessarily exclude the third possibility. There is no doubt that many protozoa are true anaerobes, although the best examples are to be drawn from commensal or parasitic types inhabiting the gut: for example, various protozoa from the rumen of cattle or sheep cannot be grown in culture except under strictly anoxic conditions, and there is no doubt that their natural environment is anoxic (Hungate, 1943). Similar conditions are found in sewage works, at any rate in the early stages of purification. Certain species are characteristic of anoxic sewage tanks, and others, including various peritrich ciliates, are found in the later stages under more aerated conditions (Lackey, 1932; Barker, 1942). In tests carried out by Lackey, the flagellate *Trepomonas agilis*, obtained from anoxic tanks, survived in the laboratory in stagnant but not in aerated sewage, whereas the peritrich *Opercularia*, an aerobic inhabitant of partly purified sewage, survived in the laboratory in aerated but not in stagnant sewage.

There is a complete lack of oxygen within the putrefying mud at the bottom of certain lakes and fiords, and at certain times the reducing conditions and lack of oxygen spread into the overlying water (as discussed by Mortimer, 1941) where they may extend to a considerable distance above the bottom owing to the virtual isolation of the deeper waters by a thermocline. The limited though characteristic fauna of the hypolimnion and of the mud bottom includes a number of protozoa, some of which must endure complete anoxia for weeks or even months at a time. For instance, the bottom-living rhizopod *Pelomyxa villosa* was found by Moore (1939), in summer-time investigations of Lake Douglas, Michigan, only in the deep oxygen-free waters. *Pelomyxa palustris* found under similar conditions was reported to survive prolonged experimental anoxia, although a number of other protozoa perished (Lindeman, 1942). A list of 'Animals known to occur in the profundal oxygen-less regions of American lakes', given by Welch (1935, p. 171), includes seventeen genera of Protozoa, and a much longer list of sapropelic Protozoa is given by Brand (1946).

In certain habitats there is a localized or temporary lack of oxygen, so that animals may move in and out of the anoxic region or may be subject to a temporary anoxia. Dung provides such a habitat (Watson, 1946). The coprophilic ciliate *Balantiophorus minutus* remained alive in purified nitrogen for 20 days, although movement was sluggish; attempts to culture it in an atmosphere of hydrogen failed (Watson, 1944). Many protozoa can survive without oxygen for a limited time (reviewed by Stout, 1956), but this usually involves a reduction in activity (Pantin, 1930, for *Amoeba* sp.; Kitching, 1939, for *Paramecium* spp.; Stout, 1956, for *Colpoda* spp.) and therefore in metabolism. The duration of survival without oxygen may be affected by a variety of other conditions, and if experiments are to be designed for ecological rather than purely physiological purposes, it is important that these other conditions should be representative. For instance, it was found (Kitching, 1939) that *Paramecium multimicronucleatum* from a flourishing hay infusion survived without oxygen for about 11 hr. in a hanging drop of its own culture medium. Its food supply was limited, and the conditions regarding disposal of excretory matter were abnormal, so that it would not be safe to suggest how long it could survive anaerobically in nature.

Conditions of reduced oxygen tension are found in a thermocline when there is oxygen-free water beneath, as well as rather generally near the bottom of muddy ponds. It is not possible to say whether the abundance of *Enchelys* sp. (Juday, 1919), *Loxodes rostrum* (Rylov, 1923), *Coleps* sp. (Ruttner, 1953), or *Stentor coeruleus* (Sprugel, 1951) under these conditions is related directly to low oxygen tension or whether the connexion is through some other factor, such as an aggregation of suitable food. *S. coeruleus* was found to be capable of living in well-oxygenated water.

Hydrogen-ion concentration and carbon dioxide concentration

The importance of controlling the hydrogen-ion concentration is well known to anyone who cultures protozoa. Much information has been published as to the limits of pH for growth or survival of various protozoa in culture (summarized by Hall, 1953, p. 479), but little fundamental information is available as to why some species are more tolerant than others of acidity or alkalinity. As an extreme example, *Euglena mutabilis* has been found at pH 1·9 in the effluent from a sulphuric acid factory (Hein, 1953).

The complexity of the problem is sufficiently illustrated by reference to the work of Schoenborn (1949) on the growth of the saprozoic flagellate *Astasia longa* in different culture media at different pH values. In a medium containing casein peptone *A. longa* was able to grow over the range pH 3·3–3·7 to 9·2–9·6, but in an inorganic medium with only acetate added the range was only from pH 4·6–5·1 to about 7·3.

In nature the pH is intimately connected with the concentration of carbon dioxide as well as with the alkali reserve of the medium, and therefore shares with the oxygen concentration the property that it is likely to be modified profoundly by the presence of living matter. Gradients are apt to be set up around aquatic vegetation, etc., and local microhabitats may become established which differ from the general mass of surrounding water. Little is known about such gradients, although it should now be possible to develop means of investigating them. Picken (1937) has suggested that chemical gradients, together with thigmotaxis, may play a part in holding together an association of free-living protozoa with filamentous algae or sewage fungus.

In view of the graded conditions of oxygen tension and pH (or carbon dioxide tension) which are found in nature, it is not surprising that some protozoa when tested in the laboratory are found to move along such gradients into what may be supposed to be better conditions. Flagellates may aggregate in response to concentrations of dissolved oxygen or carbon dioxide determined by their own metabolism. When mounted under a cover-glass, *Bodo sulcatus* was found to aggregate at the centre, but later to move out and form a ring a little way from the edge. Further tests indicated that the response was to oxygen tension rather than to carbon dioxide (Fox, 1920). On the other hand, if *Astasia longa* is exposed to a gradient of dissolved carbon dioxide concentration under certain experimental conditions, it aggregated at a pH of 5·3–6·3 (Borgers & Kitching, 1956). The response of the *Astasia* to pH was constant in spite of changes in the alkali reserve of the medium, so that it appears to depend on the concentration of H^+ and not of CO_2, HCO_3^-, or CO_3^{2-}.

There can be no doubt that hydrogen-ion concentration must play an important part in controlling the occurrence and distribution of certain protozoa in nature. For instance, the ciliate *Spirostomum ambiguum* was observed by Saunders (1924) to appear in a pond at Cambridge in

October, in water at pH 7·4 (near the bottom), to persist throughout the winter at pH 7·3–7·5, and to disappear again with the spring growth of vegetation as the pH rose above 7·6. Moreover, the *Spirostomum* in the pond remained by day among the dead leaves at the bottom, where the water was slightly more acid, but came out into the open water at night, when in the absence of photosynthesis the water was presumably less alkaline. Saunders was able to demonstrate experimentally that in a gradient of pH from 6·8 to 8·0 (obtained by adjustment of the carbon dioxide content) *Spirostomum* collected at the acid end. *S. ambiguum* is very sensitive to alkalinity. It was found to survive for a long or indefinite period at pH 7·4, but the survival time decreased sharply from pH 7·6 upwards (whether obtained by a reduction of the carbon dioxide content or by the use of a dilute borax and boric acid buffer) (Jenkin, 1927). In this case laboratory experiments have been successfully related to the survival and behaviour of a ciliate in nature.

Tidal rhythms

In many cases protozoa rely for safety on a mechanism of behaviour which brings them into a suitable range of environmental conditions. The range of behaviour possible within the anatomical limitations of a protozoon is surprising. In the case of light, oxygen tension or carbon tension, the environment often offers a gradient along which they can move. In the case of the rising tide, a microscopic organism living at the surface of mud or in a rock pool may have to descend to safety at the first wash of the water, or even earlier, if it is not to be carried away; and this may be ensured by an inherent or long-lasting rhythm of behaviour.

On the shores of the Avon at Bristol, *Euglena deses* appears on the surface of the mud 1–2 hr. after dawn and disappears near the time of sunset, the reaction being determined by the light and therefore changing in time of day in accordance with the season of the year. But super-imposed on this direct response there is a rhythm related to the tide. *Euglena* stays down while the water covers its particular stretch of mud, comes up ½–1 hr. after the water has receded, provided it is light, and disappears again with the first wash of the rising water. The *Euglena* living at the upper margin of the tidal mud is only covered for a short time at spring tides, and when brought into the laboratory responds only to light and dark. But *Euglena* collected from a zone always under tidal influence continues to burrow under the mud in the laboratory, even though not covered with water, at the time of high water, and this rhythm persists for about 3 days (Bracher, 1919). A similar observation has been made by Fauré-Fremiet (1950*b*) on a chrysomonad, *Chromulina psammobia*, which forms yellow patches on the sand near low-water mark. In this case the rhythm persisted in the laboratory for 8 days in the absence of a tide.

Another striking example is that of *Strombidium oculatum*, a ciliate with symbiotic algal cells which inhabits intertidal rock pools and is apparently confined to these. This animal remains at the bottom encysted while the tide is in but comes to the surface soon after the tide has left its pool (Fauré-Fremiet, 1948). The rhythm is continued in the laboratory and is independent of light, but gradually loses its regularity *in vitro*.

All these cases are ascribed by Fauré-Fremiet to a metabolic rhythm which is constantly maintained by natural selection. Certainly any individuals which fail to follow the rhythm are likely to be washed away from their natural habitat. In the case of *Chromulina*, Fauré-Fremiet found that the rhythm was suppressed if the temperature was lowered to $+2$ or $+3°$, and reappeared when the temperature was raised again but was then out of phase with the tide.

I am indebted to Dr H. D. Crofton for advice and to Professor J. E. Harris, F.R.S., for criticism of the manuscript.

The figures in this paper have been reproduced by permission as follows: Fig. 1, *The Journal of Experimental Zoology*; Fig. 2, The Company of Biologists Ltd. (*J. Exp. Biol.*); Fig. 3, The University of Chicago Press (*Physiol. Zool.*); Fig. 4, The Williams and Wilkins Company, Baltimore, Md.; Fig. 5, *The Biological Bulletin*; Fig. 6, *The Journal of Morphology*. I am glad to express my gratitude to the authorities concerned.

REFERENCES

ALLEN, W. E. (1928). Review of five years of studies on phytoplankton at Southern California piers, 1920–1924 inclusive. *Bull. Scripps Instn Oceanogr. tech.* **1**, 357.
ALLEN, W. E. (1940). Summary of results of twenty years of researches on marine phytoplankton. *Proc. Sixth Pacific Science Congress*, **3**, 577–83. (Held at Berkeley, 1939.)
ALLEN, W. E. (1942). Occurrence of 'Red Water' near San Diego. *Science*, **96**, 471.
ALLEN, W. E. (1943). 'Red Water' in La Jolla Bay in 1942. *Trans. Amer. micr. Soc.* **62**, 262–4.
ALSTERBERG, B. (1926). Die winklische Bestimmungsmethode für in Wasser gelösten, elementaren Sauerstoff sowie ihre Anwendung bei Anwesenheit oxydierbarer Substanzen. *Biochem. Z.* **170**, 30.
BAKER, E. S. G. & BAUMBERGER, P. (1941). The respiratory rate and the cytochrome content of a ciliate protozoan (*Tetrahymena geleii*). *J. cell. comp. Physiol.* **17**, 285.

BALLANTINE, D. (1953). Comparison of the different methods for estimating nannoplankton. *J. Mar. biol. Ass. U.K.* **32**, 129.

BALLANTINE, D. (1955). Observations on a toxic *Gymnodinium. Challenger Soc. Abstr.* **3**, no. 7, p. 15.

BANDEL, W. (1940). Phytoplankton- und Nährstoffgehalt der Ostsee in Gebiet der Darsser Schwelle. *Int. Rev. Hydrobiol.* **40**, 249.

BARKER, A. N. (1942). The seasonal incidence, occurrence and distribution of Protozoa in the bacteria bed process of sewage disposal. *Ann. appl. Biol.* **29**, 23.

BARKER, A. N. (1946). The ecology and function of Protozoa in sewage purification. *Ann. appl. Biol.* **33**, 314.

BARKER, H. A. (1935). The culture and physiology of the marine dinoflagellates. *Arch. Mikrobiol.* **6**, 156.

BEERS, C. D. (1926). The life cycle of the ciliate *Didinium nasutum* with reference to encystment. *J. Morph.* **42**, 1–21.

BEERS, C. D. (1933). The relation of density of population to rate of reproduction in the ciliates *Didinium nasutum* and *Stylonychia pustulata. Arch. Prostistenk.* **80**, 36–64.

BEERS, C. D. (1937). The viability of ten-year-old *Didinium* cysts (Infusoria). *Amer. Nat.* **71**, 521.

BODINE, J. H. (1921). Hydrogen-ion concentration of Protozoan cultures. *Biol. Bull., Woods Hole,* **41**, 73.

BORGERS, J. A. & KITCHING, J. A. (1956). Reactions of the flagellate ~~Astasia~~ *longa* in gradients of dissolved carbon dioxide. *Proc. roy. Soc.* B, **144**, 507.

BRAARUD, T. (1951). Salinity as an ecological factor in marine phytoplankton. *Physiol. Plant.* **4**, 28.

BRAARUD, T. & PAPPAS, I. (1951). Experimental studies on the dinoflagellate *Peridinium triquetrum* (Ehrb.) Lebour. *Avh. norske VidenskAkad.* (1951), no. 2.

BRAARUD, T. & ROSSAVIK, E. (1951). Observations on the marine dinoflagellate *Prorocentrum micans* Ehrenb. in culture. *Avh. norske VidenskAkad.* (1951), no. 1.

BRACHER, R. (1919). Observations on *Euglena deses. Ann. Bot., Lond.,* **33**, 93.

BRAND, T. VON (1946). *Anaerobiosis in Invertebrates.* Biodynamica Monographs no. 4. Normandy, Missouri.

BRIDGMAN, A. J. (1948). Studies on some aspects of cystment in the ciliate *Tillina magna. J. exp. Zool.* **108**, 21.

BROWN, M. G. (1940). Growth of Protozoan cultures. II. *Leucophrys patula* and *Glacucoma pyriformis* in a bacteria-free medium. *Physiol. Zoöl.* **13**, 277.

BURBANCK, W. D. (1942). Physiology of the ciliate *Colpidium colpoda.* I. The effect of various bacteria as food on the division rate of *Colpidium colpoda. Physiol. Zoöl.* **15**, 342.

BURBANCK, W. D. & GILPIN, D. W. (1946). Physiology of the ciliate *Colpidium colpoda.* III. The possible use of the division rate of *Colpidium colpoda* for identification of intestinal bacteria. *Physiol. Zoöl.* **19**, 236.

BUTTS, H. E. (1935). The effect of certain salts of sea water upon reproduction in the marine amoeba, *Flabellula mira* Schaeffer. *Physiol. Zoöl.* **8**, 273.

CARTER, L. (1957). Ionic regulation in the ciliate *Spirostomum ambiguum. J. exp. Biol.* (in the Press).

CRUMP, L. M. (1950). The influence of the bacterial environment on the excystment of amoeba from soil. *J. gen. Microbiol.* **4**, 16.

CUSHING, D. H. (1955). Production and a pelagic fishery. *Fish. Invest. London,* series II, **18**, no. 7. H.M. Stationery Office.

CUSHMAN, J. A. (1950). *Foraminifera. Their classification and economic use*, 4th ed. Cambridge, Mass.: Harvard University Press.

CUTLER, D. W. (1923). The action of Protozoa on bacteria when inoculated into sterile soil. *Ann. appl. Biol.* **10**, 137.

CUTLER, D. W., CRUMP, L. M. & SANDON, H. (1923). A quantitative investigation of the bacterial and protozoan population of the soil, with an account of the protozoan fauna. *Phil. Trans.* B, **211**, 317.

CZERNIN-CHUDENITZ, C. W. (1955). Ökologische Untersuchungen über das Phytoplankton des Klopeinersees in Kärnten. *Arch. Hydrobiol. (Plankt.)*, **51**, 54.

DEWEY, V. C. & KIDDER, G. W. (1940). Growth studies on ciliates. VI. Diagnosis, sterilisation and growth characteristics of *Perispira ovum. Biol. Bull., Woods Hole*, **79**, 255.

DROOP, M. R. (1955). A suggested method for the assay of vitamin B_{12} in sea water. *J. Mar. biol. Ass. U.K.* **34**, 435.

EDDY, S. (1928). Succession of Protozoa in cultures under controlled conditions. *Trans. Amer. micr. Soc.* **47**, 283.

FAURÉ-FREMIET, E. (1948). The ecology of some infusorian communities of intertidal pools. *J. Anim. Ecol.* **17**, 127.

FAURÉ-FREMIET, E. (1950a). Écologie des ciliés psammophiles littoraux. *Bull. biol.* **84**, 35.

FAURÉ-FREMIET, E. (1950b). Rhythme de marée d'une *Chromulina* psammophile. *Bull. biol.* **84**, 207.

FAURÉ-FREMIET, E. (1951). Écologie des protistes littoraux. *Année biol.* **27**, 437.

FELLERS, C. R. & ALLISON, P. E. (1920). The Protozoan fauna of the soils of New Jersey. *Soil Sci.* **9**, 1,

FINDENEGG, 1. (1943). Untersuchungen über die Ökologie und die Produktionsverhältnisse des Planktons im Kärntner Seegebiete. *Int. Rev. Hydrobiol.* **43**, 368.

FINLEY, H. E. (1930). Toleration of fresh water Protozoa to increased salinity. *Ecology*, **11**, 337.

FOX, H. M. (1920). An investigation into the cause of the spontaneous aggregation of flagellates and into the reactions of flagellates to dissolved oxygen. *J. gen. Physiol.* **3**, 483.

FRANZ, H. (1951). État de nos connaissances sur la microfauna du sol. *Année biol.* **27**, 241.

FRISCH, J. A. (1940). The experimental adaptation of *Paramecium* to sea water. *Arch. Protistenk.* **93**, 38.

GARNJOBST, L. (1947). The effect of certain deficient media on resting cyst formation in *Colpoda duodenaria. Physiol. Zoöl.* **20**, 5.

GAUSE, G. F. (1934). *The struggle for existence*. Baltimore, Md.: The Williams and Wilkins Co.

GAUSE, G. F. (1935). Vérifications expérimentales de la théorie mathématique de la lutte pour la vie. *Actualités sci. industr.* no. 277.

GAUSE, G. F., NASTUKOVA, O. K. & ALPATOV, W. W. (1934). The influence of biologically conditioned media on the growth of a mixed population of *Paramecium caudatum* and *P. aurelia. J. Anim. Ecol.* **3**, 222.

GIESE, A. C. (1938). Cannibalism and gigantism in *Blepharisma. Trans. Amer. micr. Soc.* **57**, 245.

GRAHAM, H. W. (1941). An oceanographic consideration of the dinoflagellate genus *Ceratium. Ecol. Monogr.* **11**, 99.

GRAHAM, H. W. & BRONIKOVSKY, N. (1944). The genus *Ceratium* in the Pacific and North Atlantic Oceans. *Publ. Carneg. Instn*, no. 565.

GRAY, E. (1951). The ecology of the bacteria of Hobson's Brook, a Cambridgeshire chalk stream. *J. gen. Microbiol.* **5**, 840.

GRAY, E. (1952). The ecology of the ciliate fauna of Hobson's Brook, a Cambridge-shire chalk stream. *J. gen. Microbiol.* **6**, 108.

GREENLEAF, W. E. (1926). The influences of volume of culture medium and cell proximity on the rate of reproduction of Infusoria. *J. exp. Zool.* **46**, 143.

GRITTNER, I. (1951). Die Nahrungswahl des Pantoffeltierchens *Paramecium caudatum* Ehrb. *Mikrokosmos*, **41**, 62.

GROSPIETCH, T. (1954). Studien über die Rhizopodenfauna von Schwedisch-Lappland. *Arch. Hydrobiol.* (*Plankt.*), **49**, 546.

HAAGEN-SMIT, A. J. & THIMANN, K. V. (1938). The excystment of *Colpoda cucullus*. I. The chemical nature of the excysting factors in hay infusions. *J. cell. comp. Physiol.* **11**, 389.

HALL, R. P. (1953). *Protozoology*, 1st ed. New York: Prentice-Hall Inc.

HALL, R. P. & SCHOTTENFELD, A. (1941). Maximal density and phases of death in populations of *Glaucoma pyriformis*. *Physiol. Zoöl.* **14**, 384.

HAMMANN, I. (1952). Ökologische und biologische Untersuchungen an Süsswasser-peritrichen. *Arch. Hydrobiol.* (*Plankt.*), **47**, 177.

HARDIN, G. (1942). An investigation of the physiological requirements of a pure culture of the heterotrophic flagellate, *Oikomonas termo* Kent. *Physiol. Zoöl.* **15**, 466.

HARDIN, G. (1944). Physiological observations and their ecological significance: a study of the Protozoan *Oikomonas termo*. *Ecology*, **25**, 192.

HARDING, J. P. (1937*a*). Quantitative studies on the ciliate *Glaucoma*. I. The regulation of the size and the fission rate by the bacterial food supply. *J. exp. Biol.* **14**, 422.

HARDING, J. P. (1937*b*). Quantitative studies on the ciliate *Glaucoma*. II. The effects of starvation. *J. exp. Biol.* **14**, 431.

HARVEY, H. W. (1955). *The chemistry and fertility of sea waters*. Cambridge University Press.

HAUSMANN, L. A. (1917). Observations on the ecology of the Protozoa. *Amer. Nat.* **51**, 156.

HEIN, G. (1953). Über *Euglena mutabilis* und ihr Verhalten in sauren Medien. *Arch. Hydrobiol.* (*Plankt.*), **47**, 576.

HETHERINGTON, A. (1933). The culture of some holotrichous ciliates. *Arch. Protistenk.* **80**, 255.

HOPKINS, D. W. (1946). The contractile vacuole and the adjustment to changing concentrations in fresh water amoebae. *Biol. Bull., Woods Hole*, **90**, 158.

HUNGATE, R. E. (1943). The culture of *Eudiplodinium neglectum*, with experiments on the digestion of cellulose. *Biol. Bull., Woods Hole*, **83**, 303.

HUTCHENS, J. O. (1941). The effect of the age of the culture on the rate of oxygen consumption and the respiratory quotient of *Chilomonas paramecium*. *J. cell. comp. Physiol.* **17**, 321.

HUTNER, S. H. & PROVASOLI, L. (1955). Comparative biochemistry of flagellates. In *Biochemistry and Physiology of Protozoa*, vol. **2**, edited by S. H. Hutner and A. Lwoff. New York: Academic Press Inc.

JAHN, T. L. (1935). Studies on the physiology of the euglenoid flagellates. VI. The effect of temperature and of acetate on *Euglena gracilis* cultures in the dark. *Arch. Protistenk.* **86**, 251.

JENKIN, P. M. (1927). The relation of *Spirostomum ambiguum* to the hydrogen ion concentration (alkaline range). *J. exp. Biol.* **4**, 365.

JUDAY, C. (1919). A freshwater anaerobic ciliate. *Biol. Bull., Woods Hole*, **36**, 92.

KIDDER, G. W. (1947). The nutrition of monocellular animal organisms. *Ann. N.Y. Acad. Sci.* **49**, 99.

KIDDER, G. W. (1951). Nutrition and metabolism of Protozoa. *Annu. Rev. Microbiol.* **5**, 139.

KIDDER, G. W., LILLY, D. M. & CLAFF, C. L. (1940). The influence of food on the structure and growth of *Glaucoma vorax* sp.nov. *Biol. Bull., Woods Hole*, **78**, 9.

KIDDER, G. W. & STUART, C. A. (1939*a*). Growth studies in ciliates. I. The role of bacteria in the growth and reproduction of *Colpoda*. *Physiol. Zoöl.* **12**, 329.

KIDDER, G. W. & STUART, C. A. (1939*b*). Growth studies in ciliates. II. The food factor in the growth, reproduction, and encystment of *Colpoda*. *Physiol. Zoöl.* **12**, 341.

KITCHING, J. A. (1939). The effects of a lack of oxygen and of low oxygen tensions on *Paramecium*. *Biol. Bull., Woods Hole*, **77**, 339.

KITCHING, J. A. (1956*a*). Contractile vacuoles of Protozoa. *Protoplasmatologia*, 3D 4*a*. Vienna: Springer Verlag.

KITCHING, J. A. (1956*b*). Food vacuoles. *Protoplasmatologia*, 3D 4*b*. Vienna: Springer Verlag.

LACKEY, J. B. (1932). Oxygen deficiency and sewage protozoa; with descriptions of some new species. *Biol. Bull., Woods Hole*, **63**, 287.

LACKEY, J. B. (1936). Occurrence and distribution of the marine Protozoan species in the Woods Hole area. *Biol. Bull., Woods Hole*, **70**, 264.

LACKEY, J. B. (1938). A study of some ecological factors affecting the distribution of Protozoa. *Ecol. Monogr.* **8**, 501.

LEBOUR, M. V. (1916). The Peridiniales of Plymouth Sound from the region beyond the breakwater. *J. Mar. biol. Ass. U.K.*, N.S. **11**, 183.

LILLY, D. M. (1942). Nutritional and supplementary factors in the growth of carnivorous ciliates. *Physiol. Zoöl.* **15**, 146.

LILLY, D. M. (1953). The nutrition of carnivorous Protozoa. *Ann. N.Y. Acad. Sci.* **56**, 910.

LINDEMAN, R. L. (1942). Experimental simulation of winter anaerobiosis in a senescent lake. *Ecology*, **23**, 1.

LOEFER, J. B. (1939). Acclimatization of fresh-water ciliates and flagellates to media of higher osmotic pressure. *Physiol. Zoöl.* **12**, 161.

LUCAS, C. E. (1955). External metabolites in the sea. *Deep-Sea Res.* **3**, suppl. p. 139.

MITCHELL, W. H. (1929). The division rate of *Paramecium* in relation to temperature. *J. exp. Zool.* **54**, 383.

MOORE, G. M. (1939). A limnological investigation of the microscopic benthic fauna of Douglas Lake, Michigan. *Ecol. Monogr.* **9**, 537.

MORTIMER, C. H. (1941). The exchange of dissolved substances between mud and water in lakes. *J. Ecol.* **29**, 280.

Mᴏᴏᴏ, J. D. (1985). Factors influencing the distribution of fresh-water ciliates. *Ecology*, **6**, 437.

NORDLI, E. (1953). Salinity and temperature as controlling factors for distribution and mass occurrence of Ceratia. *Saertr. av Blyttia*, **11**, 16.

ORMSBEE, R. A. (1942). The normal growth and respiration of *Tetrahymena geleii*. *Biol. Bull., Woods Hole*, **82**, 423.

PACE, D. M. & IRELAND, R. L. (1945). The effects of oxygen, carbon dioxide and pressure on growth in *Chilomonas paramecium* and *Tetrahymena geleii* Furgason. *J. gen. Physiol.* **28**, 547.

PACE, D. M. & LYMAN, E. D. (1947). Oxygen consumption and carbon dioxide elimination in *Tetrahymena geleii* Furgason. *Biol. Bull., Woods Hole*, **92**, 210.

PANTIN, C. F. A. (1926). On the physiology of amoeboid movement. IV. The action of magnesium. *J. exp. Biol.* **3**, 297.

PANTIN, C. F. A. (1930). On the physiology of amoeboid movement. V. Anaerobic movement. *Proc. roy. Soc. B*, **105**, 538.

PARKE, M., MANTON, I. & CLARKE, B. (1955). Studies on marine flagellates. II. Three new species of *Chrysochromulina*. *J. Mar. biol. Ass. U.K.* **34**, 579.

PAULSON, B. (1953). Some rhizopod associations in a Swedish mire. *Oikos*, **4**, 151.

PENNAK, R. W. (1951). Comprehensive ecology of the interstitial fauna of freshwater and marine beaches. *Année biol.* **27**, 451.

PHELPS, A. (1935). Growth of Protozoa in pure culture. I. Effect upon the growth curve of the age of the inoculum and of the amount of the inoculum. *J. exp. Zool.* **70**, 109.

PHELPS, A. (1936). Growth of Protozoa in pure culture. II. Effect upon the growth curve of different concentrations of nutrient materials. *J. exp. Zool.* **72**, 479.

PHELPS, A. (1946). Growth of Protozoa in pure culture. III. Effect of temperature upon the division rate. *J. exp. Zool.* **102**, 277.

PICKEN, L. E. R. (1937). The structure of some protozoan communities. *J. Ecol.* **25**, 368.

PROVASOLI, L. & PINTNER, I. J. (1953). Ecological implications of *in vitro* nutritional requirements of algal flagellates. *Ann. N.Y. Acad. Sci.* **56**, 839.

PRUTHI, H. S. (1927). On the hydrogen-ion concentration of hay infusions, with special reference to the influence on the Protozoan sequence. *J. exp. Biol.* **4**, 292.

ROTTIER, P.-B. (1936). Recherches sur la croissance de *Polytoma uvella*. L'influence de la concentration des substances nutritives. *C.R. Soc. Biol., Paris*, **122**, 776.

RUTTNER, F. (1953). *Fundamentals of limnology*. Translated by D. G. Frey and F. E. J. Fry. Toronto: University of Toronto Press.

RYLOV, V. M. (1923). Über den Einfluss des im Wasser gelösten Sauerstoffs und Schwefelwasserstoffs auf den Lebenzyklus und die vertikale Verteilung des Infusors *Loxodes rostrum* O. F. Müll. (Aspirotricha, Anphileptina.) *Int. Rev. Hydrobiol.* **11**, 179.

SAUNDERS, J. T. (1924). The effect of the hydrogen ion concentration on the behaviour, growth and occurrence of *Spirostomum*. *Proc. Camb. phil. Soc. biol. Sci.* **1**, 189.

SCHOENBORN, H. W. (1947). The relation of temperature to growth of *Astasia* (Protozoa) in pure culture. *J. exp. Zool.* **105**, 269.

SCHOENBORN, H. W. (1949). Growth of *Astasia longa* in relation to hydrogen ion concentration. *J. exp. Zool.* **111**, 437.

SINGH, B. N. (1942). Selection of bacterial food by flagellates and amoeba. *Ann. appl. Biol.* **29**, 18.

SINGH, B. N. (1955). Culturing soil Protozoa and estimating their numbers in soil. In *Soil Zoology*, by Kevan, D. K. McE. London: Butterworth's Scientific Publications.

SMITH, J. A. (1940). Some effects of temperature on the frequency of division and on the volume of starch and fat in *Chilomonas paramecium*. *Biol. Bull., Woods Hole*, **79**, 379.

SPRUGEL, G. (1951). Vertical distribution of *Stentor coeruleus* in relation to dissolved oxygen levels in an Iowa pond. *Ecology*, **32**, 147.

STOUT, J. D. (1955). Environmental factors affecting the life history of three soil species of *Colpoda* (Ciliata). *Trans. roy. Soc. N.Z.* **82**, 1165.

STOUT, J. D. (1956). Reactions of ciliates to environmental factors. *Ecology*, **37**, 178.

STRICKLAND, A. G. R. & HAAGEN-SMIT, A. J. (1947). Chemical substances inducing excystment of the resting cysts of *Colpoda duodenaria*. *J. cell. comp. Physiol.* **30**, 381.

STRICKLAND, A. G. R. & HAAGEN-SMIT, A. J. (1948). The excystment of *Colpoda duodenaria*. *Science*, **107**, 204.

SUGDEN, B. & LLOYD, L. (1950). The clearing of turbid waters by means of the ciliate *Carchesium*: a demonstration. *J. Inst. Sew. Purif.* **16**.

TAYLOR, C. V. & STRICKLAND, A. G. R. (1936). Effects of high vacua and extreme temperature on cysts of *Colpoda cucullus*. *Physiol. Zoöl.* **9**, 15.

THORNTON, H. G. & CRUMP, L. M. (1952). Micropredators in soil. *Rep. Rothamst. exp. Sta.* p. 164.

WAGTENDONK, W. J. VAN (1955*a*). The nutrition of ciliates. In *Biochemistry and Physiology of Protozoa*, vol. **2**, edited by S. H. Hutner and A. Lwoff. New York: Academic Press Inc.

WAGTENDONK, W. J. VAN (1955*b*). Encystment and excystment of Protozoa. In *Biochemistry and Physiology of Protozoa*, vol. **2**, edited by S. H. Hutner and A. Lwoff. New York: Academic Press Inc.

WANG, C. C. (1928). Ecological studies of the seasonal distribution of Protozoa in a fresh-water pond. *J. Morph.* **46**, 431.

WATSON, J. M. (1944). Studies on the morphology and bionomics of a little known holotrichous ciliate—*Balantiophorus minutus*. Schewiakoff. II. The effect of environmental factors. *J. R. micr. Soc.* **64**, 31.

WATSON, J. M. (1946). The bionomics of coprophilic Protozoa. *Biol. Rev.* **21**, 121.

WELCH, P. S. (1935). *Limnology*, 1st ed. New York and London: McGraw-Hill Book Co. Inc.

WHEDON, W. F. (1939). A three year survey of the phytoplankton in the region of San Francisco, California. *Int. Rev. Hydrobiol.* **38**, 459.

WISEMAN, J. D. H. & OVEY, C. D. (1950). Recent investigations on the deep-sea floor. *Proc. Geol. Ass., Lond.*, **61**, 28.

WOODRUFF, L. E. (1912). Observations of the origin and sequence of the Protozoan fauna of hay infusions. *J. exp. Zool.* **12**, 205.

ECOLOGY OF MICRO-ORGANISMS IN SOILS AS OBSERVED DURING THEIR DEVELOPMENT UPON BURIED CELLULOSE FILM

H. T. TRIBE

School of Agriculture, Cambridge

Most soils contain an enormous population of micro-organisms, both in numbers and diversity. Among the major biological groups found in nearly all soils are bacteria, fungi, algae, Protozoa and other small fauna. There is general similarity in the populations found in different soils. With reference to bacteria, it is possible to isolate, for example, nitrifiers, nitrogen-fixers, or anaerobic spore-formers by applying the appropriate enrichment technique, from almost any soil. Similarly, amongst the fungi, many genera may be isolated readily from a great diversity of soil types. All this population is supported through the decomposition of a variety of different kinds of organic matter, and so a knowledge of the fate of the organic matter should assist in following the disposition of the micro-organisms on it.

Aerobic decomposition of fresh organic matter, such as, for example, leaf tissues, follows a course which may be divided into two phases. The first is its conversion to humus, and the second is the breakdown of the humus to simple gaseous and mineral constituents. Considered as a physical substrate, humus is organic matter which has become so extensively decomposed that it has lost all its original structure, become broken up and dispersed amongst the mineral particles of the soil. It has originated in two quite distinct ways, from synthesis of microbial tissues and metabolic products, and by accumulation of the components of the organic matter that are decomposable with difficulty. During its formation there has been a loss of carbon as carbon dioxide, and an adjustment of nitrogen content to give a carbon-nitrogen ratio (for arable soils in general) of approximately ten to one. Some mobilization of mineral constituents has also probably occurred. The rate of decomposition slows down at about the humus stage, for reasons which are not known. Further breakdown to simple products continues over a long period.

These two phases coincide with Winogradsky's (1925) division of the soil microflora into autochthonous (indigenous) and zymogenous (fermentative) flora. The former are those micro-organisms always numerous in soil and not fluctuating much in numbers, carrying on activities which require no nutrients or sources of energy other than those normally present in soil. Soil in this context excludes organic matter which has not been humified. Winogradsky's zymogenous flora consists of those micro-organisms, developing rapidly on freshly added organic matter, which are normally present in low numbers, and to which they subside after a period of great activity.

Winogradsky regarded the autochthonous flora as primarily small coccoid bacteria, which Conn (1948) considers to be stages in the life cycle of certain normally rod-shaped bacteria, his genus *Arthrobacter*. Conn himself regards as autochthonous forms certain bacteria which are difficult to classify on account of their weak fermentative ability, chiefly non-sporing rods which either have a micrococcus stage in their life cycle (*Arthrobacter*) or remain as short rods (*Agrobacterium* Conn).

Conn regards as zymogenous micro-organisms the rest of the non-spore-forming bacteria, the spore-forming bacteria, the actinomycetes and fungi. In soil containing no fresh organic matter, the last three groups probably exist as spores, whilst the numbers of the non-spore-forming bacteria drop to a very low level, requiring special enrichment techniques to detect them.

All the soil microflora except certain non-spore-forming bacteria are therefore regarded as being responsible for decomposition of organic matter before the humus stage. Dr Garrett envisages a colonization, exploitation and exhaustion of such substrates, during which a succession of micro-organisms develops upon them. He points out that analogies can be drawn between the ecology of higher plants and the microbial ecology of soil, but with the fundamental difference that the microbial succession depletes the capacity of the habitat rather than building it up, so that the end-point of a succession of micro-organisms on a substrate is not a persisting climax association, but zero (Garrett, 1955).

Direct experimental evidence for these successions is lacking, chiefly for technical difficulties of demonstration. Indirect evidence, in the constant presence in soils of the very diverse microflora (and fauna), supports the view that particular substrates are colonized by particular micro-organisms; otherwise one would expect that in a permanent habitat such as soil the most efficient micro-organisms would have by now driven out those less efficient in decomposition of 'organic matter' and become established as a relatively small group. And since a substrate is changed by the development of micro-organisms on it, any one substrate may be expected in the course of time to provide a series of microhabitats.

It is in the study of the interrelations of micro-organisms in particular habitats that soil microbiology should be especially able to contribute to a knowledge of microbial ecology, because any substrate put into the soil will be in the presence of an almost unlimited potential of microbial species. Those developing on it will possess certain properties. They must first be susceptible to stimulation to germinate from a resting stage. They must after germination be able to coexist with any other organism which develops at the same time or soon afterwards—perhaps having been stimulated to germinate by the development of the first organism. When the substrate has become exhausted, the organism must be able to form a resting stage to continue the species.

In this contribution, organic matter is represented by Cellophane, the brand of regenerated cellulose film made by the British Cellophane Company. It has two most suitable properties. It is a relatively pure form of cellulose, and it provides perfect conditions for observation. Simply by mounting small pieces on glass cover-slips with distilled water it is possible to observe the process of decomposition to a very advanced stage. It provides a theatre on which the course of life under soil conditions may be watched and the chief characters become known.

Cellophane has been used in order to trap soil chytrids (e.g. Haskins, 1946), but seems not to have been used before in studies on general microflora. Cellulose in the form of filter paper adhering to microscope slides and buried in forest soils was used by Cholodny (1930) in a few observations, but he never followed it up. The Cholodny slide is a glass microscope slide buried in soil, removed after a period of time, cleaned of major soil particles and stained. Since no nutrient is contained in the glass, development of micro-organisms on it is supported by organic matter in the soil. The slide reflects this development in soil organic matter rather than creating its own special habitats.

TECHNIQUE

The technique as finally adopted was as follows: British Cellophane Company P.T. 300 sheet Cellophane* was cut into pieces approximately 1.0×0.5 cm. and these were boiled in a large volume of distilled water to dissolve out plasticizers. After washing in another volume of distilled water they were placed singly on $\frac{7}{8}$ in. square cover-slips, the excess water was drained off and the cover-slips buried vertically in pots of soil. If the Cellophane pieces are not supported on cover-slips, it is not usually possible to recover them after about one month. The moisture

* Kindly given by British Cellophane Ltd., Bridgwater, Somerset.

holding capcity (m.h.c.) of the soil having previously been determined, the soil was watered to 60 % of this value (after adding the cover-slips). The pots were kept at laboratory temperatures and allowed to dry out to 30–40 % m.h.c., after which they were rewatered to the original value of 60 % m.h.c. The cycle lasted about 2–4 days and ensured aeration of the soil. These moisture and temperature relations were considered to give temperate conditions which would be favourable for aerobic decomposition.

The slips were dug out and examined from time to time and permanent microscope slides made by placing the cover-slip with adherent Cellophane into picronigrosin in lactophenol (Smith, 1954) for several hours, followed by washing in lactophenol. The back of the cover-slip was then washed in water, dried, and the cover-slip mounted Cellophane side downward in lactophenol on a slide. The mount was sealed with colourless nail varnish.

Before preservation the slips were examined wet under the microscope, when fungal spores could be transferred to agar plates with fine needles. Cellophane pieces were also cut up into small fragments and plated in order to examine the growing out of certain mycelia, or brushed free of surface mycelium and then cut up to obtain cultures of fungi which produced 'rooting branches' in the thickness of the Cellophane. Originally cultures of these were obtained by placing a triple 'sandwich' of Cellophane into soil, i.e. three pieces pressed together damp. After development of the fungi, the two outer pieces were removed and the 'roots' were found almost in pure culture in the centre piece. Pl. 1, fig. 1, was taken from a centre piece made in this way. Particular care was taken to ensure that the development of cultures from these sources was checked microscopically, since unwanted colonies can rapidly grow out from tiny soil particles which it is difficult to avoid transferring to the agar plate. Using filtered agar the inocula could be observed through the back of the Petri dish under ⅓ in. objective, provided the dishes were not too full of agar.

SOILS

Some study has been made of Cellophane buried in the following soils:

(1) Black fen peat from an arable field near Stretham, Cambs, pH 7·0.

(2) Calcareous loam from a field near Cambridge, pH 7·2.

(3) Loamy sand from the University Farm, Cambridge, pH 6·8.

(4) Weathered chalk, from the side of a quarry near Cambridge, pH 7·6.

(5) Leaf litter taken from under firs at Santon Downham in the Breckland, Suffolk, pH *c.* 5·2.

(6) Acid sandy soil underlying the litter, pH *c.* 4·4.

With the exception of the Breckland soils these were put through a 3 mm. sieve. The larger pieces of debris were removed from the litter to obtain a uniform material, and the acid sand, being almost free of debris, was not treated.

OBSERVATIONS

In outline, the course of decomposition was similar in all the soils. Fungi were nearly always the first colonizers and after a time they became replaced by bacteria. Sometimes fungi, bacteria and residual Cellophane were consumed by soil fauna, some of which left characteristic excremental pellets which were very persistent.

In the first four soils, similar fungi developed. A few days after addition of the Cellophane, fungus hyphae begin to grow and large parts of the Cellophane are quickly covered by mycelium. Several species put characteristic 'rooting' or nutritional branches into the thickness of the Cellophane. These 'roots' support the superficial mycelium. They spread out to a limited extent and sometimes dissolve out definite cavities (Pl. 1, fig. 1) but more usually enzymic action is restricted and no cavity can be seen (Pl. 1, fig. 2). After some time 'rooting' branches may autolyze, leaving patches of Cellophane full of holes (Pl. 1, fig. 3), or they may persist, perhaps increase in extent and degenerate slowly without leaving cavities. The 'rooting' fungi which have so far been found on Cellophane in these soils belong to the genera *Botryotrichum*, *Chaetomium* (?), *Humicola*, *Stachybotrys* and *Stysanus*. Other 'rooting' fungi occur which give rise to nothing more than sterile mycelium when isolated on to Czapek-Dox or potato-dextrose agars. Other fungi which develop vigorously on Cellophane are species of *Aleurisma* (and probably *Sporotrichum*) and an oval-spored fungus which has not so far been identified. Chytrids often occur in the early stages, especially in the loamy sand soil (Pl. 1, fig. 4). They cause an intense local solution of Cellophane, but since their powers of linear extension are limited, they are not a major factor in its degradation. Secondary infection by chytrids is not usual, although they produce sporangia and zoospores *in situ*. This is probably because the Cellophane is usually extensively colonized by other fungi by the time the zoospores are liberated.

Of the filamentous fungi which begin invasion of the Cellophane, probably the commonest is *Botryotrichum piluliferum* (Sacc. & Marsh), which is synonymous with *Coccospora agricola* (Goddard) (Downing, 1953). It produces typical 'rooting' branches, which are difficult to differentiate from those produced by *Chaetomium* (?) and *Humicola*. Aleuriospores (chlamydospores) are produced relatively late. The fungus therefore appears as a sterile mycelium on the Cellophane and has to be isolated for proof of identity.

An almost equally common isolate is a fungus believed to be a *Chaetomium*. This grows on Cellophane as a sterile mycelium indistinguishable from *Botryotrichum*, and when isolated on to agar produces tiny microspores on tips of phialides after a few days very similar to those figured in Downing's paper on *Botryotrichum* (but which I have never found on my isolates of *Botryotrichum*). After a few weeks, some isolates produce imperfect perithecia on potato-dextrose agar. These have occasionally been found on Cellophane in weathered chalk and in loamy sand (see Pl. 2, fig. 5). Only twice have perfect perithecia been seen on Cellophane (Pl. 2, figs. 6, 7), and in neither case was it possible to germinate the spores. Colonies obtained from ascospores from a *Chaetomium* perithecium growing on filter-paper laid on top of weathered chalk resembled these isolates very closely, in form of colony, production of microspores and eventual production of imperfect perithecia. Various media, including those with added paper or straw, failed to induce proper perithecial formation in any isolate.

Humicola grisea Traaen (White & Downing, 1953) is another common 'rooting' fungus found in these soils. This fungus is synonymous with several other chlamydospore-forming fungi recorded in the literature on soil fungi, viz. *Monotospora dalae* Mason, *Melanogone pucciniodes* Wollenw. & Richter, and probably *Mycogone nigra* (Morgan) Jensen and *Basisporium gallarum* Moll. It produces large chlamydospores which may appear two-celled, since they are sometimes borne on an inflated hyphal cell. The hyphae may spread some distance over the glass away from the Cellophane, giving the effect of a Cholodny slide (Pl. 2, fig. 8).

Stachybotrys atra Corda occurs more sporadically. It produces characteristic long narrow 'roots', usually with a zone of hydrolysed Cellophane surrounding the rooting hyphae, and spores on normal conidiophores in great abundance (Pl. 2, fig. 9). Sometimes it reduces the piece of Cellophane on which it is growing to a sooty mass and develops so vigorously as to extend into the neighbouring soil particles (Pl. 3, fig. 10). It is easily identified without isolation.

A species of *Stysanus* has been found as a dominant in weathered chalk. It produces 'roots' and two types of spore: an *Echinobotryum* stage (Pl. 3, fig. 11) with ovate rough spores occurs, and also typical coremia bearing slightly smaller smooth oval spores (Pl. 3, fig. 12).

After a period commonly of about 3 weeks, but which may vary from 1 week in loamy sand to 10 or more in weathered chalk, the fungus mycelium becomes moribund, staining patchily in short lengths, and the contents then disappear. A tissue of dead hyphae results and this becomes colonized by bacteria (Pl. 3, fig. 13). At about this stage the Cellophane with its microbial population may be attacked by soil animals, though this is by no means always the case. Pl. 4, fig. 14, shows a patch of Cellophane bearing mycelium and spores of *Stysanus* after 39 days' burial in weathered chalk, which has been attacked by some soil animal, probably a mite, leaving small pellets of excrement some of which consist largely of *Stysanus* spores. In one sample of fen soil, annelid worms were found devouring Cellophane. After 17 days from one to five worms were found on each of a number of Cellophane pieces, and after 46 days most of the Cellophane pieces on slips buried in these pots of soil had disappeared. No characteristic solid excremental pellets were found near the Cellophane attacked by these worms, which produced a rather ill-defined semi-liquid excretion.

Provided that there is no development of soil animals (other than nematodes, which invariably occur, often in large numbers, on Cellophane in the bacterial stage), the Cellophane remains thus for a long period of time, at least of the order of several months. The substrate, which sometimes still contains a small proportion of cellulose as shown by the chlor-zinc-iodide reaction, has become unsuitable for fungal development. Resting fungus spores are commonly present. There is one exception to the absence of fungal growth, and that is the development of nematode-trapping fungi, which occasionally flourish. Pl. 4, fig. 15, shows small trapping networks of one such fungus, probably a species of *Arthrobotrys*, growing over a background of bacterial debris —the remains of Cellophane after 70 days in fen soil. Pl. 4, fig. 16, from the same slide, shows a nematode caught by the fungus which is growing over the surface of the cover-slip away from the Cellophane.

The microflora developing on the Cellophane buried in soil from Santon Downham, in either the litter or acid sand underlying it, is quite different from the preceding. The dominant fungi are species of *Oidiodendron* (Robak, 1932; von Szilvinyi, 1940; Smith, 1946) (Pl. 5, fig. 17). All the four species known, *O. fuscum, O. rhodogenum* and *O. nigrum* Robak and *O. flavum* von Szilvinyi are found. They develop very strongly and after 4–6 weeks may cover the Cellophane with masses of spores. Occasionally *Penicillium* spp. have been found and *P. spinulosum* Thom.

has been seen sporing. *Trichoderma* has been isolated twice from Cellophane. Actinomycetes (*Streptomyces* spp.) sometimes occur in small colonies in the earlier stages of decomposition in these soils, producing characteristic spirals of spores.

Bacterial development is less than in the neutral soils, and only occasional nematodes are found. Both fungi and Cellophane may be heavily attacked by mites. Pl. 5, fig. 18, shows Cellophane after 12 weeks' burial in litter. It has been totally destroyed, and among masses of *Oidiodendron* spores can be seen the mite pellets. The brown portions of the conidiophores scattered amongst the debris are relatively resistant to mite action. One of the mites responsible is shown in Pl. 5, fig. 18, with pellets visible inside. Pl. 5, fig. 19, shows a piece of Cellophane after 23 weeks in acid sand. All of it has been converted into mite pellets which can be seen adhering to sand grains. Slight aggregation of sand grains on to the cover-slip results from the presence of the pellets, which may be regarded as approaching the humus end of organic matter decomposition. Pl. 6, fig. 20, shows in more detail the coating forming on a sand grain. The pellets contain *Oidiodendron* spores, pieces of conidiophores and what seem to be very small bacteria, plus structureless material. Pl. 6, fig. 21, is an oil immersion photomicrograph of pellets in Pl. 5, fig. 19.

DISCUSSION

Decomposition of Cellophane pieces has been followed in a few diverse soil types under temperate conditions up to an advanced stage. There were two main phases, a fungal phase lasting perhaps from 1 to 10 weeks followed by a bacterial phase which continues indefinitely. Once the fungi had died down, they never reappeared as colonizers of the residue even after growth (and probably death of some) of the bacteria. This observation is in line with the general experience of the difficulty of demonstrating fungal hyphae growing through soil—soil being thought of in this connexion as being without unhumified organic matter.

During the fungal phase the different species often co-existed with one another. Sometimes one species would become the sole dominant, growing quickly and excluding others, such as *Stachybotrys* on the Cellophane in fen soil illustrated in Pl. 3, fig. 10; this, however, was an isolated occurrence. No evidence of antibiosis was seen. No zones of inhibition were found anywhere. The species isolated belonged to genera not noted for antibiotic production, with the possible exception of *Chaetomium*; from this genus one antibiotic has been recorded, chaetomin from *C. cochliodes* (Waksman & Bugie, 1944). In loamy sand, there sometimes appeared to be an absence of the 'rooting' fungi from the immediate neighbourhood of a Cellophane piece, and bacteria (sometimes along with chytrids) were then responsible for its initial colonization. Bacteria were nearly always present in the fungus phase, although they were not dominant, nor responsible for much decomposition.

When the fungus hyphae died, there developed a large bacterial population, often accompanied by many nematodes. Can this be regarded as an early humus stage, with a flora of autochthonous bacteria? It is highly persistent, lasting in some soils up to 8 months at least. Cellophane itself will contribute nothing to humus, being homogeneous and readily decomposable. There appear to be several sources of soluble products at this stage, and in consequence several probable habitats for bacteria. Autolysis of fungal hyphae, and probably also of the bacteria which first develop, would release soluble products. Nematode excretions too seem to be a likely source of soluble materials. They produce no pellets of any sort and presumably their excretion is liquid. Nothing seems to be known about the physiology of nematode excretion, but being members of the animal kingdom they may be expected to excrete amounts of soluble nitrogenous compounds.

The pellets produced by soil mites may also be regarded as a form of humus. Some types of humus formed under forests in Europe are mainly composed of the excreta of soil fauna (Russell, 1950, p. 514). Subsequent decomposition of the pellets seems to be very slow.

Broad differences brought out in the different soil types were chiefly in relative length of the fungus phase. Weathered chalk and the Breckland soils had a prolonged fungus phase and few bacteria, whereas in loamy sand fungi were not always the initial colonizers.

This study has been a survey of possibilities and was not planned to be quantitative. For a quantitative estimate of the fungi which produce no characteristic structures on Cellophane with constancy, isolation into culture is necessary. Some fungi can be detected on any slide; *Stachybotrys* for example, produces its conidiophores and conidia on Cellophane buried for periods as short as 9 days, and the heavy brown conidiophores and spores persist almost indefinitely. *Stysanus* produces spores of the *Echinobotryum* type from about the same time, though the first coremia have not been found before 32 days. Chytrids can be estimated in similar manner. Some indication of the frequency of these organisms can be seen in Table 1.

The chief filamentous fungi found in the neutral soils were *Botrytrichum*, *Chaetomium* (?), sterile mycelia and *Humicola*, probably in that order. The *Aleurisma-Sporotrichum* group also occurred fairly frequently in fen soil and loamy sand, but it was not easy to say whether these were primarily cellulose-decomposing fungi or merely associated with one of the former. *Oidiodendron* was dominant in the Santon Downham soils.

It is interesting to compare these species with those recorded by Siu (1951), which is the most comprehensive study yet made on the subject. Heading the list of order of abundance of genera from 4500 isolates from exposed cotton textiles (p. 131) are *Penicillium*, *Aspergillus*, non-sporing mycelia, *Fusarium* and *Trichoderma*, which comprise over 60 % of the total. Although the four genera mentioned are the commonest soil fungi, none was either observed to spore in Cellophane buried in the neutral soils or was present as large patches of mycelium. Conversely of the genera found on the Cellophane, *Chaetomium* is recorded as providing only 2·9 % of the isolates from the textiles, *Humicola* 0·8 % and *Sporotrichum* 0·7 % with no mention of the other genera.

Table 1. *Distribution of certain fungi on Cellophane buried in a range of soil types*

Soil type	No. of slides examined	No. of slides with		
		Stachybotrys	*Stysanus*	Chytrids
1. Fen	53	8	0	2
2. Calcareous loam	45	3	0	0
3. Weathered chalk	28	0	15	1
4. Loamy sand	96	6	0	54
5. Santon Downham soils	56	0	0	0

The flora found on the Cellophane in the neutral soils is much more like that recorded by Jensen (1931) from neutral soils to which filter paper and straw had been added. By plating methods he obtained *Mycogone* (= *Humicola*), *Stachybotrys*, *Coccospora agricola* (= *Botryotrichum*) and *Botryosporium*. From more acid soils he isolated *Penicillia* and *Trichoderma*. The Breckland soils with their population of *Oidiodendron* spp. may be exceptional representatives of acid soils.

SUMMARY AND PROSPECT

A technique is described and illustrated by the use of which it is possible to follow the succession of micro-organisms on a substrate from initial burial in soil to an advanced state of decomposition. The principle is that of direct microscopical observation, together with direct isolation of the dominant organisms observed.

A community of actively developing micro-organisms lives on the substrate in a soil environment. A 'normal' course of development can be studied on a chosen soil type under temperate conditions, with its usual variations due to heterogeneity of soil. After having established this course, deviations from it in other soil types or from particular conditions of soil treatment can be followed. Further, the use of thin sections of other materials, such as wood shavings, for example, will probably stimulate development of other communities from the soil population. By variation thus of substrate, soil and conditions of soil treatment, it should be possible to accumulate information on the inter-relations of quite a number of soil micro-organisms.

I wish to thank Mr E. W. Mason of the Commonwealth Mycological Institute, Kew, for identifying *Botryotrichum piluliferum* Sacc. & Marsh and *Humicola grisea* Traaen.

REFERENCES

CHOLODNY, N. (1930). Über eine neue Methode zur Untersuchung der Bodenmikro-flora. *Arch. Microbiol.* **1**, 620.

CONN, H. J. (1948). The most abundant groups of bacteria in soil. *Bact. Rev.* **12**, 257.

DOWNING, M. H. (1953). *Botryotrichum* and *Coccospora*. *Mycologia*, **45**, 934.

GARRETT, S. D. (1955). Microbial ecology of the soil. *Trans. Brit. mycol. Soc.* **38**, 1.

HASKINS, R. H. (1946). New chytridiaceous fungi from Cambridge. *Trans. Brit. mycol. Soc.* **29**, 135.

JENSEN, H. L. (1931). The microbiology of farmyard manure decomposition in soil. II. Decomposition of cellulose. *J. agric. Sci.* **21**, 81.

ROBAK, H. (1932). Investigations regarding fungi on Norwegian wood pulp and fungal infection at wood pulp mills. *Nyt. Mag. Naturv.* **71**, 185.

RUSSELL, E. J. (1950). *Soil Conditions and Plant Growth*, 8th ed. London: Longmans Green.

SIU, R. G. H. (1951). *Microbial decomposition of cellulose*. New York: Reinhold.

SMITH, G. (1946). A note on the occurrence of species of *Oidiodendron* Robak in Britain. *Trans. Brit. mycol. Soc.* **29**, 232.

SMITH, G. (1954). *An Introduction to Industrial Mycology*, 4th ed. London: Arnold.

SZILVINYI, A. VON (1940). Mikrobiologische Bodenuntersuchungen im Lunzer Gebiet. III. Teil. Die Schimmelpilzflora. *Zbl. Bakt.* **103**, 133.

WAKSMAN, S. A. & BUGIE, E. (1944). Chaetomin, a new antibiotic substance pro-duced by *Chaetomium cochliodes*. I. Formation and properties. *J. Bact.* **48**, 527.

WHITE, W. L. & DOWNING, M. H. (1953). *Humicola grisea*, a soil inhabiting cellu-lolytic hyphomycete. *Mycologia*, **45**, 951.

WINOGRADSKY, S. (1925). Études sur la microbiologie du sol. I. Sur la méthode. *Ann. Inst. Pasteur*, **39**, 299.

EXPLANATION OF PLATES

PLATE 1

Fig. 1. Cellophane 17 days in fen soil. × 150. 'Rooting' branches of *Botryotrichum piluliferum* in the thickness of the Cellophane, with surface mycelium pulled back. Note zones of solution of Cellophane near 'roots'. (See text on p. 291.)

Fig. 2. Cellophane 7 days in calcareous loam. × 150. 'Rooting' branches of *B. piluliferum* in thickness of Cellophane. Surface mycelium pulled off. No evident zones of solution.

Fig. 3. Cellophane 16 days in loamy sand. × 150. 'Rooting' branches of a *mycelium sterilium*. Surface mycelium brushed off. Note autolysis of 'roots' leaving cavities in Cellophane.

Fig. 4. Cellophane 10 days in loamy sand. × 150. Initial colonization by chytrids.

PLATE 2

Fig. 5. Cellophane 53 days in weathered chalk. × 150. Imperfect perithecia of *Chaetomium* (?) sp. developing on edge of Cellophane.

Fig. 6. Cellophane 53 days in weathered chalk. × 150. Part of *Chaetomium* perithecium showing hairs and ascospores.

Fig. 7. Cellophane 67 days in calcareous loam. × 150. Perithecium of *Chaetomium*.

Fig. 8. Cellophane 22 days in loamy sand. × 150. Hyphae and chlamydospores of *Humicola* growing out over the cover slip from Cellophane. Note heavy bacterial development on hyphae on and near Cellophane.

Fig. 9. Cellophane 16 days in calcareous loam. × 150. Conidiophores of *Stachybotrys* with characteristic long 'roots' in the background.

PLATE 3

Fig. 10 Cellophane 23 days in fen soil. × 150. Soil particles just above Cellophane showing heavy growth of *Stachybotrys*.

Fig. 11. Cellophane 32 days in weathered chalk. × 600. *Echinobotryum* stage of *Stysanus* sp. Note absence of bacteria.

Fig. 12. Cellophane 46 days in weathered chalk. × 150. *Stysanus* coremia.

Fig. 13. Cellophane 22 days in loamy sand. × 150. Network of decayed hyphae over which bacteria are developing.

PLATE 4

Fig. 14. Cellophane 39 days in weathered chalk. × 150. *Stysanus* tissue and Cellophane consumed by soil fauna, probably mites. Note excremental pellets in which are *Stysanus* spores.

Fig. 15. Cellophane 70 days in fen soil. × 150. Nematode-trapping networks on hyphae growing over Cellophane in 'post-fungal' stage.

Fig. 16. Same slide showing nematode trapped on the cover-slip, and hyphae extending over glass away from Cellophane.

PLATE 5

Fig. 17. Cellophane 14 days in acid sand. × 150. Conidiophore of *Oidiodendron* sp. in

Fig. 18. *Above:* Cellophane 82 days in litter. × 150. Total disintegration through fungus and mite action. Background of *Oidiodendron* spores, partly eaten conidiophores and mite pellets. *Below:* Mite with two pellets *in situ*.

Fig. 19. Cellophane 161 days in acid sand. × 150. Total disintegration leaving pellets only, which adhere to sand grains. For *A* and *B* see Pl. 6.

PLATE 6

Fig. 20. Detail of debris coating sand grain in fig. 19 at *A*. *Oidiodendron* spores and broken conidiophores. × 600.

Fig. 21. Detail of pellets at *B*. *Oidiodendron* spores, pieces of conidiophore and tiny bacteria amongst amorphous material. × 1400.

PLATE 1

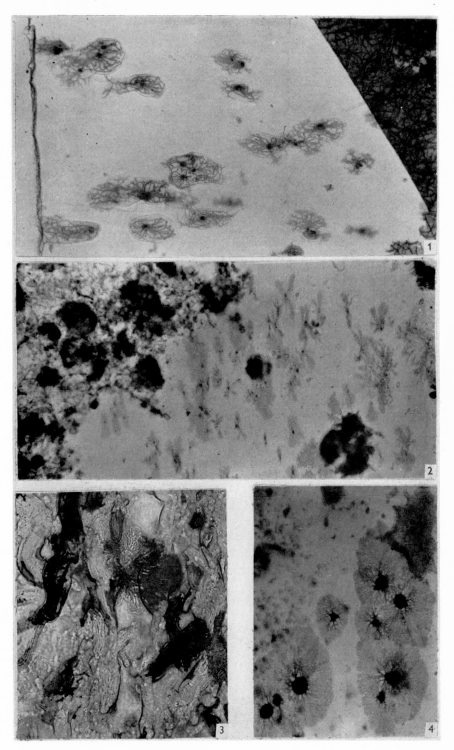

PLATE 2

PLATE 3

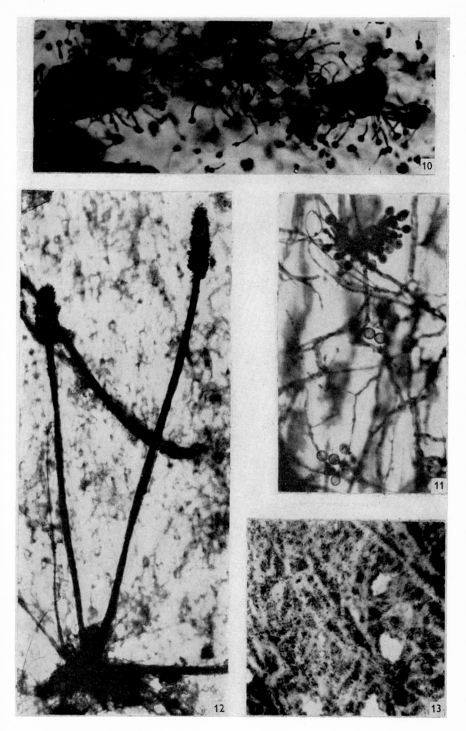

PLATE 4

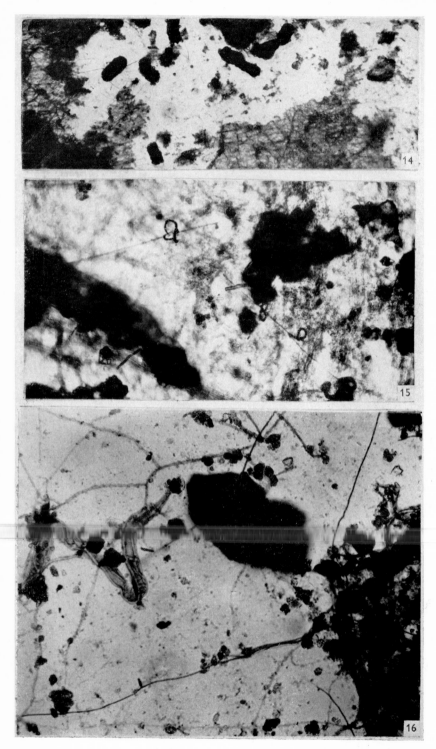

PLATE 5

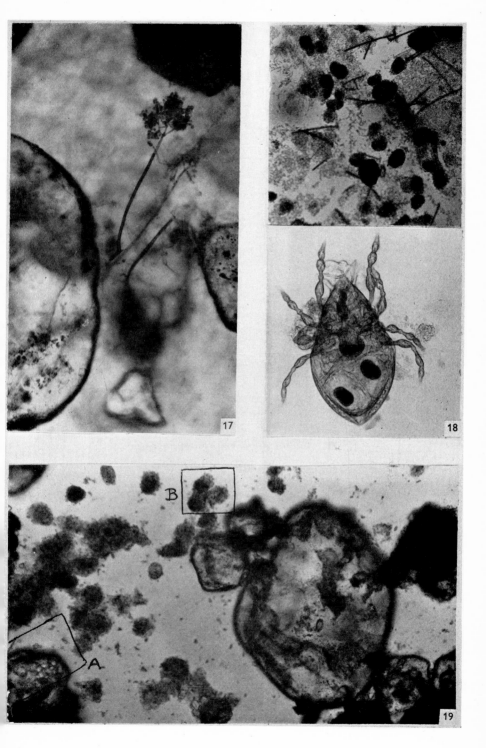

PLATE 6

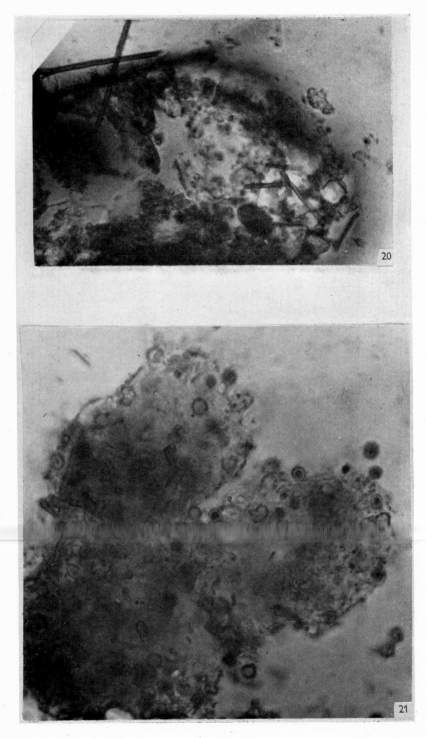

THE ROLE OF PLANT HOSTS IN MICROBIAL ECOLOGY

F. C. BAWDEN

Rothamsted Experimental Station, Harpenden, Herts

Had I been wise enough to consider my subject carefully before agreeing to contribute a paper on it, I should almost certainly have refused the invitation. However, I gave it so little thought that the only serious doubt I then had was that, with the plant host seeming to play such an obvious role in microbial ecology, it might be difficult to present self-evident facts without being too platitudinous. Now that the passage of time has forced me to contemplate the subject in detail, I have become increasingly appalled by its size and complexity and by my growing awareness that I am singularly ill-equipped to deal with it. As I now see it, I am asked to cover, not only the whole of plant pathology, to which can be added infections with avirulent or beneficial microbes, but also large chunks of soil microbiology and evolution. Avoiding clichés about 'the balance of nature' now seems a minor part of my task.

Clearly I shall have to make some rather arbitrary selections from this embarrassingly large subject, and I shall be forced to generalize. Generalization necessarily means over-simplification and inevitably entails errors. For instance, although I shall in the main deal with viruses and with pathogenic microbes that infect flowering plants, this still leaves ample scope for great differences in behaviour. Arguments developed around the behaviour of obligate parasites cannot be expected to hold in detail for facultative parasites, or those developed around soil-borne pathogens to apply precisely to air-borne ones. Also, if I am not to be bogged down in detail, I shall have to assume that, when a parasite meets a host plant, conditions are always such that the parasite will infect and multiply. This, of course, is so far from the truth as to be ludicrous, but I cannot qualify all my statements to cover the many and varied ways in which the environment can affect either host or parasite, or both, and determine the result of an encounter between the two.

GROSS EFFECTS OF CHANGING THE COMPOSITION
OF PLANT COMMUNITIES

Green plants directly or indirectly provide food for nearly all other kinds of organisms, including most microbes. As different kinds of plants have different constitutions and different microbes have different nutritional capabilities, the microflora of any area must necessarily depend greatly on the character of the macroflora. This is true for both saprophytes and parasites, but the population of parasites is likely to respond quicker and more obviously when the character of the macroflora changes, not only because saprophytes will linger on dead remains, but because parasites are usually more restricted in the number of plant species they can infect than are saprophytes in the types of dead tissue on which they can exist.

Resistance to infection is the normal condition of plants, and susceptibility the exception. This, the basic thesis of my subject, needs stressing, and, at the risk of being tedious, it is worth expressing in different ways. Putting the host first, it means that any one plant species is immune from most parasites; or putting the host as the object, any one parasite can infect only a few plant species. The age-old agricultural practice of rotating crops, found empirically as a method of decreasing losses from soil-borne pathogens long before the germ theory of disease was established, derives directly from it, but the fact is much more immediately obvious with air-borne pathogens that are either obligate parasites or only precarious saprophytes. A cursory look at crops is enough to show that a sure way of avoiding attacks by the potato-blight fungus is to grow, say, wheat, and that wheat rusts or smuts do not occur where only beans are growing. Logic, too, suggests that the survival of both hosts and parasites demands some limitation of host range; a virulent pathogen with an unlimited host range would presumably lead to a lifeless world. However, I must add that logic may be a faulty tool for either elucidating the reasons underlying ecological situations or for forecasting evolutionary trends.

There is no need to do experiments to show that large-scale changes in the character of plant populations affect the population of parasites; the information is writ large in the history of agriculture by the immense losses from crop diseases, events relevant enough to our subject to deserve some discussion.

Plants, of course, get diseased when growing in areas untouched by agriculture, and diseases have doubtlessly sometimes limited the increase of wild species that might otherwise have become predominant. But in most 'wild' habitats the plant populations are varied, mixtures of very many different species, and pathogens do not have too easy a time. If one plant becomes parasitized, its neighbours are likely to be different species and not to be susceptible to the same parasites. Each plant is a selective ecological niche, favouring only a few parasites, and spread from one suitable niche to another is a chancy thing. With neighbouring plants supporting different populations of parasites (and saprophytes), the microflora in any region is proportionally as rich in species as is the macroflora, and no one microbe is especially numerous.

This we can assume was the general condition when, some 10,000 years ago, man started to abandon hunting as a way of life and increasingly adopted the cultivation of crops. Until then the vegetation in any region was relatively stable, made up of different types that had slowly become adapted so that they were in equilibrium with one another and with their pests and diseases. We can assume, too, that the microflora, with seasonal cycles reflecting the seasonal growth of the plants, was changing only slowly. The growing of crops entailed replacing the stable mixed populations of wild plants, over ever-increasing areas, by single or very few species. This, the earliest application of the 'pure culture technique', had revolutionary results, particularly as the few plant species chosen for cultivation were not those that competed too well in the 'wild'; they had not previously been extensively exposed to pathogens and susceptible types had not been culled by natural selection. Grown over large areas they were inevitably easily found by their parasites, which, having once gained a foothold, spread rapidly in these new communities where all neighbour plants were their hosts. As agriculture changed the macroflora from few individuals of many species to many individuals of few species, so it created a new microflora, much less rich in variety than the old but immensely more in total numbers.

QUALITATIVE EFFECTS OF HOST PLANTS ON PATHOGENS

The selective action of different plant species in encouraging some species of parasites and prohibiting others is only the obvious part of a more complex story. To leave it there would seem to imply that a species is a collection of identical units, whereas in all biological systems the only unequivocal unit is the individual. Variability can be taken for granted and every species is axiomatically a collection of units with different capabilities. Thus, even when changing a plant does not appear to influence the prevalence of a parasitic species, it may nevertheless be

profoundly affecting the composition of the parasite's population, by
encouraging the multiplication of those individuals best able to infect
it and discouraging others. Competition between parasitic species may
sometimes be severe, but it is usually a minor affair compared with
competition between individuals of one species. It could not matter
less to *Phytophthora infestans* what parasites are attacking a wheat crop,
and a spore encountering a potato plant it can infect is usually not
seriously inconvenienced by the fact that the plant is already supporting
a population of other parasites, but it matters a great deal to its future
whether or not the plant is already extensively infected by spores of
other races of *P. infestans*.

The changes in the character of the population of a parasite produced
by changing the variety of the host plant is only too evident in the record
of crop varieties bred to resist important diseases. For a time these have
fulfilled their function, but after a while, sometimes only a depressingly
short while when air-borne pathogens are concerned, the varieties
succumb to the diseases they were bred to resist.

How does this come about? The resistance of such varieties is sometimes said to have 'broken down', so the first thing to emphasize is that
there is no reason to consider the variety has lost any intrinsic character.
It still resists the forms of the parasite it was bred to resist, but it has
now met some with different capabilities. Immediately it was grown on
a large scale it introduced a new ecological factor, an additional subtlety
into the 'pure culture' technique, excluding the older forms of the parasite and allowing a free field for any 'new' ones that can infect it. But
saying this still leaves us far from a full explanation of the phenomenon.
Does a resistant variety actively help to create forms able to infect it?
Or does it simply provide a medium that selects forms which would have
occurred anyway, but which, had the variety of plant not existed, would
never have reached a noticeable population?

Many of the early workers who studied variability in fungi would have
answered 'yes' to the first question. Now almost everybody would
answer 'no' and give an emphatic 'yes' to the second. The reasons for
this change in outlook have been fully discussed by Stakman &
Christensen (1953). They conclude that the phenomena, which led
Marshall Ward and others to postulate such a thing as adaptive
parasitism and that one plant could act as a 'bridging host' and change
a parasite so that it becomes able to infect a previously resistant plant,
all arose from the use of mixed inocula, which contained biotypes with
different parasitic capabilities and from which the bridging host selected
only one or a few. There is no need to suspect the correctness of this

conclusion. The genetic variability now known to occur in fungi, combined with population statistics, mutation rates, and the possibilities of genetic characters combining in new ways, adequately explain almost every phenomenon that is likely to be encountered. The mechanism for gene segregation and recombination is obvious enough with fungi that have sexual stages, and with those that do not there is always hetero-karyosis or some other mechanism to allow different individuals to exchange genes. Even with no such mechanisms, the enormous popula-tions achieved by parasites in crops provide, at very modest mutation rates, ample opportunities for many genetic variations.

I do not intend to disagree with the modern view that the ecological consequences of introducing new varieties of plants is usually to select and favour biotypes of pathogens that would have existed even without the new varieties. But I do suggest that the idea of adaptive parasitism should not be wholly abandoned. Because an idea was advanced in the wrong context does not mean that it is wrong in all contexts. In culture, fungi vary greatly, not only by mutation but also phenotypically, and there seems no *a priori* reason why they should not also yield a range of phenotypes when infecting host plants. Phenotypic changes in plants can determine whether or not they act as hosts for a given parasite (for example, some wheat varieties are immune from race 15B of wheat black-rust fungi when grown at 18° and very susceptible at 29° (Stakman & Christensen, 1953)), and it is not obvious to me why all changes in the infective capabilities of parasites must arise from changes in their genetic constitution.

There is now ample evidence that many bacteria, which usually do not produce a given enzyme, will produce it when they are exposed to an environment containing the specific substrate. The continued pro-duction of some adaptive enzymes seems to call for the continued stimulus of the substrate, but sometimes one exposure to a substrate is enough (Pollock, 1950). If bacteria can undergo such changes, why not fungi? Unfortunately, it is almost impossible to design critical experi-ments to find whether or not host plants can similarly change the patho-genic capabilities of fungi, for, despite the immense number of words that have been written on the subject, there is still virtually nothing known about the factors that determine susceptibility to one form of a parasitic fungus and resistance to another. Until it is known whether resistance is a positive thing, the presence of some specific toxin in the plant, or negative, the lack of some essential metabolite, there seems little that can be done to carry the subject further.

Viruses, no less than pathogenic microbes, can also change their behaviour as a consequence of moving from one host to another. The most common change is either enhanced or decreased virulence towards the original host, and is again adequately explained by the preferential selection of one genetically different type from a mixture. There are, though, some changes that seem not to fit easily into this simple explanation. One strain of tobacco mosaic virus with which I have been working recently (Bawden, 1956) will infect both leguminous and solanaceous plants systemically, but it undergoes striking changes while making the move from one host to the other and it adopts different forms in the two hosts. The two forms are only remotely related serologically, they differ considerably in their contents of different amino acids, have different physical properties and produce different types of local lesion in *Nicotiana glutinosa*. As obtained from leguminous plants, the virus produces no lesions in *N. glutinosa* that resemble those produced by the virus from tobacco plants. Yet the virus from legumes infects tobacco plants, from which later the solanaceous form of the virus is recoverable. This, then, seems not to be the selection of a minor form occurring in a mixed inoculum. Selection, perhaps, but from forms produced in the inoculated tobacco plant and not obtained from the legume which provided the inoculum.

The virus can be transferred between legumes and solanaceous plants repeatedly, and at each transfer to the other host it undergoes these major changes in properties to give a form that readily invades the new host systemically. The phenomenon can, of course, be explained by postulating a readily reversible mutation, but phenotypic variation seems equally likely. Certainly the physiological condition of tobacco plants seems to be concerned in the change, for, whereas the tobacco form is readily produced in young White Burley tobacco plants kept at 20° after they are inoculated from infected French beans, it rarely occurs in older plants at this temperature and it has never appeared when inoculated plants are kept at temperatures above 30°. At 30° both forms of the virus will multiply when tobacco plants are inoculated with them, but in plants inoculated from beans only the leguminous form is produced, and this form reaches much larger amounts than in plants at 20°.

Multiplication in different host plants can change the ability of some viruses to be transmitted by a given species of insect, a property of great ecological importance. Some viruses have been found to lose (Black, 1953) this ability or to have it greatly impaired (Hollings, 1955), and one to gain it (Watson, 1956), when propagated in a new host. No doubt some of these changes can be explained by the differential multiplication of chance mutants, some of which are insect-transmitted and others not.

But not all the results seem to fit this idea too happily. Potato virus C, a strain of the aphid-transmitted potato virus Y, was not transmissible by aphids when first transmitted from potato plants to *Nicotiana* sp. (Bawden & Kassanis, 1947). It became aphid-transmitted after propagation in these species for some years (Watson, 1956), although much less readily so than type strains of potato virus Y. If this were because of a chance mutant to an aphid-transmissible form, then transmission by aphids would be expected to select this form and to increase the readiness with which the culture is transmitted by aphids, but it does not.

For this symposium I may have given more attention than I should to discussing whether the plant plays an active part in creating its own pathogens. Our subject is ecology, and in this context the mechanism underlying that fact is, perhaps, less important than the fact that all that is needed to get a different population of parasites, not only of different species but also of types within a species, is to change the plant population. These new parasites will now occur mainly because some of the microbes and viruses that come into an area with the new plant population will be able to develop there, whereas previously they could not, but sometimes they may derive from forms of microbes already present but previously unimportant. The basis of plant quarantines rests on the thesis that when a crop is newly introduced into an area it will remain free from a given disease until the causal pathogen is brought into that area from elsewhere. No doubt this is often true, and it may always be so with obligate parasites and with most air-borne pathogens, although even these had to originate somewhere, some time; and if it happened once, why not again? But with soil-borne pathogens that also exist generally as saprophytes, it seems rash to expect quarantines to be all that is necessary to prevent specific pathogenic forms from occurring. Fungi like *Fusarium oxysporum* occur in almost all soils, and to get the specialized forms that infect different kinds of plants, say banana, pea and flax, all that may be necessary is to expose the heterogeneous 'wild type' to the selective or adaptive influence of the appropriate host plant often enough.

SOIL-BORNE MICROBES

The specialized, pathogenic forms of *Fusarium oxysporum* have often been differentiated from those that commonly occur in many soils by giving them different names, such as soil invaders and soil inhabitants. In his detailed review of the ecology of root-infecting fungi, Garrett (1956) redefined the two types under the names root-inhabiting and soil-inhabiting fungi. He characterizes the root-inhabiting fungi as having 'an expanding parasitic phase on the living plant and a declining sapro-phytic phase after its death', and the soil-inhabiting ones as having the 'ability to survive indefinitely as saprophytes'. Garrett states that the saprophytic phase of root inhabitants is restricted because of competi-tion from other soil microbes, and he suggests that most root-disease fungi could be placed in one or other of these categories. That some fungi are more active saprophytes than others is as unquestionable as that some are more active parasites than others, but it does not neces-sarily follow that because a fungus can live as a parasite, it must there-fore be a worse saprophyte than if it lived wholly saprophytically. Certainly some active parasites do not survive long in the immense numbers they can reach while a susceptible crop is being grown. For example, one year without a susceptible crop is usually enough to decrease *Ophiobolus graminis* from levels where it would ruin wheat to levels where it causes little or no loss. But pathogenic forms of sapro-phytic fungi that occur regularly in soil need not behave in the same manner. The growing of a crop that can be parasitized by a form of, say, *Fusarium oxysporum* will increase the population of that form, and when the crop dies there will be proportionally more of that form in the soil than there was previously. I know of no reason to assume that this form will then decline proportionally more than the other forms that have continued to live only as saprophytes while the crop was growing. Indeed, records of wilt diseases, occurring the first time a susceptible crop is taken after many years under immune ones, are common enough to suggest that pathogenic forms do persist in soil for long periods as saprophytes.

It seems important to distinguish between what is inherently possible in a species and what is not. If a species is intrinsically a weak sapro-phyte, then the only time it can reach large populations, which favour evolutionary changes, is when it is living as a parasite, and so it is likely to become increasingly adapted for life as a parasite with much less likelihood of increasing its activity as a saprophyte. The growing of crops susceptible to *Ophiobolus graminis* seem largely merry interludes in its life with usually no permanent effect on its incidence. The only way in which these interludes seem likely to aid its survival in larger numbers is by the chance occurrence of forms that are better saprophytes, for the survival of a soil-borne fungus seems more favoured by increasing its saprophytic activity than by increasing its parasitic activity. The position is different with air-borne pathogens, which have ready means of dispersal, because increasing the numbers of these not only increases the likelihood of evolutionary changes in the stock, but also increases their chances of reaching new host plants. Also, with soil-borne fungi like *Fusarium oxysporum*, which are active saprophytes, the growing of a crop susceptible to one form of the fungus could well have lasting effects, by adding to the soil large quantities of a previously minor form, probably still as saprophytic as the main types, but if not, able to recombine genes for parasitism with those for saprophytic activity.

The effect of growing any given type of plant shows most obviously on the microflora because of changes in types of pathogenic microbes, which publicize themselves by the diseases they cause. However, there are comparable changes with microbes that are not obviously pathogenic and with those that seem to be beneficial. The growing of various tree species will usually lead to the development in or on their roots of characteristic mycorrhizal fungi. Most of these are higher Basidiomycetes; some are active saprophytes, able to live freely by decomposing pieces of dead plants; although others will grow saprophytically on agar plates, they can rarely be isolated from soil organic matter; still others have not yet been found to grow except as parasites. Some of the facultative parasites seem to require simple sugars as sources of energy, but with such a varied collection of fungi adopting a similar spatial association with their host plants, it would be only idle to look for a single explanation of their curiously restricted habitat. The association between mycorrhizal fungi and higher plants is usually regarded as symbiotic rather than parasitic, with the fungi aiding the roots to acquire nutrients and also protecting the roots against some pathogens. Garrett (1956) calls such fungi 'the most highly developed parasites known to us'. This description is fully acceptable if a highly developed parasite is defined as one that does not harm, or confers some benefit on, the host, but the word 'developed' carries implications that may not be fully justified. No doubt such a condition may sometimes have been reached by a long association between a host and a parasite, which might at first have been pathogenic. But there seems no need to assume that such conditions only arise from a long period of evolution, or that parasites must always evolve from virulence through avirulence to symbiosis. Microbes will grow where they can and, presented with a host, they will infect it regardless of the consequences. Towards some they will be virulent and towards others not, and there seems no reason why a microbe should not sometimes encounter a new host in which it can immediately live commensally or symbiotically.

More obvious than the effects of plants in encouraging their mycorrhizal fungi is the effect of growing leguminous plants on the incidence of *Rhizobium* sp. The benefits of symbiosis with a nitrogen-supplying bacterium may well be reflected in the wide distribution of the Leguminosae, but even here, with the benefits so apparently obvious, evolution seems not to lead smoothly to an inevitable association between host and forms of the symbiont that fix most nitrogen. Even when a strain that fixes much nitrogen is sown along with leguminous seeds, it may still fail to establish well on the growing plants, because the growing of the legume stimulates all forms present in the soil to multiply, and those better able to fix nitrogen are ousted by those less able in this activity but favoured by some other (Thornton, 1956). In the complexities of interactions between host, parasite (or symbiont), and the many other factors introduced by the environment and by other organisms, it may be only vain to expect what, by analogy with human affairs, would seem to be a rational outcome. Similarly, a situation or relationship that appears to present a sensible end to a logically postulated series of events may well have come about in quite other ways.

STIMULATION OF MICROBES BY HOST PLANTS

Although the prime part of the host in microbial ecology is to provide a source of food that can be used by some but not all microbes, its other roles must not be disregarded. For instance, actively metabolizing tissues of plants often produce substances that stimulate dormant organs to activity, microbial spores and seeds of higher plants to germinate, and eelworm cysts to hatch. Such effects have usually been described by workers who, studying some given parasite, have mainly tested the effects of exudates or extracts from host-plant species on the particular parasite engaging their attention. This approach may sometimes have suggested that the substances have a greater specificity of action than they have, and so given more support than is fully justified to the idea that it is sensible behaviour for a parasite to be stimulated by its host and suicidal to be stimulated by other plants. However, tests have been extensive enough to show that some insusceptible plants, or plants in which the parasite does not complete its life cycle, also produce substances with similar activities, and this discovery has raised the possibility of using such plants as 'decoy' crops to rid infested soil of persistent parasites.

Such 'decoys' have decreased the numbers, both of resting spores of *Plasmodiophora brassicae* (Macfarlane, 1952) and of *Spongospora subterranea* (White, 1954), and of cysts of the potato-root eelworm (Jones, 1954); and a decrease rather than elimination is, perhaps, as much as could reasonably be expected from the method. When root exudates produce their striking effects *in vitro* and stimulate all spores or cysts to germinate, conditions are very different from those in soil, where the exuded substances probably rarely get far before they are absorbed by something or are broken down by some microbe. Indeed, were this not so, it is difficult to see how resting organs of some species could persist in soil; not only would they be stimulated to activity when there was no host-plant root near enough for them to infect, but they can be activated by such a variety of substances (Brown, 1946) that it seems they could not long remain dormant even though no host-plant tissues came anywhere near them.

On present knowledge it is reasonable to interpret the results of experiments with 'decoy' plants as a direct effect of the host substances in stimulating resting organs to abortive activity, but it may be far from the whole story. The incidence of disease in succeeding crops can certainly be decreased in other ways and, seemingly, sometimes by the growing of plants that inhibit rather than promote spore germination. For example, Buxton (1957a, b) found that exudates from the roots of pea varieties resistant to infection by some races of *Fusarium oxysporum* f. *pisi* stimulate the germination of spores of races to which the varieties are susceptible and inhibit that of races they resist; yet he also found that, when a variety of pea resistant to the race present in soil was grown, the incidence of wilt in a subsequent planting of a susceptible variety was decreased. The growing of a given type of plant must have many other effects on the soil microflora than stimulating or inhibiting spore germination; in the same way that we cannot begin to interpret the action of substances that do stimulate germination, because their constitution is unknown, so also too little is known about the factors influencing the soil microflora for observed effects on disease incidence, when one type of plant is grown instead of another, to be attributed surely to any one cause.

Like earlier workers (West & Lochhead, 1940; Timonin, 1941) studying wilt diseases of other plants, Buxton (1957b) found that pea varieties highly susceptible to wilt diseases supported a denser and richer microflora in the immediate vicinity of their roots than did resistant varieties. That this region normally maintains more microbes than does soil not contiguous with living roots, even in soils rich in organic matter, has been known since Hiltner (1904) first called this region the rhizosphere. The rich population here may in part reflect the action of the root exudates in stimulating dormant microbes to activity, but there are probably many other contributing factors. Some of the microbes may be living on sloughed-off root hairs or epidermal cells, and others on sugars and amino acids secreted by the thin-walled living cells; as the root grows and respires, it must alter the soil locally, both physically and chemically, and so present habitats in which microbes with special needs can multiply. It is important to remember that, even with a dense stand of plants, the soil is still far from filled by roots and, on microbial standards, much of the soil microflora remains remote from living tissues. Distances that are ecologically unimportant for larger organisms become highly significant for soil microbes, and the occurrence of living tissues in their immediate vicinity creates an environment quite different from that when the tissues are only fractions of a millimetre away.

The quality of the rhizosphere microflora, as with the quality of root parasites, depends on the identity of the plant providing the roots. As Harley (1948) has pointed out, the phenomenon of mycorrhiza is not readily separable from the general rhizosphere effect, and it may be a consequence of local conditions in which one species of a fungus is so affected by the roots of a given plant as to become dominant. I have sometimes been told that the beneficial effects of mycorrhiza are obvious and do not need arguing because the biggest and best trees have most mycorrhiza, but I do not find this wholly convincing. It could have another explanation, based on the ecological probability that the mycorrhizal fungi are sparsely distributed in soil; namely, that only large trees produce roots in sufficient quantity to explore the soil thoroughly enough to encourage the fungi into activity.

The stimulating effects of host tissues on spore germination have been mainly studied with extracts or exudates of roots, but Brown (1922) showed that materials which encourage the germination and subsequent growth of fungus spores also occur on the surfaces of other plant parts. Last (1955) found that leaves, like roots, can carry a dense population of microbes, which seem to be neither harmful nor beneficial to the host. The quality and quantity of this microflora, growing in what he calls the 'phyllosphere' of cereal leaves, varies through the season and with the state of activity of the plants. Whether the species he found to predominate on wheat and barley also predominate on other species has yet to be determined.

Host plants affect the microflora in other ways than by secreting substances that either encourage or discourage spore germination or growth. This fact, I think, will be sufficiently indicated by making the point that the spread of air-borne microbes, dependent on a high humidity or free water for sporulation or for spore germination, will be favoured more by the conditions in a dense stand of a leafy crop than in an open stand which wind and sun will dry more rapidly.

ALTERNATE AND ALTERNATIVE HOSTS

Some parasites that can infect more than one kind of plant behave in much the same manner in all their hosts, each of which provides a similar kind of ecological niche. For others, though, and especially with obligate parasites, typified by the rust fungi and viruses, one host may play a very different role from another.

The well-known history of *Puccinia graminis*, with its movement between wheat and barberry entailing five different types of spores, makes a particularly vivid illustration of the phenomenon implied by the phrase alternate hosts. The fungus reaches its greatest populations in wheat, where it mainly spreads by successive generations of uredospores, produced asexually in vast numbers. Provided there is a continuous succession of susceptible cereals within reach of these spores, and conditions are otherwise favourable, the parasite can continue indefinitely in this state. As infected wheat matures, however, resting spores (telia) are formed, by which the fungus can survive through a period when there are no susceptible plants to infect. These become diploid, and there is a reduction division when they germinate to produce the haploid sporidia, which infect only species of *Berberis* and *Mahonia*. These infections give rise to pycnia containing pycnospores, which function as gametes. When pycnospores of opposite sex fuse, cluster cups or aecia are formed on the barberry and in these develop aecidiospores, with paired nuclei. The aecidiospores cannot infect barberry but only wheat or some other susceptible member of the Gramineae, on which then are produced in increasing numbers the uredospores with paired nuclei that again spread the parasite widely.

Here, then, we have two hosts playing very different parts. The one, growing over vast areas, mainly produces enormous numbers of clonal-line spores, but also the spores by which the parasite survives; the other, much more sparsely distributed, produces only one generation of airborne spores in a season, but this provides the initial inoculum for wheat in an area that otherwise would be free from the parasite, and produces it in a range of genetically different forms. The genetic variability is not simply a postulate from what is known of the life history of the fungus, but has been demonstrated by field surveys in North America, where the number of races of *Puccinia graminis tritici* and *P. graminis avenae* recovered from cereals growing near barberry greatly exceeds the number in areas free from the alternate host (Stakman & Christensen, 1953).

The effect of barberry in initiating outbreaks of cereal rusts is mainly local, for although many millions of aecidiospores may be produced, they seem to be deposited unusually rapidly for fungus spores (Gregory, 1945), the great majority falling within a few metres and only a minute proportion reaching as far as a kilometre. This, too, is implied by the success achieved in controlling wheat rust in some areas by eradicating barberry bushes. That it has not eradicated the disease from other areas, such as North America, is explicable by the fact that areas of wheat to the south continuously maintain the fungus in the uredospore stage, and the uredospores, although greatly diminished in numbers during the journey north, still arrive in numbers more than adequate to start epidemics. Eradicating the barberry over large areas, however, has certainly played a great part in decreasing losses from wheat rust, for not only has it delayed the start of rust outbreaks but it has helped to stabilize the pathogenic forms of the fungus so that cereal varieties bred for resistance have had a longer useful life than they might otherwise have done.

Most viruses have no method of surviving except in infected plants, so that their continued existence depends on the continued occurrence of living susceptible plants. Only a few are seed-borne, and so most plants raised from seed start life virus-free. Hence annual crops, unless vegetatively propagated, become infected by viruses coming into them from other plants. Where there is a succession of susceptible crops through the year, as with the cabbage tribe in Britain, so there is a continual movement of viruses from old infected plants to seedlings, and the incidence of virus diseases in a new crop often reflects the proximity of an older one. So, too, with sugar beet, the yellows virus that often becomes epidemic in the root crop, which is grown as an annual, comes initially from plants growing as biennials, grown for seed or some other purpose, and in which the virus survives through the winter.

Although viruses are obligate parasites, not all of them have narrow host ranges, and some of the viruses that become prevalent in annual crops of one species derive from perennial plants of quite different species, genera or even of different families. Most gladioli, for instance, are infected with yellow-bean mosaic virus, which they will supply to any French beans grown near, and many of the perennial plants so popular in herbaceous borders are hosts for the viruses that cause the diseases of tomato spotted wilt and cucumber mosaic. The statement made earlier, that pathogens spread less in mixed populations of plants than in pure stands, is not invalidated by this, but when a pathogen has a range of alternative hosts, growing these hosts together will obviously encourage its spread and survival.

Again, all hosts are not equal to a virus. Some it may harm, or even kill, whereas others seem unaffected. In some it reaches high populations and spreads rapidly from plant to plant, whereas in others it reaches only low populations and spreads rarely; the former are the plants in which they cause important diseases; the latter are often those that continue to supply virus for the former, and although they may well pass unnoticed, are perhaps of greater ecological importance to the survival of the virus.

One other relevant point: most viruses common in plants are insect-transmitted, and so the nature of the plant affects the spread of virus in two ways. First, by its direct interactions with the virus, whether it is susceptible and, if so, the extent to which the virus multiplies in it and the time for which it survives, and secondly, whether the insects that transmit the virus will feed on it, and, if so, whether it is a host on which the insects will breed readily.

CONCLUSION

I have outlined only some of the more obvious ways in which plant hosts affect the microbial population and have dealt very inadequately even with what is known. However, had I covered this fully, the picture would still be far from complete, because the roles of the plant host are undoubtedly far more varied and complex than have as yet been disclosed. I have usually not attempted to explain the effects that have been observed, for most of the changes that lead to them are still concealed and knowledge of the many systems on which natural selection is continually operating is only fragmentary. Some things can be explained plausibly, but in our present state of knowledge, or ignorance, we are well advised not to accept explanations simply because they are plausible. I hope I have at least indicated that the interactions between hosts and parasites are so varied that every ecological situation is best considered as though it were unique. Generalizations are easy enough to make because so little is known and so few habitats have been thoroughly explored, but they will inevitably have to be abandoned when more information is gained, and so they are hardly worth the making. Information about the behaviour of one parasite and one host can provide a useful guide, suggesting things to look for and experiments to make with others, but to do the looking and the experiments in the expectation of establishing general theories, applicable to widely differing situations and to different microbes, is almost certainly only to court disappointment.

REFERENCES

BAWDEN, F. C. (1956). Reversible, host-induced, changes in a strain of tobacco mosaic virus. *Nature, Lond.*, **177**, 302.

BAWDEN, F. C. & KASSANIS, B. (1947). The behaviour of some naturally occurring strains of potato virus Y. *Ann. appl. Biol.* **34**, 503.

BLACK, L. M. (1953). Loss of vector transmissibility by viruses normally insect transmitted. *Phytopathology*, **43**, 466.

BROWN, R. (1946). Biological stimulation in germination. *Nature, Lond.*, **157**, 64.

BROWN, W. (1922). Studies in the physiology of parasitism. VIII. On the exosmosis of nutrient substances from the host tissue into the infection drop. *Ann. Bot., Lond.*, **36**, 101.

BUXTON, E. W. (1957*a*). Some effects of pea root exudates on physiologic races of *Fusarium oxysporum* f. *pisi*. *Trans. Brit. mycol. Soc.* **40** (in the Press).

BUXTON, E. W. (1957*b*). Differential rhizosphere effects of three pea varieties on physiologic races of *Fusarium oxysporum* f. *pisi*. *Trans. Brit. mycol. Soc.* **40** (in the Press).

GARRETT, S. D. (1956). *Biology of root-infecting fungi*. Cambridge University Press.

GREGORY, P. H. (1945). The dispersion of air-borne spores. *Trans. Brit. mycol. Soc.* **28**, 26.

HARLEY, J. L. (1948). Mycorrhiza and soil ecology. *Biol. Rev.* **23**, 127.

HILTNER, L. (1904). Über neuere Erfahrungen und Probleme auf dem Gebiete der Bodenbakteriologie unter besonderer Berücksichtigung der Gründüngung und Brache. *Arb. dtsch. LandwGes.* **98**, 59.

HOLLINGS, M. (1955). Investigation of Chrysanthemum viruses. 1. Aspermy flower distortion. *Ann. appl. Biol.* **43**, 86.

JONES, F. G. W. (1954). First steps in breeding for resistance to potato-root eelworm. *Ann. appl. Biol.* **41**, 348.

LAST, F. T. (1955). Seasonal incidence of *Sporobolomyces* on cereal leaves. *Trans. Brit. mycol. Soc.* **38**, 221.

MACFARLANE, M. (1952). Factors affecting the survival of *Plasmodiophora brassicae* Wor. in the soil and its assessment by a host test. *Ann. appl. Biol.* **39**, 239.

POLLOCK, M. R. (1950). Penicillinase adaptation in *B. cereus*: adaptive enzyme formation in the absence of free substrate. *Brit. J. exp. Path.* **31**, 739.

STAKMAN, E. C. & CHRISTENSEN, J. (1953). Problems of variability in fungi. In *Plant Diseases*. Washington: United States Department of Agriculture.

THORNTON, H. G. (1956). The ecology of micro-organisms in soil. *Proc. roy Soc.* B, **145**, 364.

TIMONIN, M. I. (1941). The interactions of higher plants and soil micro-organisms. III. Effect of by-products of plant growth on activity of fungi and actinomycetes. *Soil Sci.* **52**, 395.

WATSON, MARION A. (1956). The effect of different host plants of potato virus C in determining its transmission by aphids. *Ann. appl. Biol.* **44**, 599.

WEST, P. M. & LOCHHEAD, A. G. (1940). Qualitative studies of soil micro-organisms. IV. The rhizosphere in relation to the nutritive requirements of soil bacteria. *Canad. J. Res.* C, **18**, 129.

WHITE, N. H. (1954). The use of decoy crops in the eradication of certain soil-borne plant diseases. *Aust. J. Sci.* **17**, 18.

THE BIOLOGICAL INFLUENCES OF MAN AND ANIMALS ON MICROBIAL ECOLOGY

R. LOVELL
Royal Veterinary College, London

There are two habits which living things have developed in the universal struggle for the easiest way to obtain food and shelter; they are the predatory and the parasitic habit. Although parasitism is a physiological habit and in essence a balance between two living things, this phenomenon is accompanied by predatory processes whenever opportunity is offered to one or other of the parties. The influences of man and animals in microbial ecology may therefore be studied by attention to pathological and physiological affairs. Metazoa, protozoa, fungi, bacteria and viruses may be parasitic in man and animals and our knowledge of their presence, their kind, their numbers and variations has been gleaned from studies of normal individuals and from studies of disease processes. The pathological manifestations of parasitism are merely incidents in a developing parasitism. There are some infective agents which habitually cause disease in a particular host; those individuals who harbour the micro-organism but are able to withstand its pathogenic effects are called healthy carriers or are referred to as being 'latently infected'. There are other micro-organisms which cause disease less frequently and only under relatively well-defined conditions; when these are carried on the mucosa or in some organ of the animal body, they are referred to as 'the normal flora' and their frequency distribution is recorded under this heading. There is apparently no biological difference between these relationships; one is regarded as a normal relationship because it is of more frequent occurrence and the other as an abnormal one. Is there any real difference between the relationship of the many who harbour pneumococci and the few who are carriers of the typhoid bacillus?

Man has interfered with parasitism in his own life and in the lives of the lower animals. Domestication may protect animals, which in a state of nature would be preyed upon by parasites; on the other hand, overcrowding tends to encourage parasitism. There are then two conflicting processes which vary from one host-parasite relationship to another and with the degree of interference. There is no stability and the relationships are changing; these changes are associated with our changing habits and ways of living.

Estimates of the distribution of a particular parasite may sometimes be made by observations on the geographical distribution of the host; this is possible when distribution of host and microbe coincide. The micro-organism is, in these circumstances, an obligatory parasite and lives in a particular species of animal only and is not able to exist outside of that animal species. This simple relationship apparently exists in regard to man and *Neisseria meningitidis*. The meningococcus is found in the nasopharynx of a proportion of human beings and is not known to exist elsewhere. It is therefore safe to assume that meningococci will not be found where man is not known. *Babesia bovis* may be found within the red blood cells of cattle; its final host is a species of tick and it is not found naturally anywhere but in ticks and cattle. *Trichomonas foetus* is another specific parasite in that it is found in the genital tract of cattle, and possibly deer as well but in no other species of animal.

There are other examples whereby the distibution of a micro-organism bears a 'time' relationship to the geographical distribution of a particular species of animal. *Erysipelothrix rhusiopathiae* is found in some soils, and there is the association with the earlier residence of pigs in the neighbourhood. Normal and diseased pigs may carry this organism and pigs appear to be the prime reservoir, although infection of birds, sheep, man, other mammals and possibly fish may occur. Many species of *Clostridium* have a similar time relationship; tetanus occurs more frequently in areas in which the soil is highly cultivated and well manured. There is a clear association with the use of natural manure and the presence of *C. tetani* in the faeces of domesticated animals. 'Tetanus areas' and 'Braxy areas' are well known; in one case the spores of *C. tetani* are common and in the other the spores of *C. septique*.

Corynebacterium ovis is commonly found in the soil of sheep-shearing compounds in Australia, and this is associated with the presence of sheep in close confinement during the shearing periods. The reservoir of the bacteria is the intestines of domesticated animals and the soil becomes contaminated; the bacteria may survive for varying periods.

There are other relationships whereby the micro-organism is found in a large variety of animal species. *Pasteurella tularensis* has been found in six species of birds and twenty-eight species of mammals in North America, and in fourteen other species of mammals in parts of Europe and Asia. In all there are forty-eight vertebrates in addition to man, in which tularaemia is or has been recognized (Burroughs, Holdenried, Longanecker & Meyer, 1945). *Trypanosoma brucei* is another catholic parasite, and may be found in horses, cattle, sheep, pigs, camels, dogs and goats as well as in some species of monkey, in elephants, hyaenas, wart hogs and the reed and water buck.

The relationship between micro-organisms and animals may range from one in which one species of animal appears to be able to support the growth of an organism under natural circumstances to that whereby many species of animal may play this role. The narrow host-specificity implies a more intricate and intimate relationship and suggests a marked loss of power of the parasite to synthesize its essential nutritional requirements. All parasites have lost some of this power, but the degree of loss and the degree of host-specificity should be in some way correlated. This degree of host-specificity limits the usefulness of assessing the geographical distribution of a microbe by an evaluation of the distribution of a particular animal host.

NORMAL BACTERIAL FLORA OF DIFFERENT ANIMAL SPECIES

From time to time reports appear of surveys which have been made of the bacterial flora of a group of individuals. In some cases there is a description of the nasopharyngeal flora of a sample of human beings over a considerable period (*Report*, 1930; Straker, Hill & Lovell, 1939), in others a description of the carrier rate of one type of organism in a sample of the population in a particular geographical area (Taylor, 1949). The figures recorded for either type of survey give an incomplete picture of the incidence of the bacteria concerned. The nasopharyngeal flora of a sample of the population in London and south-east England was examined at frequent intervals over a period of 7 years just before the Second World War. Each organism studied had its order of frequency of isolation; for example, *Streptococcus pneumoniae* was carried by about 30 % and *Neisseria meningitidis* by from 10 to 20 % of the persons examined. Thus, provided the same technique was used, the frequency distribution at one examination closely resembled that at an examination of a similar group of people made a few weeks earlier. This similarity of range of frequency could have been ascribed to the assumption that some persons tend to harbour certain bacteria over long periods of time, whilst others tend to be comparatively free of them. The picture was, however, more complicated, and it was revealed that some individuals persistently carried an organism, others were intermittent carriers, some carried an organism for a short time and then lost it, whilst others were apparently free for long periods and suddenly acquired it. If a person was under survey for a long time, then it was highly probable that sooner or later he or she would become a carrier of the bacterium under study. The figures given in the above report suggest that within a period of some 6 years every person in one sample of the population examined would have been shown to be harbouring *S. pneumoniae* and three-quarters would have yielded *N. meningitidis*. Had it been possible to undertake more frequent examinations there is little doubt that each of the bacteria under study would have been recovered from each of the persons examined.

A similar picture is revealed in the report issued by the Agricultural Research Council (*Report*, 1944) on the persistence and spread of *Streptococcus agalactiae* in dairy cattle. This bacterium was isolated from 38·8 % of 16,482 samples of milk and from 23·1 % of 5433 teat swabs; when cattle in nine herds were examined at approximately weekly intervals the cumulative carrier rate reached 100 % for both milk samples and teat swabs.

One single examination of the distribution of bacteria in or on man and animals yields an imperfect picture of the true incidence. It is therefore justifiable to assume that the bacillus of Johne's disease is present in more than 15 % of cattle (see Taylor, 1949), and that *Coryne-bacterium pyogenes* is present in the tonsils of more than 18 % of cattle (see Francis, 1941). The technique utilized as well as the frequency of examination may also be responsible for revealing a lower incidence than that which exists. *Salmonella* bacteria were not isolated from the tissues or intestinal contents of normal healthy pigs, cattle or horses by many who attempted it between the years of 1906 and 1934 (see Lovell, 1934). In 1940 Scott recovered thirty-eight strains from the mesenteric glands of 1000 pigs and in 1947 (*Report*, 1947) 133 strains were isolated from 3285 pigs. The high frequency of meningococci in the nasopharynx of healthy adults in the inquiry cited (Straker *et al.* 1939) differed markedly from that obtained during the First World War when a carrier rate of from 10 to 20 % would have been regarded as unduly high and one of 20 % considered as a warning of an impending epidemic.

There is a strong probability that these changing pictures were in some measure associated with the introduction of better techniques and of media designed to facilitate isolation of the organism sought.

Parasitism of man and animals by bacteria, protozoa and inferentially by viruses is a well-recognized phenomenon. Attention has been paid very largely to those micro-organisms which are regarded as pathogenic or potentially pathogenic, so that some problems of epidemiology may be more fully understood. Whilst the relationship is constantly changing, there is a suggestion that the number of a sample so parasitized is frequently under-estimated and that the techniques utilized play a great part in the accuracy of assessment.

Some micro-organisms have a simple relationship with one species of host. Thus *Corynebacterium renale* occurs in cattle, and the meningo-coccus, group A streptococci, the pneumococcus and the diphtheria bacillus are essentially human parasites. Their presence in other animals is exceptional; group A streptococci have been known to parasitize the bovine udder, the pneumococcus has been recovered from guinea-pigs, from calves, and from an occasional monkey, and the diphtheria bacillus has caused superficial lesions in horses, elephants and an occasional cow. In general, however, these are examples of a fairly strict host-specificity.

Others show a wider range; *Corynebacterium pyogenes* occurs in cattle, sheep, pigs and goats, and has on rare occasions been found in man or in horses. *Pasteurella pestis* occurs in rats and in man, whilst variants of *Pasteurella septica* (or *multocida*) are found in cattle, sheep, pigs, horses, fowls and occasionally in man. All the varieties of *Brucella* are being found in an increasing number of animal species although it is fair to say that the comparative incidence of *B. melitensis, abortus* and *suis* bears a close relationship, in some countries at least, to the distribution of sheep and goats, cattle and pigs. The types of tubercle bacillus show a similar kind of distribution; the main reservoir of the bovine type is cattle, even though strains of this type may be isolated from man, pigs, dogs, cats and horses; the human and avian types range beyond the human and avian hosts. There are some peculiar relationships such as the recovery of the avian type from the wallaby on several occasions even though exposure to other types may have been as frequent.

The problems which are raised here concern the adaptation of one type of microbe to a particular host species and the subsequent adaptation to others. This apparent preference is shown in some of the examples cited and may also be demonstrated in the frequency with which some serological types of bacteria are associated with one species of host. *Salmonella typhi* is a human pathogen; *S. dublin* is found mainly in cattle; *S. pullorum* occurs in poultry. Types of bacteria may be determined on cultural and on serological grounds; whichever criterion is used the general phenomenon remains and relationships between microbes and animal hosts vary from a strict one to one which is catholic.

DISTRIBUTION OF INFECTIOUS DISEASES AS INDICATIVE
OF MICROBIAL ECOLOGY

Some indication of the influence of animals on microbial ecology may be obtained by a study of the distribution of some infectious diseases. The degree to which this is applicable depends largely upon the specificity of the disease for a particular host and upon the reservoir of the infective agent.

Measles is one of the important exanthemata of the human race, and its morbidity rate in children is very high. Most adults have had the disease and it is not known to occur in any other host. The distribution of the virus and its perpetuation is clearly associated with mankind. Swine fever, or hog cholera, is similar in this respect; the virus of this disease is found in pigs and its distribution and perpetuation associated with the pig population. This virus may be adapted to rabbits and to sheep, but it is maintained that pigs are the reservoir of the virus. This specific reservoir of the virus has been questioned, but the virus does not appear to have been recognized in other sites or in other animal species. There is thus a close relationship between the incidence of measles and of swine fever and the distribution of man and of pigs. The same close relationship occurs between the virus of myxomatosis and rabbits; apparently no other species of animal, with the possible exception of the hare, is infected under natural circumstances. The story has been told frequently of the inoculation of two rabbits with virus in France in June 1952 (Thompson, H. V., 1956). These two rabbits were released within a walled park and by September 1953 myxomatosis was present in half of the ninety departments of France; by the end of the year all but five departments were affected. The disease spread to Belgium, Germany, Luxemburg, the Netherlands, Spain, Switzerland, Austria and Italy; the disease appeared in Kent in the late summer or autumn of 1953, and by the end of 1955 it was present in most parishes of England, Wales and Scotland. The mortality in Great Britain was estimated to be of the order of 99 %, and the rabbit population has decreased accordingly. Attenuated strains of virus have since appeared in Britain; this was not unexpected as weaker strains of virus are known in Australia. This disease has profoundly affected agriculture and wild life in Britain because the rabbit is no longer a common animal; crops have been grown in fields previously grazed bare by rabbits, whilst buzzards, stoats and foxes may have had to alter their diet or breed less prolifically. The impact of a specific virus upon a susceptible population may have considerable influence far beyond the actual host-parasite relationship.

Studies of the epidemiology of an infective disease will indicate whether one or more species of animal affect the distribution of a particular microbe. Although the reservoir of infection may possibly be the same species as that attacked, as in measles, swine fever and myxomatosis, a great number of infections are derived from another animal species. Reference has already been made to the variety of mammals and birds attacked by tularemia. *Leptospira icterohaemorrhagiae* may produce disease in man and in dogs, whereas the reservoir of infection is the rat; on the other hand, *L. canicola* infects dogs and occasionally man, with the dog as its reservoir. These common observations pose many problems concerning the cultural requirements of these infective agents. What are the mechanisms which allow the anthrax bacillus to grow and produce disease in sheep, cattle, pigs, horses, man and in some carnivores with an apparently decreasing severity, whilst the glanders bacillus is confined to asses, horses and man? Are the mechanisms similar to those which allow the mammalian types of tubercle bacilli to be infective for so many species and yet prevent the bacillus of Johne's disease from infecting other than cows and sheep?

There is a vast field of investigation open to the field naturalist who is a microbiologist. Many microbial agents, some of them infective for man or animals, are possibly to be found in wild animals. Additional hosts of the psittacosis group of viruses are being discovered; these range from petrels and snowy egrets to small rodents and opossums. The studies on food poisoning in man have stimulated investigations to observe the distribution of *Salmonella* bacteria in nature. In the U.S.A. it has been maintained that chickens are the largest single reservoir. The role played by pigs, cattle, rodents and domestic pets has also been investigated. Some attention has been paid to their presence in reptiles, and Boycott, Taylor & Douglas (1953) now show that *Salmonella* bacteria may occur in tortoises imported into this country. Seventeen species were recovered from tortoises imported from Morocco, but knowledge of the species of *Salmonella* in current circulation in Morocco is scanty and the significance of the findings is discussed in this light. The authors take the view that the testadine bowel is a favourable site for the survival of *Salmonella* and there is little object in trying to define their existence there as saprophytic or as the result of infection. It may be that geographical location may be a greater factor than that of species of animal, and that the high carrier rate may have been associated with infection in transit.

THE INFLUENCE OF VARIATIONS WITHIN A SPECIES IN THE DISTRIBUTION OF MICROBIAL AGENTS

Under natural circumstances animals and man carry and support bacteria, protozoa and possibly viruses. Such parasites are not essential for the life of the host. Reyniers and his colleagues at the University of Notre Dame, Indiana, U.S.A., have studied 'germ-free' animals for about 25 years. Their 'germ-free' animals are free of bacteria, fungi, protozoa and presumably viruses. The animals are introduced into the 'germ-free' environment by Caesarean section or by the sterilization of the shell of fertile eggs. All operations are performed in sterile cages, and samples of hair or feathers, food, milk, water, urine and faeces are collected in sealed tubes, removed from the cage through sterile locks and subjected to rigorous tests for the presence of living microbial agents. Such animals have no experience of microbial agents, and therefore many so-called normal defence mechanisms have not functioned. There are no normal or natural antibodies, phagocytosis is unknown and the lymphatic system is underdeveloped and in what has been expressed as 'an idling state'. When such animals are deliberately infected with a specific bacterium unexpected results are obtained. No change in the cultural characteristics of a *Lactobacillus* was observed when passaged through three generations of germ-free rats. On the other hand, a strain of *Streptococcus liquefaciens* gave rise to an increasing number of variants which did not liquefy gelatin; there appeared to be a loss of some of the proteolytic activity; these loss-variants therefore appeared to be more akin to *S. faecalis* in cultural characteristics. It is suggested therefore that antigenic changes and alterations in virulence may also occur (Reyniers, personal communication); *Bacillus subtilis* is able to induce an epidemic with a high mortality when introduced accidentally in herds of experimental animals which are 'germ-free'. These studies (see Reyniers, Trexler, Wagner & Gordon, 1955) raise questions concerning the influence of the status of an individual animal in microbial ecology. Status may in this context include such variables as sex, age, environment and the immunological and nutritional states. The variables are difficult to maintain or exclude and the provision and maintenance of 'germ-free' animals is a costly adventure.

Age and sex are variables which influence the ecology of micro-organisms. Brucellosis is a disease of maturity which is reflected in the resistance of young calves to *Brucella* infection up to or near the beginning of ovulation. Furthermore, infection of children with *Brucella* is uncommon. There are other infective agents which have an age or sex incidence and therefore demonstrate the influence of these variables. The physiological changes which occur in mammals may have some bearing upon the distribution of micro-organisms. Infection of the endometrium occurs frequently in cattle, but there is some protective mechanism which functions at the oestrogenic phases of the cycle. Age alone may be the prime factor, and H. W. Smith (personal communication) found in a group of eight calves that the number of viable *Bacterium coli* per gram of faeces varied enormously during their first 5 months of life. The range at 2 days old was from 400 million to 6000 million, then counts diminished until at 50 and 150 days there were marked diminutions, and at the latter date the numbers ranged from 20,000 to 5 million viable *B. coli*.

The relative resistance of a host to a particular agent is not constant and the 'carrier state' may frequently be judged by serological tests. Cattle may carry *Brucella* and the latently infected animals may be detected by the agglutination of *Brucella* by their sera. Tuberculous animals may be detected by allergic tests. These indirect tests are of value in certain defined infections only; horses may contain in their sera agglutinins for the glanders bacillus with no evidence of present or past infection (Lovell, 1935). Indirect methods of assessment are subject to error unless supported by other evidence.

INFLUENCE OF HUMAN ACTIVITIES ON MICROBIAL ECOLOGY

The changing face of disease in man and in animals is a reflexion of the change of habits of man and the changes occurring in our management of animals. Two hundred years ago the cattle in England strayed away among the stubble in search of their food. Stock were slaughtered at the end of the autumn because of lack of feeding supplies. To-day domesticated animals are assured of a good food supply; they are housed, fed, watered, immunized and given antibiotics. These changing habits have changed microbial ecology and will continue to change it, and this is shown by the incidence of certain infective diseases.

Unfortunately, early records of some diseases are sparse and it is difficult to evaluate the factors which have led to the rise and fall of diseases, or to their apparent change in virulence. Scarlet fever was a dreaded disease of childhood in the early part of this century, whilst to-day it is a mild incident. In some infective diseases credit must be given to methods of prophylaxis as in the present low incidence of diphtheria compared with relatively few years ago. Little is known of the mechanisms at work in the complex host-parasite relationship, and one hazards a guess as to the reasons for the diminution of distemper in the dog and the increase in the disease colloquially known as 'hard pad'. Changes which are forced upon our animals by changes of habits may lead to these alterations and differences. In some cases we are able to trace the causal event and praise or blame. Disease, a reflexion of the distribution of the infective agent, may be increased or decreased. Clear-cut examples are rare except in remote areas or in islands.

Sheep farming is one of the chief agricultural pursuits in the island of Iceland, and because of the climate the sheep are housed for two or three of the winter months. In the summer they roam the mountain pastures and are rounded up and penned in the autumn before being housed on their separate farms for the winter months. This sheep husbandry is different from that occurring in more temperate climates, and until 1933 the island was supporting about three-quarters of a million sheep. In that year, twenty sheep were imported into Iceland from Germany; they were all apparently in good health and after a period of quarantine were distributed to sixteen different farms. Five years later, Johne's disease was discovered for the first time in Iceland on one of the farms. At the same time infection was found on four more of the sixteen farms into which the rams had been introduced. It is estimated that more than 75,000 sheep died in the island from Johne's disease in the years 1938–53. The incubation period of Johne's disease is long, and it appears as if at least five of the imported sheep were latently infected with the bacillus of Johne's disease and that the Icelandic sheep, coupled with the methods of husbandry practised in Iceland, made ideal conditions for its spread. At least two of the imported sheep carried the virus of maedi, a chronic pneumonia of sheep with a period of incubation of two or three years. Maedi was prevalent in Iceland from 1939 to 1953, and it is estimated that during those years 150,000 animals were lost from the disease. Another chronic disease of sheep, infectious adenomatosis or jaagsiekte, was probably introduced into the island at the same time, and this too caused serious losses. The climatic and geographical conditions compel sheep farmers to adopt methods of husbandry which are not known in more temperate climates, and these conditions are probably responsible for the devastating effects of the diseases introduced by latently infected sheep. The three diseases, one bacterial in origin and the other two probably caused by viruses, are not known in those areas from which the infected sheep originated. Microbial ecology has been markedly influenced by man's interference, and still further changes occurred when about 170,000 sheep were slaughtered in attempts to control these diseases (Sigurdsson, 1954).

The changing incidence of tuberculosis in man has been estimated by mortality rates, morbidity rates and recently by infection rates. It is thought that an epidemic wave must have spread over England and Wales in the eighteenth century, reaching its peak in about 1810. This high incidence was brought about by the change in our habits of living because of the deterioration occasioned by the Industrial Revolution. People flocked from the country to the towns and lived in squalid, overcrowded dwellings and worked in dark insanitary factories. The fall in incidence has been accompanied by the slow improvement of housing and general social conditions. It was estimated that the death-rate in 1810 was about 6000 per 1,000,000 living; in 1855 the death-rate from tuberculosis was estimated at 3626 per million; 50 years later it was 1632 and 100 years later 148 (Thompson, D., 1956). It has been accepted that this variation in incidence of tuberculosis with its variables in host according to age, sex, social and economic status gives a good indication of the distribution of the human type of the tubercle bacillus. The rate of infection from the bovine type, though far from being negligible, has decreased during the last few years and is without doubt correlated with the increase in the amount of milk treated by heat and by the decrease in tuberculosis in cattle.

The distribution of the bovine tubercle bacillus throughout a particular area may be estimated by subjecting the cattle in an area to the tuberculin test. It is true that a small number of human beings, pigs, horses, dogs and cats may be infected with this type of tubercle bacillus, but the reservoir of infection is the bovine species of animal. The tuberculin tests, as made to-day, are reliable within an extemely high degree and able to detect tubercle-infected cattle and to differentiate between those infected by the bovine or avian types. Endeavours made to control bovine tuberculosis in Great Britain depend upon the detection of animals by this test, their elimination and the building up of herds free from tuberculosis. Attested herds and attested areas are those herds and areas in which, as far as may be ascertained by the test, no bovine tuberculosis exists. By well-marked steps, such areas are being formed and the country is being cleared of bovine tuberculosis in these defined stages. In 1945 it was estimated that of 8,697,376 cattle in Great Britain 788,020 or 9·06 % of them were in attested herds and therefore presumed free from tuberculosis. This distribution of attested herds is shown in Fig. 1. Ten years later, in December 1955, it was calculated that of 9,764,800 cattle in Great Britain, 6,052,000 were in attested herds or areas. This means that 62 % are free from tuberculosis and the distribution of these is shown in Fig. 2. These figures are given to show how the distribution of a given micro-organism may sometimes be estimated by a biological test made on a host, in this case an allergic one. Furthermore, though the changing habits of man and animals may in some way lead to increasing disease, there are deliberate attempts being made in many directions to decrease infective diseases in man and in animals. This has marked effects on microbial ecology.

GENERAL DISCUSSION

In many ways a discussion of the influence of man and animals in microbial ecology is similar to some of the aspects of epidemiology; it is a study of host-parasite relationships. It is known that mammals may survive under 'germ-free' conditions, whereas under natural circumstances they carry bacteria, protozoa and probably viruses. The main attention has been paid to those agents which may cause disease; it becomes difficult to define in exact terms what is meant by a 'carrier animal' or a 'latently infected animal' and to distinguish between these relationships and the relationship enjoyed by the normal bacterial flora of an animal. Latent viral infections are known in the field (Koprowski, 1952) and in the laboratory and one assumes that similar relationships therefore exist.

The extent of these host-parasite relationships may be judged by surveys of the agents carried by normal animals and in some cases by the incidence of specific diseases. Variations within the host influence the extent to which populations contain or carry a microbial agent. These variations may be normal ones such as the distribution of the sexes and of different age groups. On the other hand, there are populations, normally susceptible to an immigrant micro-organism, but containing a high proportion of immune animals. This immunity may be a natural one or one which has been induced artificially; interplaying factors increase the complexity of these relationships. The different habits of mankind and the changes in management of domesticated animals increase still further these complexities. Dogs in kennels and horses in stables are more frequently infected with some of the common bacterial infections than their fellows with more freedom. The selective influences which are at work will continue to change; a study of the mechanisms may provide explanations, but the story will never finish.

I am very grateful to Mr J. N. Ritchie, C.B., B.Sc., F.R.C.V.S., D.V.S.M., Chief Veterinary Officer to the Ministry of Agriculture, Fisheries and Food, for the supply of the maps (Figs. 1, 2) and for the data which accompany them.

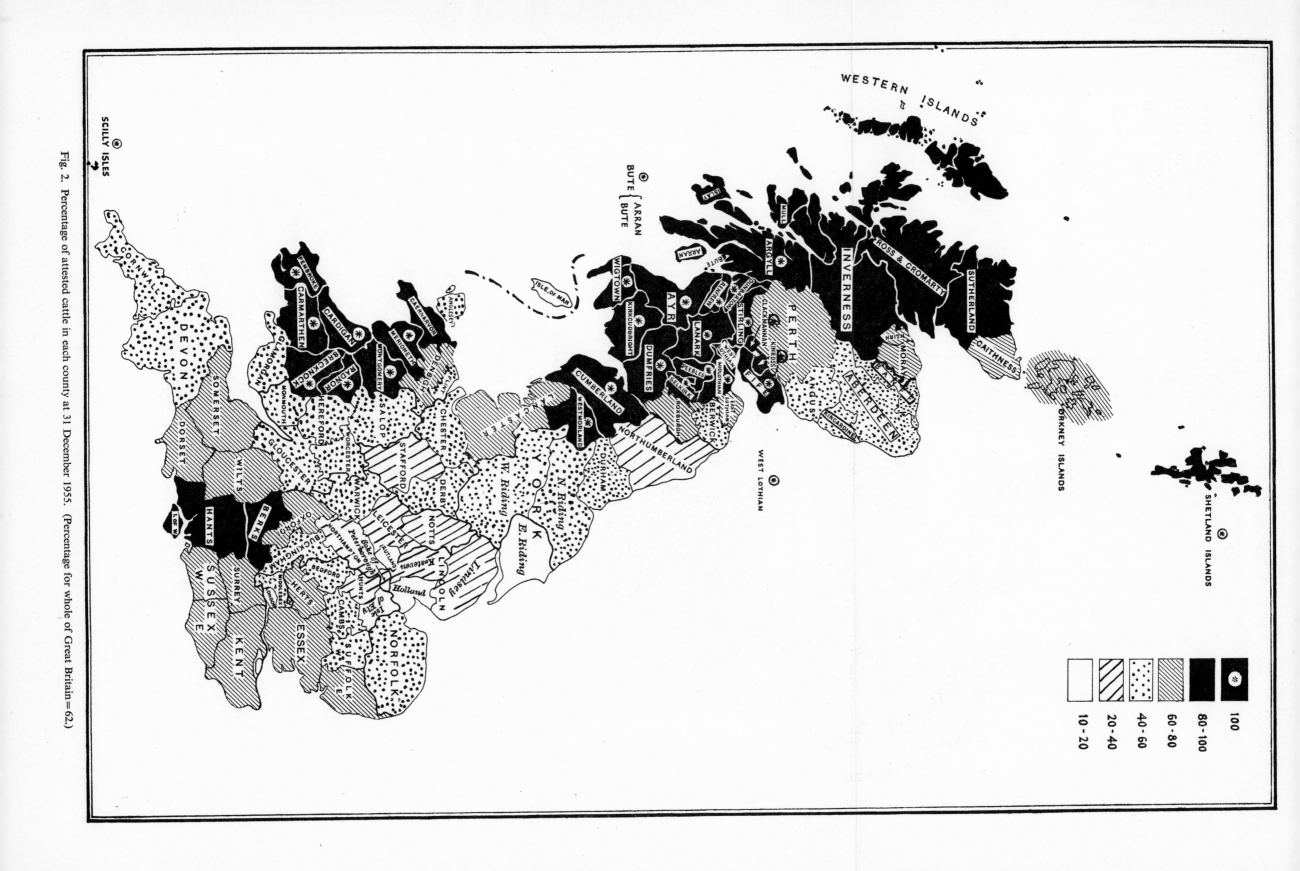

Fig. 2. Percentage of attested cattle in each county at 31 December 1955. (Percentage for whole of Great Britain = 62.)

10 - 20
20 - 40
40 - 60
60 - 80
80 - 100
100

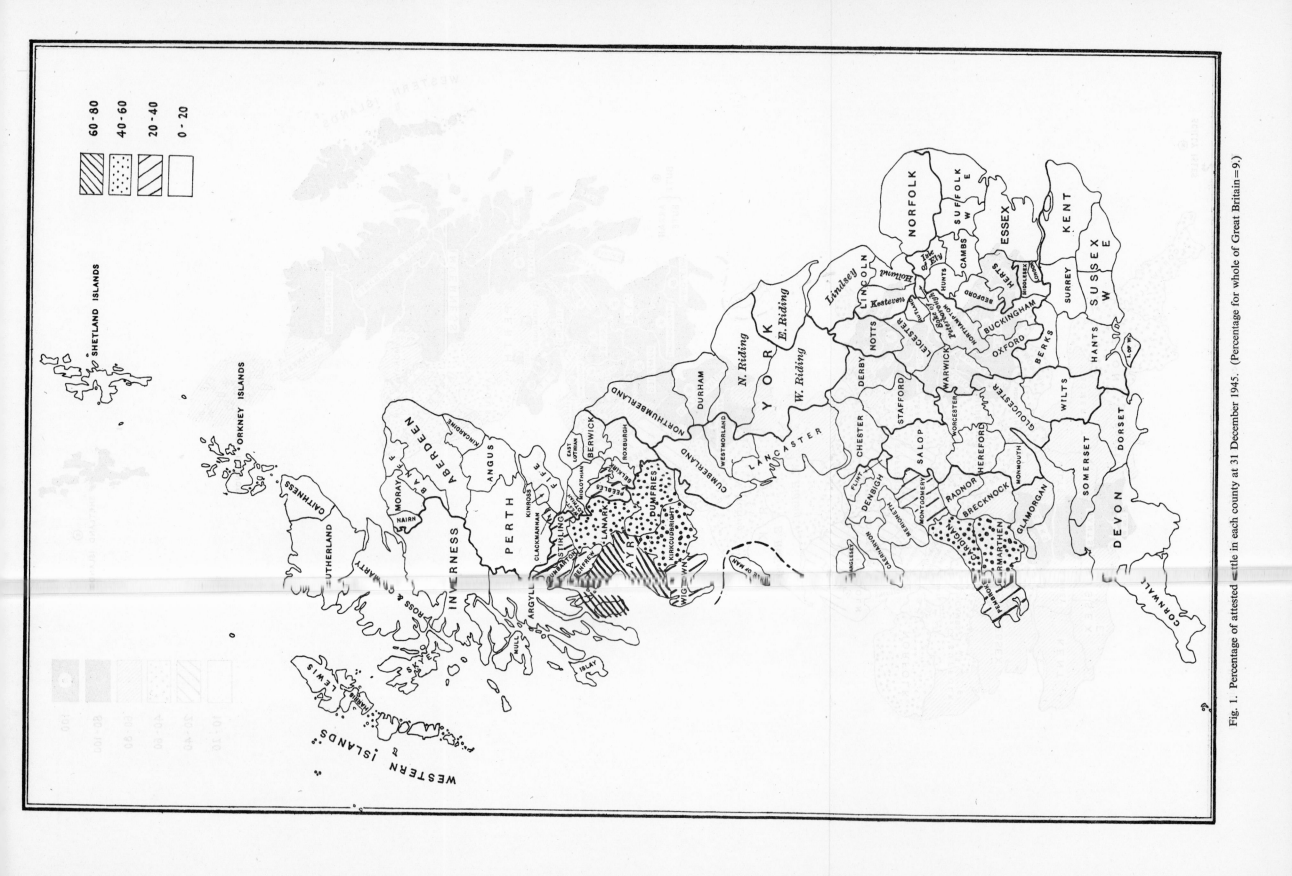

Fig. 1. Percentage of attested cattle in each county at 31 December 1945. (Percentage for whole of Great Britain = 9.)

REFERENCES

BOYCOTT, J. A., TAYLOR, J. & DOUGLAS, S. H. (1953). Salmonella in tortoises. *J. Path. Bact.* **65**, 401.

BURROUGHS, A. L., HOLDENREID, R., LONGANECKER, D. S. & MEYER, K. F. (1945). A field study of latent tuberculosis in rodents with a list of all known naturally infected vertebrates. *J. infect. Dis.* **76**, 115.

FRANCIS, J. (1941). A bacteriological examination of bovine tonsils and vaginas. *Vet. J.* **97**, 243.

KOPROWSKI, H. (1952). Latent or dormant viral infections. *Ann. N.Y. Acad. Sci.* **54**, 962.

LOVELL, R. (1934). The presence and significance of agglutinins for some members of the *Salmonella* group occurring in the sera of normal animals. *J. comp. Path.* **47**, 107.

LOVELL, R. (1935). Studies on normal agglutinins. The agglutination of *Pf. mallei* by normal horse sera. *J. R. Army vet. Cps*, **6**, 69.

Report (1930). A study of the nasopharyngeal bacterial flora of a group of the Manchester population during the period July 1925 to September 1927. *Rep. Publ. Hlth med. Subj. Lond.* **58**.

Report (1944). Modes of spread of *Streptococcus agalactiae* infection in dairy herds. *Rev. Ser. Imp. Bur. anim. Hlth*, no. 2.

Report (1947). Bacteriology of sprayed dried egg with particular reference to food poisoning. *Spec. Rep. Ser. med. Res. Coun., Lond.*, no. 260.

REYNIERS, J. A., TREXLER, P. C., WAGNER, M. & GORDON, H. A. (1955). Germ free research. A basic study in host-contaminant relationship. *Bull. N.Y. Acad. Med.* **31**, 231.

SCOTT, W. M. (1940). *Salmonella* in healthy pigs at slaughter. *Proc. R. Soc. Med.* **33**, 366.

SIGURDSSON, B. (1954). Observations on three slow infections of sheep. *Brit. vet. J.* **110**, 255, 307, 341.

STRAKER, E., HILL, A. B. & LOVELL, R. (1939). A study of the nasopharyngeal bacterial flora of different groups of persons observed in London and south-east England during the years 1930–37. *Rep. Publ. Hlth med. Subj. Lond.* **90**.

TAYLOR, A. W. (1949). Observations on the incidence of infection with *M. johnei* in cattle. *Vet. Rec.* **61**, 539.

THOMPSON, D. (1956). Tuberculosis—the changing emphasis. *Mon. Bull. Minist. Hlth Lab. Serv.* **15**, 99.

THOMPSON, H. V. (1956). Myxomatosis. A survey. *Agriculture, Lond.*, **63**, 51.

ECOLOGY OF VIRUSES

C. H. ANDREWES

National Institute for Medical Research, Mill Hill, London, N.W.7

One can consider the ecology of viruses from several viewpoints—virus in relation to its intracellular environment, as a parasite of the body as a whole, or as an infecting agent of a population of susceptible hosts; and finally there is the ecology of virus disease. In practice, these views have to be fused to give us a multi-dimensional picture. We have to discuss the factors affecting the ability of a virus to survive, multiply and spread; in so far as its properties are liable to modification and change, we cannot avoid considering virus evolution in relation to environment.

An ideal virus has certain natural advantages. It can potentially multiply at an astronomical rate. A phage can increase its numbers 200-fold in 20 min. Influenza A virus may be hard to find anywhere in a country, and yet within a month or two it may infect there some millions of people in any one of whom tens of millions of virus particles may be present. The tiniest drop of infected material may suffice to set up a fresh infection. Viruses are so small that, so far as we know, they are not subject to the attentions of either predators or parasites. How, then, do higher organisms avoid being overwhelmed by them? To answer this question we must look rather deeply.

For the cycle of infection to be fulfilled, four things are necessary. (1) Virus must be brought into contact with and be able to initiate infection in a susceptible host—or, if one chooses to look more closely, in a susceptible host cell. (2) It must be able to multiply adequately in the host, not merely in the cells first infected, but spreading to other cells and tissues. (3) It must be capable of being freely dispersed, as in excreta or by means of biting arthropods, so that it is in a position to reach a fresh host. (4) It must be able to survive outside the original host in a state in which it can produce a fresh infection.

We have now to consider the environmental factors which help or hinder it in each of these four activities—getting in, multiplying, getting out, getting about.

Latency and chronicity of virus infections

One thing must be made clear at the outset. The simple picture outlined above has probably been greatly modified in the course of evolution. A lethal attack by virus upon host is a relatively uncommon state of affairs; still rarer is a destructive epidemic. A long association between virus and host has commonly led to a state of equilibrium, so that many virus infections are wholly inapparent. Clearly, the longer an infected host survives and acts as a source of infection to other hosts, the better it is for the virus. We do not have to guess that this must happen; we can see it happening. Traub (1936, 1939) studied a colony of mice infected with lymphocytic chorio-meningitis virus and in the course of a year or two saw a change from an apparent to a wholly inapparent infection. At the end, the virus was so modified as to be relatively harmless to foetuses *in utero*—all individuals were infected before birth and carried the virus throughout life without any obvious ill-effects.

Perhaps even more interesting, because easier to study at leisure, are the changes taking place in myxomatosis of rabbits. This South American virus, introduced into Australia, at first killed about 99·5 % of the rabbits it infected. Within less than two years some attenuation had taken place so that mortality was only about 90 %; and there is a lot of difference between 100 survivors amongst 1000 attacked and only 5! Mykytowycz (1953) found an association between longer survival and lesser mortality; it seemed reasonable that the longer surviving rabbits would have a chance of infecting more mosquito vectors and that the virus would thus be favoured. It appears rather unexpectedly in practice that the most attenuated viruses are not becoming dominant, but rather those of intermediate virulence. Apparently the lesions produced by the weakest viruses are not ideally adapted to transferring infection to the mosquito proboscis (Fenner, 1955).

A particularly interesting point has become clear lately. The Australians view with much alarm the spread of milder strains which will allow survival of more of the hated rabbits. They have therefore in some localities introduced a more virulent virus from Europe. This has at first spread well and for some months has probably killed its expected 99·5 %; but before long the attenuated local strain has once more gained the ascendancy (Fenner, 1955).

In Britain, in Sherwood Forest in Nottinghamshire, an attenuated virus producing chronic nodular lesions has appeared; this kills perhaps only half the infected rabbits in the laboratory (Hudson, Thompson & Mansi, 1955). Great efforts have been made to kill the rabbits in

Sherwood Forest to prevent the attenuated virus from spreading, but one must expect that the effect will at best be to delay its extension. It is too early to see how the difference in the vectors (fleas in Britain, mosquitoes in Australia) will affect the ecological pattern. It does appear, however, that with a seasonal vector in Australia, there tend to be seasonal epizoötics, such as we have not yet seen in this country.

Breakdown of equilibria

Instances of balanced associations are too numerous to mention—prophage in lysogenic bacteria, ectromelia and other latent infections of mice, paracrinkle virus in King Edward potatoes (Salaman & Le Pelley, 1930) and so on. The most important ecological factors as regards virus *disease* are those which cause a breakdown in an equilibrium. In the laboratory one can induce lysis by irradiating a lysogenic phage; one can activate a latent animal virus by serial passages of tissue suspensions through apparently normal animals; one can grow out a latent virus in cultures of apparently normal tissues. Analogous things must be happening in nature. The rapid serial passage in the laboratory is paralleled by the bringing together of large numbers of susceptible people or animals; we are familiar with epidemics of respiratory virus infections amongst recruits and among boarders at the beginning of school terms. Another example is afforded by outbreaks of psittacosis among young budgerigars crowded too close together (Meyer, 1942). Man is asking for trouble when he grows his crops in pure culture, giving maximal opportunity for vectors, often specific ones, to spread virus infections. In fact very many troublesome virus infections are brought about by man's rash habit of aggregating his own kind, his herds and his crops under somewhat artificial conditions. He further encourages some virus infections by breeding his domestic plants and animals so as to select for some obvious useful property, in ignorance of the risk of activating a hitherto latent virus infection in the process.

Viruses in strange hosts

A virus and its host are not isolated in the world. There may intrude strange viruses and strange hosts. Often an infection which is harmless in the normal host is lethal in another one. One may instance encephalo-myelitis viruses in America, harmless to their normal avian hosts but often killing man or horse when carried over by a mosquito. In this instance the infection is apparently a blind alley for the virus; the viraemia occurring in the new host is not great enough to permit transfer by an insect to a fresh victim. But it need not always be so. Presumably the jungle yellow fever of the African monkeys and the tree-top mosquitoes was similarly carried by chance to man; and then, perhaps after many blind-alley ventures, an *Aedes aegypti-Homo sapiens* cycle became established.

These general considerations are necessary to establish that our four 'activities' (getting in, multiplying, getting out and getting about) must not be looked at in too naïve a manner as explaining everything about virus ecology. We can now pass on to considering the activities separately, so far as they can be separated.

CONTACT WITH HOST AND ENTRY

Exceptionally it may be possible to produce a florid infection with one or very few virus particles. In general, the mass of virus gaining access to the potential host is of great importance. Thus for arthropod-borne viruses we have to consider vector efficiency. The result is, of course, affected by the capacity of the virus to multiply in the vector. Mechanical transfer of infection by an insect is rarely effective, except apparently in the case of myxomatosis and Australian mosquitoes. (No studies of mechanism have been made in the case of the equally successful vector in Europe—the rabbit flea.) Of importance are such things as the biting habits of the vector, the numbers of blood meals it takes, and the intervals between these, the regularity of its occurrence in the same habitat as the host. Many mosquitoes have been shown to be capable of transmitting a virus infection in the laboratory, and yet are of no practical importance in the field.

I have elsewhere (Andrewes, 1956) used the terms horizontal, vertical and zigzag to describe methods of parasite transmission. 'Horizontal' describes infection through virus liberated in secretions and excretions; 'vertical' (following Gross, 1951) covers transfer of infection from one generation to the next; and 'zigzag' that in which a living vector is concerned.

With horizontal transmission the amount of virus reaching a host may determine the establishment of infection and production of disease. Non-specific defence mechanisms may stop a tiny dose of virus at the outset; with large doses disease may result, while with intermediate quantities a subclinical immunizing infection may be the outcome. It is likely that with respiratory infections such as influenza and the common cold, the last result is a very common one.

Ecology of influenza

The influenza virus presents such a fascinating array of ecological problems that we must consider it in some detail. In the course of evolution the virus has apparently learnt how to achieve two things: to spread widely when all is favourable for it and to survive when things are bad, quietly awaiting its chance to re-emerge.

The ability of the virus to spread in epidemic fashion is related to the ability to vary antigenically (Andrewes, 1953). A previously infected population will for some years have sufficient herd immunity to prevent the occurrence of a widespread epidemic due to a familiar type of virus. An antigenically changed virus, however, will be in a very different position. Studies from the World Health Organization's network of influenza laboratories have shown how extensive virus spread is linked with antigenic change. Serological types are known for many viruses but for none other than influenza has it been clearly shown that one type tends to succeed another, the older type dying out with fair rapidity, making room for its successor. At the World Influenza Centre laboratories at Mill Hill we have at times had some success in prophesying the further course of events from the appearance of a particular antigenic type at a particular place and time. Antigenic novelty is, however, by no means everything for the virus. Single, strikingly novel, antigenic types have at times appeared and failed to spread, as, for example, one received from Japan in 1953. The happenings of 1955–6 are dramatic in a negative sort of way and recall Sherlock Holmes and 'the curious incident of the dog in the night'. To Watson's comment that the dog did nothing in the night, Holmes replied that '*that* was the curious incident'. In the spring of 1955, after the failure of an expected A epidemic to occur, we obtained from widely separate places (India, Eire, the United Kingdom and New York State) viruses of a rather novel make-up but all similar to one another. There was a strong temptation to prophesy that this virus would appear in epidemic form in the autumn of 1955 in equally widely scattered places. But it was not so. Outbreaks in Britain and elsewhere were of a very modest and limited nature, and all viruses examined by us proved to resemble an older type of virus (Scandinavian) first isolated in 1951. The new 1955 virus apparently lacked some property enabling it to persist through the warm months until the chills of autumn should encourage it to come forth. In the circumstances the absence of a big influenza epidemic in three successive winters is indeed a 'curious incident'. We cannot guess why the 1955 virus failed to survive, for we do not as yet know how successful influenza viruses manage to persist between outbreaks; that they can do so in a particular area in the absence of clinical influenza seems fairly certain. There is here a very important gap in our knowledge of the ecology of the virus.

VIRUS MULTIPLICATION

Whether a virus can multiply when it has gained a foothold in a host will depend upon the body's power of resistance, and the factors concerned may be innate or acquired; the latter we will regard as synonymous with immunological.

Natural resistance

What are the factors which decide that children do not catch dog distemper nor puppies measles? One might be tempted to imagine that it is a question of need for a specific surface receptor, a specific enzyme system or a specific substrate which the measles virus, for instance, finds in the child's cells and not in the puppy's. Recent work on rabbit myxoma throws a little doubt on this notion (Chaproniere & Andrewes, 1956). Myxoma virus, believed to be one of the most specific, has been shown to be capable of multiplying in tissue cultures of supposedly insusceptible species such as squirrels, guinea-pigs, rats and even human beings. For rats in particular, the age of the host furnishing the tissues seems to be all important, embryonic tissues being the most favourable. (It is of course familiar that many viruses will grow in developing hens' eggs but not in chicks.) Many animal sera contain heat-labile factors capable of neutralizing certain viruses, but there is as yet no evidence that these play any part in determining the specificity of the attacks of viruses upon their hosts. The field, in view of recent developments in tissue culture techniques, is a fertile one for study.

Immunological resistance

The presence of a specific immunological resistance amongst potential hosts is a major ecological factor controlling virus growth and spread. Where infection is blood-borne and antibodies are accordingly peculiarly well-favoured, viruses have managed to survive by operating as infections of childhood, attacking one young victim and then getting out and into another one before specific resistance has time to develop. As another example besides measles, we can think of yellow fever in endemic areas. In the latter instance, introduction of susceptible adults from non-endemic areas provides a source of victims in addition to the local children, a source, moreover, in which the disease is likely to appear in an overt instead of a subclinical form.

Viruses have found other methods of by-passing inconvenient immunological obstacles. They may enter the body by a gate where the immunological watchdog is less alert, especially the upper respiratory tract. True, some antibody to viruses can be detected in respiratory mucus, but there is less of it than in the blood, and it seems to be only moderately efficient against influenza and still less so against the common cold. Its presence in high titre is apparently only transient, so that recurring infections are possible and infection is not confined to childhood.

Influenza virus, as we have already seen, can attain its ends also by appropriate antigenic mutation.

Yet another method for the virus is to remain within the infected cell, not destroying it and even causing indefinite cellular proliferation, as do the viruses of warts and tumours generally. Cotton-tail rabbits may carry for many months papillomata rich in virus, and at the same time have circulating blood rich in antibodies. So, too, herpes virus in man probably resides intracellularly in between the periods when some stimulus activates it; potent antibodies to it are found in people carrying such a latent infection.

DISPERSAL FROM THE HOST

Some viruses produce a disease which itself assists their spread: the encephalitis of rabies makes dogs go mad and, by biting, spread the infection; the common cold virus is well aware that 'coughs and sneezes spread diseases'; asters infected with yellows virus nourish leafhoppers better and spread of the infection is thereby favoured (Severin, 1946).

More frequently, however, the tendency is towards mutual toleration so that a chronic infection is produced. This favours the virus so long as the infectious agent is being shed into the environment. We have already seen how an attenuated myxoma virus has an advantage over a rapidly lethal one. The classical evolutionary course of a virus is towards latent infection, toleration and so to vertical transmission from parent to offspring; its perpetuation is thus assured but it can never get out of its chosen groove. Only the adaptable, opportunist virus will get into the medical history books.

Influenza A virus seems to owe its success largely to its exploitation of the technique of rapid epidemic spread alternating with a period of quiescence. Such an alternation may be commoner amongst viruses than is generally realized. A vertically transmitted prophage has its perpetuation ensured while it divides *pari passu* with its host cell. The induction of lysis in the laboratory is surely paralleled by similar happenings in nature, and a resulting liberation of free lytic phage gives an opportunity for the phage to infect hosts of new types and thus invade fresh fields. Many other virus infections may be regarded from a similar point of view; the agents which switch the virus from one phase of activity to the other will then be seen as the ecological factors of major importance.

SURVIVAL OUTSIDE THE HOST

Most viruses are labile compared with bacteria, and have to get rapidly from one host to another, or perish. Influenza A virus will survive a few days in dust (Edward, 1941), but it is unlikely that dust-borne infection is of real importance. Rift Valley fever virus, again, can survive for months in dust and has caused laboratory infections in consequence (Francis & Magill, 1935); and this is odd because it is believed to be an arthropod-transmitted disease. On the other hand, the toughness of the virus of panleucopenia of cats is a matter of importance to its ecology; one hears of cats dying of the disease and of fresh cats contracting the infection when introduced months later into a household in question. The powers of resistance of foot-and-mouth virus are all too well known.

Daylight appears to be lethal to many viruses, though more so when they have been purified than in their natural state.

Most arthropod-borne animal viruses can survive for the lifetime of their insect or acarine vector; multiplication within the vector is probably the rule, though it has only been proved for a few. We come back again to myxoma (this virus and influenza between them seem to exemplify almost every aspect of virus ecology); myxoma has not been proved to multiply in mosquitoes, but it can survive on the mouthparts of *Anopheles atroparvus* for more than 6 months, enough to carry infection over from one season to another (Muirhead-Thomson, Andrewes & Stevenson, 1956).

Complex aspects of virus ecology

Murray Valley fever affords an instance of how varied may be the factors affecting viruses (cf. Burnet, 1955). The virus is believed to inhabit migrating birds as normal hosts. In very wet seasons these may change their habits and travel much farther south than usual on the Australian continent; and we may have here the explanation of the infrequent outbreaks of the disease in New South Wales.

Pseudorabies in cattle in mid-western America occurs in outbreaks as a result of close contact in markets between susceptible cattle and the pigs which may be symptomless or almost symptomless carriers of infection (Shope, 1935). Few people now doubt that improved sanitation prevents the universal distribution of polioviruses in childhood, a time of life when most infections are inapparent. We pay the penalty now in seeing more paralytic cases in older people. In fact almost any interference with the ecology of animals and vegetables will be reflected in the activity of their virus parasites.

Control of viruses

Thus only too often man's activities unconsciously favour the viruses he fears. He can, however, use his knowledge of their ecology to control them. Active immunization is a means of tipping the scale in favour of the host. Man can destroy virus vectors—the carnivores which carry rabies, the *Aedes aegypti* which transmit yellow fever. Improved sanitation will not always favour the virus, as in poliomyelitis; one may hope by appropriate hygienic measures to control infectious hepatitis and to use quarantine to stop smallpox. The more one thinks of virus control, the more obvious it becomes that almost everything that favours or hinders a virus does so through affecting its ecology; it seems therefore wise to bring this dissertation to an end or it will inevitably cover the entire field of virology.

REFERENCES

ANDREWES, C. H. (1953). Epidemiology of Influenza. *Bull. World Hlth Org.* 8, 595.

ANDREWES, C. H. (1956). Factors in virus evolution. *Advanc. virus Res.* 4 (in the Press).

ANDREWES, C. H., MUIRHEAD-THOMSON, R. C. & STEVENSON, J. P. (1956). Laboratory studies of *Anopheles atroparvus* in relation to myxomatosis. *J. Hyg., Camb.*, 54, 478.

BURNET, F. M. (1955). *Principles of animal virology*, p. 355. New York: Academic Press Inc.

CHAPRONIERE, D. M. & ANDREWES, C. H. (1956). Host specificity of myxoma virus. *J. gen. Microbiol.* 15, ii.

EDWARD, D. G. ff. (1941). Resistance of influenza virus to drying and its demonstration on dust. *Lancet*, 2, 664.

FENNER, F. (1955). Changes in the virulence of myxoma virus associated with its natural transmission in populations of the rabbit Oryctolagus cuniculus. *J. Aust. Inst. agric. Sci.* 21, 137.

FRANCIS, T. & MAGILL, T. P. (1935). Rift Valley fever: report of three cases of laboratory infection and transmission of disease to ferrets. *J. exp. Med.* 62, 433.

GROSS, L. (1951). Pathogenic properties and 'vertical' transmission of the mouse leukemia agent. *Proc. Soc. exp. Biol., N.Y.*, 78, 342.

HUDSON, J. R., THOMPSON, H. V. & MANSI, W. (1955). Myxoma virus in Britain. *Nature, Lond.*, **176**, 783.

MEYER, K. F. (1942). The ecology of psittacosis and ornithosis. *Medicine, Baltimore*, **21**, 175.

MYKYTOWYCZ, R. (1953). An attenuated strain of the myxomatosis virus recovered from the field. *Nature, Lond.*, **172**, 448.

SALAMAN, R. N. & LE PELLEY, R. H. (1930). Paracrinkle: a potato disease of the virus group. *Proc. Roy. Soc.* B, **106**, 140.

SEVERIN, H. H. P. (1946). Longevity or life-history of leaf-hopper species on virus-infected and on healthy plants. *Hilgardia*, **17**, 121.

SHOPE, R. E. (1935). Experiments on epidemiology of pseudo-rabies: mode of transmission of disease in swine and their possible role in its spread to cattle. *J. exp. Med.* **62**, 85.

TRAUB, E. (1936). Epidemiology of lymphocytic choriomeningitis in white mice. *J. exp. Med.* **64**, 183.

TRAUB, E. (1939). Epidemiology of lymphocytic choriomeningitis in mouse stock observed for four years. *J. exp. Med.* **69**, 801.

THE SELECTIVE ACTION ON BACTERIA OF VARIOUS FACTORS INSIDE AND OUTSIDE THE ANIMAL BODY, WITH PARTICULAR REFERENCE TO THEIR EFFECT ON VIRULENCE

G. S. WILSON

Public Health Laboratory Service

The problem of virulence constitutes what is undoubtedly the greatest challenge to the medical bacteriologist of to-day. The early workers, from Pasteur onwards, were fascinated by it. Its importance was recognized in relation not only to the production of disease, but also to protection against it. Vaccination against chicken cholera and anthrax, and the still greater achievement of vaccination against rabies, rested on the ability to make use of changes in virulence of the causative organism. Comprehension of its nature seemed to be within man's grasp when Almroth Wright with a few simple reagents reproduced within the compass of a capillary tube what appeared to be a replica of the defence mechanism of the animal body. And then came disappointment, gradually but none the less convincingly. The problem was realized to be far more complex than it appeared at first sight. Our knowledge up to 1910 was reviewed with true German thoroughness by Laurent (1910), who collected the various published observations on virulence into a work of nearly a thousand pages. The main thesis running throughout the book is that pathogenic organisms undergo fluctuations in virulence, and that the degree of virulence determines the type and severity of the disease they produce. This was of course no more illuminating than the explanation of the medieval doctors, ridiculed by Molière, that opium promoted sleep by virtue of its soporific properties. Laurent's review contributed little to our understanding of the essential nature of virulence, and reflecting, as it did, the impasse that had been reached, might well have led the disillusioned bacteriologist of the time to say with Faust:

Und sehe, daß wir nichts wissen können!
Das will mir schier das Herz verbrennen.

With one or two notable exceptions, the first fifteen years of the present century were a barren period for medical bacteriology. No advance was made in the study of virulence till a new concept, that of variation, swam into the scientific consciousness. Hitherto virulence had been regarded as a property uniformly possessed by all the cells in a culture. The observations, however, of Weil and Felix on *Rickettsia prowazeki*, of Arkwright and of Bruce White on the dysentery and coli-typhoid groups of organisms, and of de Kruif on *Pasteurella septica* revealed an unsuspected degree of heterogeneity in various properties between different cells in the same culture, and established a relation between certain of these properties and the property of virulence.

Though this was an interesting advance, it did little more than push the problem one stage further back. The first real step towards understanding something of the intrinsic mechanism of virulence came in 1928 with Fred Griffith's demonstration, almost unbelievable as it seemed at the time, that a rough avirulent *Pneumococcus* of one type could be changed by suitable means into a smooth virulent one of a different type. This feat had the effect of bringing in the biochemist to investigate a problem that had hitherto lain solely in the province of the biologist. It was not long before Griffith's *in vivo* transformation of pneumococci had been reproduced *in vitro* by the action of an ethanol precipitate of material from lysed pneumococcal cells, and before the transforming agent itself had been identified as a polymer of deoxyribonucleic acid.

The problem now would seem to resolve itself mainly into an understanding of the mutual interaction of the chemical constituents and enzyme mechanisms of the bacterium with those of the host. Very little work has so far been undertaken along these lines, and the little that has been done has been with the viruses. The method of attack in the immediate future will have to be by means of the electron microscope, radioactive isotopes, chromatography, infra-red spectrography, tissue culture, and selective bactericidal agents used in conjunction with the time-honoured methods of colonial and antigenic analysis and animal inoculation. How far they will take us I do not profess to say, but I suspect it to be true that the more we learn about the mechanism of virulence, the greater will become our knowledge of bacterial metabolism as a whole, and the nearer we shall get to the goal of freeing the animal kingdom from the bane of infectious disease.

DEFINITION OF VIRULENCE

This Symposium is concerned with the ecological aspect of bacteriology, and I do not want therefore to write an essay on virulence. Were I to do so I should have to devote a preliminary section of considerable length to defining what virulence is supposed to be. For the present purpose all that is needed is to give a general definition of virulence, freely admitting that factors in the environment which lead to an alteration in virulence may well be acting in different ways on what is essentially a composite property.

Arkwright's (1929) definition will do as well as any: 'Virulence in the general sense is the property by which a pathogenic micro-organism causes death or reaction of the part or parts of the body invaded and so leads to disease.' This is practically synonymous with pathogenicity, but it presupposes the existence of non-virulent strains of pathogenic organisms—a distinction worth preserving. One of the operative words in this definition is 'invaded'. It is not sufficient for an organism to grow freely in the body for it to be classed as virulent. The lower part of the human intestine is full of multiplying organisms, but though some of them may be potentially virulent, they cannot be regarded as actually virulent until they pass into or through the lining mucosa and cause damage to the tissues. It is conceivable, of course, that the organism, while remaining free in the lumen of the intestine, might produce a toxin which on absorption caused damage to the tissues, but it is very doubtful whether this in fact happens. Even in cholera the organisms are found in the superficial layers of the mucosa, where, presumably, their irritant action is most manifested. Many organisms, such as the diphtheria bacillus and the tetanus bacillus, remain localized to the site of lodge-ment and produce their effects on the distal myocardium or central nervous system by means of powerful exotoxins; but these toxins are not produced unless the organisms are able to multiply in the tissues to which they have gained access. There is therefore every justification for regarding them as virulent in Arkwright's general sense. Why some organisms remain localized to a superficial mucosa, whereas others are able to pass readily into the circulatory system and reach other parts of the body is a problem of considerable interest, but one that is not strictly germane to our present discussion. It does, however, exemplify what has already been mentioned, namely, that virulence is a composite and not a single property.

It is sometimes stated that virulence is a purely relative term, meaning-less apart from the host that is invaded. This is intended to imply the existence of an equilibrium between the parasite and the host. When the parasite overcomes the resistance of the host, the organism is said to be virulent; when the host successfully resists invasion, the organism is said to be avirulent. This is a useful concept and true up to a point, but it does not go far enough. It is justifiable to talk about absolute virulence, so long as the word 'absolute' is used in the biological and not in the physical sense. An organism may well be virulent for some members of a given species of animal and not for others according to the degree of relative resistance of the host; or it may be virulent only for members of the species at one age of life and not at another; or it may be avirulent until the resistance of the host is artificially depressed by cold, fatigue, radiation, or some other agent. In these instances the term relative virulence is appropriate. But when the virulence of the organism transcends all the fluctuations in resistance of the host—apart from those resulting from immunization—and proves uniformly virulent, the term absolute virulence is justifiable; or when the organism is virulent to one species of animal, and not to another, the same term may be applied.

It must, of course, be understood that even absolute virulence is dependent on numbers of organisms. There are very few species in which a single organism can establish itself in the tissues and give rise to disease. With the majority of species a critical minimal number of organisms must gain access to the body, naturally or artificially, before true invasion can occur. Though the truth of this is well known, it is perhaps not so widely recognized that virulence and numbers are often very difficult to dissociate. Is the ability of an organism to invade a host in particular circumstances due to an increase in its virulence or to the increased numbers in which it is gaining access to the host? At times this may be impossible to decide, but any strict analysis of virulence must take numbers into account.

It must also be assumed that the organism is in what we may call good condition. In other words it must not have been recently subjected to any noxious influence that diminishes its vitality. For example, an organism such as *Leptospira icterohaemorrhagiae* on exposure to acid water may no longer prove virulent on first injection into animals, though it may fully recover its virulence on animal passage.

With this introduction I propose to consider some of the numerous factors in the host and outside that affect the property of virulence.

FACTORS IN THE HOST AFFECTING VIRULENCE
Route of infection

Numerous examples might be quoted of organisms that are virulent when introduced into the body by one route and not by another, or are virulent in smaller numbers by one route than by another. In man tubercle bacilli are more likely to cause disease when introduced into the respiratory than into the alimentary tract; and even in the respiratory tract they are more likely to cause disease when introduced in the form of very fine droplets, $1-5\mu$ in diameter, that can pass directly to the bronchi, than in the form of coarse droplets that are held up by the filtering action of the nasal mucosa. The anthrax bacillus is far more virulent by the skin than by the alimentary tract. The same holds true of *Staphylococcus aureus*. On the other hand, the typhoid bacillus, the cholera vibrio and the large group of food-poisoning organisms belonging to the genus *Salmonella* are typical intestinal pathogens that infect via the mouth but are unable to penetrate the lightly abraded skin. Tetanus spores introduced into healthy tissue in any part of the body are completely avirulent, but when injected into damaged tissue or along with an agent that causes local necrosis are able to germinate, give rise to vegetative bacilli and produce their fatal toxin. Some organisms that grow freely in the alimentary tract are quite harmless unless trauma occurs to give them access to the blood stream or the peritoneal cavity. *Streptococcus viridans*, for instance, is an organism that is present in large numbers in the saliva of the healthy mouth. So long as it remains there it causes no trouble, but if septic teeth are extracted it may pass into the circulation and give rise to the long-drawn-out and fatal disease, infective endocarditis. Similarly *Escherichia coli*, a normal inhabitant of the human intestine, may, if the intestine is damaged mechanically or in other ways, traverse the wall of the gut and give rise to septic peritonitis. Even organisms that are normally pathogenic by one route may prove virulent in much smaller numbers when introduced by some other unnatural route. For example, in mice *Salmonella typhi-murium* may prove virulent in a dose of 100 organisms when inoculated into the peritoneum, though when given by the mouth may fail to infect in a dose of less than 100,000.

Some pathogenic organisms seem to be considerably more dangerous in the laboratory than in nature. Ostlers and knackers in frequent contact with glandered horses seldom contract glanders themselves, but workers with *Pfeifferella mallei* are very liable to become infected. *Brucella tularensis* is another organism so dangerous to work with that many bacteriologists refuse to have it in their laboratory, yet when encountered in diseased hares and rabbits by hunters and butchers it gives rise to no more than an occasional infection. Is this, one wonders, due to a difference in the route of access to the human body, or to a difference in the number of organisms gaining access to the tissues, or to some other cause?

Closely allied to the route of infection is the mode of transmission.

With strict parasites it may be assumed that the shorter the time spent in passage from one host to the next, the less damage is the organism likely to suffer from various inimical agents in the external environment. The ways in which this is assured vary greatly. Most of the respiratory pathogens rely on rapid transmission by the cough spray. Pathogenic organisms infecting through the skin may take advantage of venereal transmission; others depend on the infliction of wounds such as those received at post-mortem examination or made by the bite or scratch of an infected animal. The streptococcal septicaemia of the morbid anatomist and the *Pasteurella* infection after the scratch of a cat may be quoted as examples, though most people's minds would turn first to the virus disease hydrophobia following the bite of a rabid dog.

One method of ensuring rapid transmission from host to host that is common with protozoa, but uncommon with bacteria, is by means of arthropods. The outstanding example of this among the bacteria is the plague bacillus, which is transmitted by the flea. Since the flea itself affords an environment in which the plague bacillus can multiply, it follows that the organisms are never exposed to the rigours of the outside world. Why is it, one wonders, that more bacteria have not taken advantage of this apparently almost ideal method? True, it would not be ideal under modern conditions of hygiene, but for ages in the civilized world conditions must have existed when infestation with lice and fleas, and exposure to the bites of mosquitoes, sandflies and ticks were the usual experience of mankind. This method, of course, is possible only in diseases characterized by bacteraemia of more than transitory duration and is therefore limited in man to the plague bacillus, *Bartonella bacilliformis* (the cause of Oroya fever and verruga peruana), and *Treponema recurrentis* (the cause of relapsing fever). Of these, *Bartonella bacilliformis* is an actual parasite of the red blood corpuscles. If one is allowed to include the rickettsiae, then a wide range of typhus and typhus-like fevers is brought into this category.

In general, the diseases of the intestine resulting from alimentary infection are caused by organisms whose resistance in the outside world is greater than that of the organisms infecting by the respiratory or venereal routes. Two of the most important—the typhoid bacillus and the cholera vibrio—are normally borne by water, which presupposes a life of at any rate some hours outside the human body. Members of the *Salmonella* group may remain alive in sewage and food products for days, and apparently even for weeks or months, without losing their virulence, but in such situations either they are able to multiply or they are protected from adverse agencies by a dried covering of protein.

Some of them resemble *Brucella abortus* and *B. melitensis* in gaining adventitious access to man by means of milk in which they are excreted by the infected udder.

These examples should suffice to indicate the importance of the immediate environment to the survival and virulence of the organism on its first coming into contact with the tissues of the host. Space does not allow consideration in detail of the various defence mechanisms in operation at the portal of entry. Some are mechanical, such as the protective layer afforded to the underlying tissues by the skin, or to the bronchi and bronchioles by their covering layer of mucus; some are chemical, such as the high acid content of the normal gastric juice that virtually sterilizes the contents of the stomach, or the moderately high Eh of the subcutaneous tissues and muscle that prevents the development of anaerobic organisms; some are enzymic, such as the lysozyme that protects the conjunctiva from bacteria that might otherwise invade it; some are cellular, such as the leucocytes that ingest bacteria and prevent their forming a nidus of infection; and some are normal antibodies that interfere with the growth of invading organisms. The more precise mode of action of many of these agents has already been considered by previous contributors to this Symposium.

Site of growth in tissues

Apart from the operation of the defence mechanism at the site of lodgement, bacteria may be exposed to influences during their residence in the tissues themselves that profoundly affect their virulence. As an example we may take the tubercle bacillus. Numerous attempts to demonstrate differences in virulence between strains of human-type tubercle bacilli isolated from the lung have failed. Almost without exception these organisms have been found to possess a uniformly high degree of virulence as judged by inoculation into experimental animals. The same holds true of strains cultivated from nearly every other part of the body. But there is one exception—the skin. The late Stanley Griffith (1957) showed that over half the strains of tubercle bacilli—human and bovine—isolated from cases of lupus were below standard virulence. There were several reasons for believing that the attenuation in virulence had occurred in the skin itself. Two of these will suffice. In the first place the degree of attenuation was associated to some extent with the duration of the disease; a higher correlation would have been noted had it not been for the fact that the process of attenuation ceased once it had reached a certain point. And secondly, when tubercle bacilli were isolated at the same time from lupus lesions and from lesions in the internal tissues of the same patients, the internal strains were often found to be fully virulent while the lupus strains were no longer so. Apart from scrofulodermia, which is likewise a tuberculous disease of the skin, there is only one other situation in which attenuated strains of tubercle bacilli are at all commonly found; and that is in the horse. Tuberculosis of the horse is a comparatively rare disease and is caused by the bovine type of bacillus, but something like half the strains of tubercle bacilli isolated from tuberculous lesions in the horse are found to be of modified virulence. What is it, one may ask, in the human skin or in the tissues of the horse that is responsible for lowering the virulence of the tubercle bacillus? Ultra-violet light, as has already been shown, has profound effects on bacterial vitality and reproduction, and may perhaps be the responsible agent in the skin, but it clearly cannot be invoked to explain the reduction in virulence of tubercle bacilli isolated from the thoracic or abdominal organs of the horse. If it is assumed that the human skin and the viscera of the horse are relatively unfavourable sites for the growth of the tubercle bacillus—and there is some reason for believing this—and that the attenuation of virulence is the result of prolonged slow growth under these conditions, why do the unfavourable tissues of the cat and the dog not have a similar action? Present evidence suggests that virulence in tubercle bacilli is associated with a high lipid content and a low catalase activity (Desbordes & Fournier, 1954). Conditions in the human skin and the tissues of the horse may be unsuitable for the normal metabolic activity of the organisms by which these properties develop. The problem might well repay study. It is interesting to note that the changes in virulence are not accompanied by any change in the cultural characters of the organisms.

Another example that may be quoted is the diminution in virulence often observed in *Streptococcus pyogenes* in the throat during the convalescent stage of scarlet fever. Epidemiological evidence indicates that most scarlatinal patients lose their infectivity for their fellow men within 3–4 weeks, even though many of them are still carrying the causative streptococcus in the throat. There is some reason to believe that the diminished virulence of the organism is associated with a loss of the protein M antigen responsible for type-specificity, but the documentation is not complete. The effect may possibly be ascribed not so much to something in the tissues of the throat itself as to the action of antibodies formed in response to the infection. The mechanism is still not understood.

Passage through tissues

Both the examples just quoted have been of organisms that have lost some of their virulence through residence in the tissues. Other examples, however, may be quoted in which the reverse happens and the virulence of the organism increases. The most striking instances of this process are seen during the passage of organisms through the tissues of a given species of animal to which at first they are comparatively avirulent. Numerous observations on a variety of organisms have been made by different observers from Pasteur onwards. Not all of them are trustworthy, and many were made on too small a scale to justify the conclusions they were called on to bear. None the less there is now ample evidence of the most satisfying kind to show that by repeated passage through a given species of animal the virulence of a practically avirulent organism may be raised, often to quite a high level.

A few examples will suffice. Reference has already been made to the fall in virulence of the tubercle bacillus that often occurs during residence in the skin of patients affected with lupus. Stanley Griffith (1957) in a series of fully recorded experiments showed that the virulence of some, but not all, of these attenuated strains could be completely restored by passage through laboratory animals. It may be noted that success was limited to strains of bovine type, and to only some of these. None of the strains of human type could be raised to full virulence. Whether this was due to the much smaller number of human strains tested or to some fundamental difference in the behaviour of human and bovine strains, it is impossible to say, but discrepancies of this sort are always worth noting.

The pneumococcus is an organism whose virulence is apt to fall rapidly in artificial culture. It can often be restored completely by animal passage. The effect is most striking. Sometimes a strain that proves harmless to a mouse on intraperitoneal injection in a dose of 10 million organisms may be so exalted in virulence by animal passage that a dose of one or two organisms may suffice to kill the mouse in 24 hr. Again experience has shown that not every strain reacts in the same way. Some strains prove refractory to all attempts to raise their virulence.

Similar observations have been made on the haemolytic *Streptococcus* ever since Marmorek (1895) showed that, by alternate cultivation in serum broth and passage through rabbits, strains of this organism could be raised in virulence till, like the *Pneumococcus*, one or two organisms on injection proved fatal.

Increase in virulence on animal passage has been noted with several other organisms such as *Pasteurella pestis*, *P. septica*, *Erysipelothrix rhusiopathiae*, *Pfeifferella mallei* and the cholera vibrio.

The mechanism of action of animal passage is probably complex. In some instances it appears to act as a pure sorting mechanism. When, for example, a strain through cultivation in artificial media or other means has become rough, animal passage will gradually bring about a restoration of the strain to the smooth state by favouring the growth of the virulent smooth elements. If, however, the strain has become completely rough and there are no smooth elements surviving in it, then animal passage may fail to effect any increase whatever.

There are, however, instances on record in which a single cell culture of a rough strain has been rendered virulent by animal passage. Fred Griffith (1929) made such an observation on the pneumococcus. Clearly the mechanism here must be different. The effect of the tissues must be to bring about a change in the organism itself whereby it is transformed, gradually or rapidly, into the smooth virulent state. Fred Griffith injected the living R pneumococcus in conjunction with a dense suspension of killed smooth pneumococci, which provided, as subsequent investigators showed, an agent that effected the transformation. It may be objected that this is not a true example of the effect of animal passage on virulence, since the induction of the S form has now been accomplished in the test-tube. This is true up to a point, but it is also true that the animal tissues afford the most favourable medium in which the induction can be accomplished.

Incidentally it is worth noting that Griffith's observations, which have opened up such a big field of inquiry in bacterial variation and genetics and have pointed to the enormous biological importance of deoxyribonucleic acid, were made in a very similar way to those of Turró (1908) on the glanders bacillus 20 years earlier. At that time S and R variation had not been recognized, but Turró succeeded in raising the virulence of the glanders bacillus for guinea-pigs by injecting it along with an extract of killed glanders bacilli. The experiments of Turró might be worth repeating to see whether the rise in virulence was due to the sorting out of S and R organisms or to a true induction of an S variation in a rough organism.

Another mode of action of animal passage appears to be adaptation. This has been observed particularly in the field of viruses. Numerous viruses, or strains of a given virus, prove avirulent to the chick embryo, the mouse, or some other animal till they have been passed, often several times, through the tissues. This so-called blind passage may have to be continued for some time before the virus begins to grow appreciably in its new host and ultimately to assume virulence for it. Examples are the influenza virus for the fertile egg and the foot-and-mouth virus for the guinea-pig.

It is of interest to note that the raising of virulence by passage for one species of animal may not be accompanied by a similar rise in virulence for another species. It may even have the opposite effect. Nicolle (1906), for example, found that passage through guinea-pigs greatly raised the virulence of the glanders bacillus for guinea-pigs, but lowered it for rabbits and white mice. This is to some extent in conformity with the observations of Tillett (1927), who, studying the virulence of Type III strains of pneumococci for different animals, found that, of eleven strains which were virulent for mice, only one was virulent for rabbits. It indicates again that virulence is a complex quality and is ultimately dependent on the metabolism of the organism in the tissues.

Observations of this sort are not restricted to laboratory animals. Van der Hoeden (1955) brought evidence to suggest that passage in nature of *Leptospira canicola* through the jackal raised the virulence of this organism for cattle. More striking is the behaviour towards man of the murine typhus virus—*Rickettsia mooseri*. Normally this organism is spread by rat fleas, and gives rise to sporadic disease which has a very low case-fatality rate. Under certain conditions, however, it is spread by the body louse. It then takes on a much more serious complexion, becoming epidemic and being accompanied by a high case-fatality rate, similar to that of classical louse-borne typhus fever caused by *Rickettsia prowazeki* (Mooser, Varela & Pilz, 1934). It seems improbable that this change is dependent on the numbers of organisms constituting the inoculum; it is more likely to result from an increase in the virulence of the organism for man resulting from growth in the louse's tissues.

Tissue specificity

Closely allied to the effect on virulence of growth in the tissues is the tissue specificity of certain organisms. Why is it, for instance, that, in teleological language, *Neisseria meningitidis* prefers the meninges, *Streptococcus viridans* the endocardium, *Rickettsia prowazeki* the vascular endothelium, *Leptospira icterohaemorrhagiae* the epithelial cells of the liver and kidney, the poliomyelitis virus the anterior horn cells of the spinal cord, and the louping-ill virus the Purkinje cells of the cerebellum? Why is *Streptococcus pyogenes* Type 12 so closely associated with nephritis and *Staphylococcus aureus* phage type 71 with impetigo? Why does the tubercle bacillus in childhood affect any part of the lung, but in adults settle most frequently at the apex? I have selected these examples as being probably independent of the mode of access of the organism to the body. Numerous other examples might be quoted in which the mode of infection may determine the apparent tissue-specificity, such as the preference of the anthrax and the leprosy bacillus for the skin, the cholera vibrio for the intestine, the Morax-Axenfeld bacillus for the conjunctiva, the mumps virus for the salivary glands, and the pneumococcus for the lung.

Some examples of apparent tissue-specificity can be explained by the presence of an obvious localizing cause. Thus, in man, gas gangrene of the muscles results from a wound or other agent that produces a necrotic focus in the muscle in which anaerobic spore-bearing organisms such as *Clostridium welchii* or *C. septicum* can multiply and produce their toxin. In sheep the so-called black disease results from multiplication of *C. oedematiens* in the liver of animals infested by the liver fluke, *Fasciola hepatica*, which causes the necessary degree of hepatic necrosis to enable the spores of *C. oedematiens* to germinate.

Various workers have attempted to explain the localization of the tubercle bacillus at the apex of the adult lung in terms of relative immobility of the lung, or of its poor vascular supply, or of the partial pressures of oxygen and carbon dioxide prevailing at this site, but so far all is guess-work. The fact that some organisms prefer the epithelial tissues of the body and others the interstitial tissues, and that among the viruses some prefer the cytoplasm and others the nucleus of the cell, suggests either that nutritional conditions are particularly favourable in these sites for the parasite in question, or that in these sites the organism is spared the inhibitory effect of some substance conveyed by the blood or lymph. In this connexion the impermeability of the blood-brain barrier to the passage of circulating antibodies to the nervous tissue may be of importance, though it cannot explain why the poliomyelitis virus, the rabies virus and the louping-ill virus should each select a different part of the central nervous system in which to multiply.

Though not strictly relevant to the subject of tissue-specificity, a few related phenomena may be mentioned here. Some pathogenic organisms, such as the leprosy bacillus, the rat leprosy bacillus, and the acid-fast organism that gives rise to subcutaneous nodules in cattle, have not yet been cultivated in the laboratory. It must be supposed that they gain something from the tissues which so far no culture medium has been able to supply. Conversely, it must be supposed that the failure of some organisms to grow in the tissues of certain animals is due to the absence in the tissues of essential nutrients. This, of course, is only one of the possible explanations of animal insusceptibility; there are probably numerous others.

With certain other organisms the effect of the tissues is to make possible the formation of some substance that is formed poorly or not at all under the artificial conditions of the laboratory. One of the oldest examples is the formation of capsules; these always develop best in the animal body, and sometimes fail to develop at all *in vitro* in the absence of blood serum or other animal fluid. A more recent example is afforded by the anthrax bacillus which, according to Smith, Keppie & Stanley (1955), forms a specific toxin only in the animal body. This differs from the capsular substance, and is of particular interest because it appears to be responsible for stimulating the development of active immunity against the bacillus.

Age and sex

Among the bacteria there are not many examples of the influence of the age or sex of the host on the growth and virulence of the organisms. Most of the exanthematic fevers are commonest in childhood; this is due, however, not so much to any specially high susceptibility of the tissues at this age as to the development of a lasting immunity that protects against a second attack. It is true that, in general, infants appear to be more susceptible to infection than children and adults. This is presumably dependent on the immature state of the antibody-forming mechanism at birth. There are instances of the reverse, in which the infant appears to be less susceptible than the adult. Poliomyelitis is a case in point; but in this instance, as in some of the others, it is difficult to dissociate the innate susceptibility of the tissues from the resistance conferred on them by the passive immunity received by transfer of the maternal antibodies.

Tuberculosis in man affords one or two suggestive examples of a true age susceptibility. Judging by the type and severity of the disease, one may say that the tissues are most susceptible to the attack of the tubercle bacillus in infancy. There then comes a period between 5 and 15 years of age when the mortality of tuberculosis falls to a minimum. After the schooling period is over, the mortality rises again to reach a maximum among females in Great Britain at about 25 years of age. In males, on the other hand, the incidence continues to rise to the age of 65 years, when the mortality is between four and five times that among females. The minimum mortality between 5 and 15 years of age may perhaps be explained partly by the comparatively secluded life led by school children and partly by the development of an immunity in some of the children as the result of a primary infection, but the evidence on the whole does not suggest that either of these factors is sufficient to account for the phenomenon completely. There is certainly no question that the tissues at this age are less well suited for the development of the tubercle bacillus than those of the infant. Again the reason for the much higher mortality among old than among young males, and among old males than among old females is a matter for conjecture. Both differences are most striking, and suggest that in the elderly male some influence is at work to lower the susceptibility of the tissues to invasion by the tubercle bacillus.

Another example of the effect of age may be taken from cattle. Contagious abortion is a widespread disease. The causative organism, *Brucella abortus*, though invading the uterus and udder of adult females and the testicles of bulls, is unable to establish itself in the calf from the time of birth to the initial oestrous cycle (Huddleson, 1955). It is difficult here to avoid the conclusion that the insusceptibility of the tissues of the calf is related to the absence of the hormones governing fertility.

Coming to laboratory animals, we may note that the young rabbit is very much more susceptible to experimental infection with pneumococci than is the adult animal. Robertson & Sia (1924) showed that the blood of resistant rabbits had destructive properties for these organisms; and Woo (1926) was able to relate the high susceptibility of the young rabbit to the absence of pneumococcidal bodies in the blood.

Another example, exhibiting a rather different principle, is the insusceptibility of the adult rat to disease caused by *Haemobartonella muris*. Most adult rats—those of the Wistar breed constitute an exception—suffer from a latent infection with this organism. So long as the spleen is intact, this causes no inconvenience; but, if the spleen is removed, severe progressive anaemia develops within a few days, proving fatal in a fortnight. Unlike *Brucella abortus* in the calf, *H. muris* is able to establish itself in the young rat, but is prevented from becoming pathogenic by the controlling influence of the spleen. How the spleen acts is doubtful, but there is evidence to suggest that it may be by controlling the metabolism of copper. When it is removed there is increased elimination of copper, leading to insufficient formation of haemoglobin for the requirements of the body.

All these examples are of a disturbance of the equilibrium between the host and the parasite caused apparently by an alteration in the resistance of the host rather than by any change in the organism itself. The same holds true of the more striking examples to be found among the viruses. Some years ago Dalldorf & Sickles (1948) described a virus that was pathogenic to suckling mice but not to adult mice. Not only so, but the time during which the suckling mouse was susceptible was limited to a few days after birth. This strain was found to belong to a large group of viruses which collectively is now known as the Coxsackie group. Though adult mice are normally resistant to the Coxsackie viruses, Dalldorf & Gifford (1954), working with a strain attacking the pancreas, observed that females became susceptible during the last week of pregnancy. Their increased susceptibility disappeared immediately after delivery. This observation, taken in conjunction with the fact that the natural resistance of mature mice may also be overcome by cortisone (Kilbourne & Horsfall, 1951), suggests a hormone mechanism; and the further fact that in the foetus the adrenal glands are disproportionately large but undergo involution after birth suggests that excessive production of an adrenal hormone is responsible for lowering the resistance of the animal.

Since Dalldorf's original observations on the Coxsackie group, other examples have been noted of viruses that are virulent to the suckling but less virulent to the adult animal. One of the best of these is the foot-and-mouth virus, which gives rise on intraperitoneal injection to a mild disease in adult mice, but to a fatal disease in unweaned mice a week old (Skinner, Henderson & Brooksby, 1952). In man the rubella virus may be quoted. Normally this virus produces an extremely mild disease in the child or adult, but in the foetus it often causes severe nervous or myocardial damage, and may even prove fatal.

These various examples should suffice to show that the relative virulence of certain bacteria and viruses is raised or lowered by the state of the tissues at different ages. There is a good deal of evidence, which cannot be even summarized here, to indicate that the susceptibility of the tissues depends partly on the stage of development and activity of the antibody-forming apparatus and partly on the abundance of hormones, particularly those of the adrenal cortex.

Genetic constitution of the host

There are diseases, such as tuberculosis and rheumatic fever, that appear to run in families, suggesting that among the members there is a genetically lower degree of resistance than among those of other families. Though this may well be true, it is almost impossible to prove because of the difficulty of separating susceptibility of the tissues from the risk of exposure to infection. Members of a family are more liable to develop the disease when they are in contact with a patient in the family suffering from it than are members of healthy families; this is not necessarily because they are genetically more susceptible, but because they are exposed to a risk of infection which the others are spared. There are, however, several examples of unusually high susceptibility that cannot be explained completely in this way. Measles, for instance, is a highly infectious disease, attacking in western Europe 90 % or more of children exposed to infection and seldom proving serious unless complicated by secondary bacterial invasion. But when imported into island populations that have been free from it for a long time, it attacks persons of all ages without discrimination, and often proves most malignant. Thus in 1875, when it was introduced into the Fiji islands, it killed something like a quarter of the whole population.

Tuberculosis likewise, when introduced into virgin populations, assumes a degree of virulence characterized by early generalization and rapid death quite unlike that seen in the ordinary adult of civilized countries. A low level of personal hygiene among the natives may play a part in spreading infection, but can hardly be held responsible for the completely altered character of the disease. It is difficult to escape the conclusion that the relatively high resistance of the civilized population to diseases such as measles and tuberculosis is due to the effect of natural selection over the centuries in weeding out the more susceptible members. There is some evidence that the longer this process has continued, the higher is the average genetic resistance of the population.

This process may well explain the great modification that has occurred in the behaviour of syphilis during the 500 years or so that have now elapsed since its introduction into Europe. Medical records, and the frequent allusions to it in Shakespeare, leave no doubt that in the sixteenth century it was a most virulent disease causing a degree of tissue destruction that is quite unknown nowadays.

Attempts in human beings to dissociate genetic immunity from the risk of exposure to infection have been made by studying the comparative behaviour of twins. The underlying assumption is that monozygotic twins, which are derived from a single fertilized ovum, should behave more alike in their resistance to infection than dizygotic twins, which are derived from two separate fertilized ova. Most of the observations by this method have been made in relation to tuberculosis. There is no space to describe them in detail, but reference may be made to papers by Diehl & von Verschuer (1933) in Germany, Uehlinger & Künsch

(1938) in Switzerland, and Kallmann & Reisner (1943 *a*, *b*) in the United States. The results are open to criticism in some respects, but taken together they suggest quite strongly that the innate resistance of monozygotic twins is more uniform than that of dizygotic twins.

Observations on animals likewise lead to the conclusion that the degree of resistance varies within the same species and is genetically transmitted. The comparative immunity of Algerian sheep to anthrax was noted by Chauveau (1880) in the last century. In Uganda, Carmichael (1939) found that the incidence of tuberculosis among the long-horned Hamitic cattle was much higher, as judged by the tuberculin test, than among the humped Zebu cattle. The proportions were 80 % to 1 %, in spite of the fact that the Hamitic cattle were less exposed to infection than the Zebu.

Experimentally, Lurie (1941) studied six inbred families of rabbits and found a considerable difference between them in their resistance to inoculation with tubercle bacilli. In the members of the most resistant family the resulting disease tended to be localized and to progress slowly, whereas in those of the least resistant family it became generalized and progressed rapidly. Analysis of the various factors responsible for this difference led Lurie to the conclusion that the principal one was the degree of phagocytic activity.

Effect of diet

It is often lightly assumed that poorly nourished children are necessarily more prone to infectious disease than are well nourished children. This may be so, but it is very difficult to prove. As with genetic immunity, there are complicating factors that confuse the evidence, and may indeed point to the opposite conclusion. For example, it used to be a common observation in Great Britain that poliomyelitis tended to affect the plump healthy children of the upper social classes more often than the lean half-starved children of the lower classes. The explanation of this, however, probably lay not in any nutritional difference in the susceptibility of the tissues themselves to invasion by the poliomyelitis virus, but to the fact that, owing to their higher standard of personal hygiene, the children of the upper classes had not experienced in early life the latent immunizing infections that were usual among the children of the lower classes.

The evidence on the influence of diet on susceptibility to infection is so complex that it is impossible to consider it here (for a brief review see Wilson & Miles, 1955). Broadly speaking, the effect is very much less than might be anticipated and is often completely masked by more powerful factors. There is some evidence that deprivation of vitamin A and vitamin C, of proteins, and of fats may lower the resistance to certain infections, but the deprivation has often to be so severe as to lead to general inanition. A great deal of further work is required to define the effect of diet on the susceptibility of the tissues to invasion by bacteria and viruses, but from what has so far been carried out it would appear that the body has a surprising capacity under adverse nutritional conditions to maintain constant the biochemical composition of the cells and tissue fluids that are responsible for its defence against infection.

Antibodies

The effect of antibodies on virulence was for a long time controversial, but the evidence now accumulated seems to show that, with a few possible exceptions, organisms grown in the presence of antibodies become less rather than more virulent. The evidence up to 1926 was reviewed by Hadley (1927), who, after analysing the observations made by numerous different workers on various species of organisms, concluded that growth *in vitro* or *in vivo* in the presence of antibodies led as a rule to the occurrence of the S–R variation with an accompanying diminution in virulence. Subsequent observations have merely confirmed this conclusion.

Without discussing for the moment the S–R variation (see p. 357) we may consider the more general effect of antibodies on the survival of the parasite. If, in teleological language, the aim of a micro-organism is to find an environment in which its future is guaranteed to it, then for pathogenic organisms a high degree of virulence may be more of a hindrance than an advantage. An organism, for example, such as the virus of measles, which is highly invasive, which causes an acute disease, and which then either kills the host or is killed by it, can survive only when there is a sufficiently large supply of normal hosts to serve for its continued propagation. In isolated populations, such as those of Fiji, susceptible hosts are rapidly used up and the virus, being unable to multiply outside the human body, dies out. It is quite possible that a number of pathogenic organisms have flourished in the past and perished from this very cause. There are in fact records of numerous diseases whose aetiology we can but guess at now. Some of these may have been caused by virulent variants of organisms that to-day we know in a less virulent form, or they may have been caused by organisms which, like many of the prehistoric animals, failed to adjust themselves to their surroundings and died out completely.

The ideal state for a pathogenic organism is one in which a well-balanced equilibrium is established between the parasite and its host, allowing each of them to flourish without causing too much damage to the other. For this purpose a host is needed, which, as the result of either natural or acquired immunity, has a moderate degree of resistance to the parasite, enabling it to multiply in the tissues to an extent sufficient to ensure its passage to other susceptible hosts without at the same time destroying its own source of nourishment. If this premise is granted, then it follows that the production of antibodies serves the dual purpose of guarding the host against rapid death, and of providing for the parasite a medium in which it can live more or less indefinitely, protected from the perils of the outside world.

FACTORS OUTSIDE THE HOST AFFECTING VIRULENCE

Age of culture

It is not unreasonable to suppose that the virulence of an organism is associated with its rate of growth. Organisms taken from a culture in the logarithmic phase of growth might be expected to prove more virulent on injection into a susceptible animal than those taken from the lag or the decline phase. Plausible as this supposition may be, there is very little evidence to support it. Wadsworth & Kirkbride (1918), who compared the virulence of pneumococci to mice at different stages of the growth period, found that cocci taken from a broth culture at 6 hr. killed a higher proportion of animals than those taken from the same culture at 4 or 24 hr. The number of animals tested was, however, too small to justify the conclusion drawn by the authors that the virulence of the organisms varied with the stage of growth, reaching its maximum during the logarithmic phase. The same criticism applies to the similar conclusions of Felty & Bloomfield (1924), who worked with a haemolytic streptococcus.

Wilson (1926), studying the virulence of *Salmonella typhi-murium* to mice and working with sufficiently large numbers of animals to give significant results, could find no appreciable difference in virulence between organisms taken from the same culture during the logarithmic, the stationary and the decline phases. Webster (1925a), without giving protocols, stated that equal numbers of *S. typhi-murium* and of *Pasteurella lepiseptica* induced similar responses in mice and rabbits respectively, whether taken from cultures incubated for 2 hr. or for several days.

The discrepancy between the results of Wadsworth & Kirkbride and of Felty & Bloomfield on the one hand and of Wilson and of Webster on the other may have been due (*a*) to the small number of animals used by the former group of workers, or (*b*) to the fact that they were measuring dosage in terms of volume of culture instead of numbers of living organisms, or (*c*) to the difference in the organisms studied. It is known that pneumococci die off very rapidly during the decline phase owing to the production of hydrogen peroxide and the absence of catalase to destroy it (Chesney, 1916; McLeod & Gordon, 1922). The numbers therefore of organisms contained in an inoculum of 0·5 ml. in the experiments of Wadsworth & Kirkbride were probably far less in their 24 hr. than in their 6 hr. cultures. This may well have been responsible for the fewer deaths caused by the older culture.

Taking the evidence as a whole we must conclude that there is at present insufficient justification for relating virulence *in vivo* to the growth activity of the organisms at the time of injection.

Repeated cultivation

Working with the pneumococcus, Wadsworth & Kirkbride (1918) brought convincing evidence to show that the virulence for mice of organisms grown in broth and subcultured at intervals of 24 hr. fell rapidly. Within 6 weeks a strain that initially had killed mice in a dose of 0·000001 ml. failed to kill in a dose of 1 ml. On the other hand, the organisms, when subcultured at 8 hr. intervals, retained their virulence intact over a period of 13 weeks. Indeed, there was some evidence that, when an attenuated culture was used, the virulence might actually increase as the result of repeated 8 hr. transfer. Even more striking results were recorded by Felton & Dougherty (1924), who subcultured a single-cell strain of pneumococcus at 8-hourly intervals in skim milk. Initially, 1 ml. of culture failed to kill mice; after 150 transfers the culture was so virulent that the injection of one coccus proved fatal.

During the 10 years or so after the First World War numerous workers, studying different species of organism, found that, in broth cultures incubated for 24 hr. or longer, dissociation was apt to occur of the S–R form (for references see Hadley, 1927; Wilson, 1930). The S form was associated with virulence, the R form with lack of virulence. The explanation of Wadsworth & Kirkbride's observations is almost certainly that dissociation occurred in their 24 hr. cultures with a progressive replacement of S by R forms, whereas in their 8 hr. culture series the organisms remained permanently in the S form.

Different species of organism vary in the readiness with which they lose their virulence in artificial culture. Some appear to retain it indefinitely; others lose it in a few days. Generally speaking, however, organisms subcultured in the logarithmic phase are less liable to undergo the S–R variation than are those subcultured in the decline phase of growth.

Nature of medium

The S–R variation is greatly influenced by the nature of the medium in which the organisms are grown and by the atmospheric conditions under which they are incubated. As a rule, variation occurs more rapidly in fluid than on solid media. It tends to be inhibited or even reversed by the presence of blood, serum or other animal protein. Working with *Pasteurella lepiseptica*, Webster (1925b) found that the S–R variation (or D–G, as it was called), which occurred readily in broth incubated in air, could be inhibited either by incubating the culture under a lowered atmospheric pressure or by adding blood to the medium. This result seemed to be explicable on the assumption that the S–R variation was favoured by the formation of peroxide. Wilson (1930), working with *Salmonella typhi-murium*, obtained rather different results. He sub-cultured the organisms daily in broth for several weeks under different partial pressures of oxygen, and tested their virulence from time to time on batches of twenty mice. In 21 % oxygen the organisms very largely lost their virulence. In atmospheres of 1 and 5 % oxygen the virulence declined, but not so much as at 21 %. Under anaerobic conditions the organisms retained their initial degree of virulence unaltered, and in atmospheres of 40, 75 and 100 % of oxygen their virulence appeared actually to increase somewhat. Two possible explanations of these findings were put forward. The first supposed that some substance favourable to the S–R variation and the consequent loss of virulence was formed in cultures incubated in the presence of oxygen, but not in its absence, and that in high partial pressures of oxygen it was destroyed —presumably by oxidation in an alkaline medium. The second interpreted the results in terms of intracellular pH. In air and in low partial pressures of oxygen the intracellular reaction was supposed to become more alkaline owing to the breakdown of protein with the consequent production of ammonia, whereas in high partial pressures of oxygen the increased amount of carbon dioxide produced was sufficient to neutralize the ammonia, so that the intracellular pH remained at about its original value.

Of more recent years considerable attention has been paid to the factors controlling the virulence of the anthrax bacillus. Bail's (1904) original observation that virulent cultures grown in the body give rise to oedema fluid which can be used for the vaccination of other animals has been confirmed many times. Observations have now shown that the anthrax bacillus forms a toxin *in vivo* that is liberated into the extra-cellular fluids (Smith *et al.* 1955). The toxin appears to contain at least two components, both of which are able to give rise to active immunity in the rabbit. One of these is a non-toxic soluble antigen that can be prepared *in vitro* (Gladstone, 1948); the other is a mildly toxic anti-phagocytic lipoprotein containing a small amount of carbohydrate that has so far been isolated only from exudates of infected guinea-pigs (Smith & Gallop, 1956). Both components differ from the capsular substance of *Bacillus anthracis* and from sodium polyglutamate, which has also been isolated from infected exudates.

The formation of capsules, so closely associated with virulence in organisms such as the pneumococcus and *Pasteurella pestis*, always occurs best in the animal tissues, though in artificial culture it can often be promoted by the addition of serum or other natural animal protein to the medium. It is noteworthy that the capsule of the plague bacillus is formed best at 37° C., even though the optimum temperature for growth of the organism is about 30° C.

Bacterial antagonism

Little need be said about the effect of bacterial antagonism, since it is doubtful whether virulence is directly affected by this cause. That staphylococci under certain conditions may suppress the growth of diphtheria bacilli in the throat and prevent the development of disease appears to be highly probable. The older workers would have recorded this as an example of diminution in virulence of the diphtheria bacillus, but it seems more likely to be explicable in terms rather of numbers than of virulence. The position, however, is complex, because staphylococci may act in the opposite way. Thus, according to Thompson & Johnson (1947), the inhibitory action of saliva on the growth of diphtheria bacilli is mainly due to the hydrogen peroxide produced by the salivary streptococci, and this is neutralized by the catalase produced by staphylococci.

Numerous other instances might be quoted of bacterial antagonism in the body, but as these do not appear to affect the virulence of the organisms concerned, they need not be considered.

Effect of bacteriophage

Dr Anderson has already referred to the conversion of non-virulent into virulent forms of diphtheria bacilli under the influence of bacteriophage. So far as is known at present, the effect is limited to non-virulent strains that are susceptible to phage; the resulting virulent variant is of the same antigenic type as the parent strain, and is necessarily lysogenic; and, as the effect can be produced starting with single-cell cultures, selection of virulent variants from a mixed population cannot be held responsible for it. Other examples may be forthcoming in the course of time, but this is the only one of which we know at present.

DISCUSSION AND CONCLUSIONS

Many other factors affecting virulence might have been referred to, and most of the ones I have mentioned have been treated rather summarily; but this, I am afraid, is inevitable. My concluding task is to try to generalize from the various observations that have been recorded.

The main question is to decide what part naturally occurring alterations in virulence play in the genesis of epidemic disease in man and animals. I have specified several mechanisms by which the virulence of a given organism may be raised or lowered in the laboratory, but I have not attempted to assess the frequency with which they operate in nature. The S–R variation doubtless occurs quite commonly—almost always under the influence of antibodies—but has it any real significance, except transitory and local, in determining the occurrence of disease in the surrounding population? So long as there are some virulent S forms left and susceptible hosts for them to invade, it seems improbable that the variant avirulent R forms are of any particular importance. The same conclusion holds true, I suspect, of other less common mechanisms leading to a natural fall in virulence of the causative bacterium. It is conceivable, of course, that progressive reduction in virulence of the invading organisms might lead to the gradual disappearance of an infectious bacterial disease, but I can think of no example to quote in favour of such a conception. Tuberculosis and syphilis admittedly are very much less serious diseases in this country now than they were 500 years ago, but this I would ascribe to a rise in the genetic immunity of the population, as the result of the killing off of the more susceptible members, rather than to any diminution in the intrinsic virulence of the tubercle bacillus or of *Treponema pallidum*.

What is more difficult to decide is whether natural increases in virulence occur of a magnitude sufficient either to change a saprophyte into a parasite or a pathogenic organism of low virulence into one of high virulence. I am not trying here to reconstruct the bacteriological history of mankind. It seems not improbable that both these changes have occurred from time to time. What I am asking is whether the various ecological influences and pressures that have been considered in this Symposium are at the present time operating in nature in such a way as to determine the course of epidemic disease. Let us leave aside the minor phase variations that have been so thoroughly studied in the *Salmonella* group, and concentrate on major changes in virulence, such as those accompanying the transformation of the pneumococcus under the action of deoxyribonucleic acid or of the diphtheria bacillus under the action of bacteriophage. Are these mere laboratory tricks or are they of common occurrence in nature? This is not an easy question to answer. Medical bacteriologists of experience cannot but be impressed by the apparent fixity of bacterial species. There are, of course, great difficulties in defining the limits of bacterial species, particularly in a group such as the Enterobacteriaceae in which there is an almost infinite variety of gradations between the nodal points; but the changes that have been observed concern only one or two characters of an organism insufficient in themselves to alter its specific rank. Moreover epidemiological studies in both man and animals have failed to bring convincing proof of any change in virulence, or even in serological or phage type, during the course of an outbreak. Even though a rise in virulence has often been postulated for the genesis of an epidemic and a fall in virulence for its decline, there is remarkably little evidence to support this supposition. One is therefore left to wonder how often in nature spontaneous changes in virulence occur, and how often they are responsible for modifying the epidemiological picture. I refer here specifically to bacteria, and not to viruses, which appear to be more prone to variation. It may be that these changes occur so rarely as to have little, or only very occasional, epidemiological significance. This is perhaps to err on the conservative side, but I do think that we should wait for stronger evidence than we have at present before we conclude that bacterial transformations of one sort or another play any considerable part in determining the course of infectious disease in man or animals. I do not deny the occurrence of strains of varying degrees of virulence, or that changes in virulence may occur from time to time, but I agree with Topley (1942) when he says that the evolution within any parasitic species of a strain of high epidemicity is an occasional event, rather than part of a normal or periodic process. We are at any rate on fairly safe ground in relying on the day-to-day stability of phage types and serotypes in the prosecution of our epidemiological studies. Should any major transformation occur in bacterial virulence, then I think we are in a better position now, with our close co-ordination of field and laboratory studies, to recognize it and to study its mechanism than at any time in the past.

REFERENCES

ARKWRIGHT, J. A. (1929). The virulence of the micro-organism in infective disease. *Lancet*, **2**, 963.

BAIL, O. (1904). Untersuchungen über natürliche und künstliche Milzbrand-immunität. *Zbl. Bakt.* **36**, 266.

CARMICHAEL, J. (1939). Bovine tuberculosis in the tropics, with special reference to Uganda. *J. comp. Path.* **52**, 322.

CHAUVEAU, A. (1880). Nature de l'immunité des moutons algériens contre le sang de rate. *C.R. Acad. Sci., Paris*, **91**, 33.

CHESNEY, A. M. (1916). The latent period in the growth of bacteria. *J. exp. Med.* **24**, 387.

DALLDORF, G. & GIFFORD, R. (1954). Susceptibility of gravid mice to Coxsackie virus infection. *J. exp. Med.* **99**, 21.

DALLDORF, G. & SICKLES, G. M. (1948). An unidentified filtrable agent isolated from the faeces of children with paralysis. *Science*, **108**, 61.

DESBORDES, J. & FOURNIER, E. (1954). La virulence des mycobactéries. *Rev. Immunol.* **18**, 50.

DIEHL, K. & VERSCHUER, O. F. VON (1933). *Zwillingstuberkulose. Zwillingsforschung und erbliche Tuberkulosedisposition*. Jena: Gustav Fischer.

FELTON, L. D. & DOUGHERTY, K. M. (1924). Studies on virulence. II. The increase in virulence in vitro of a strain of pneumococcus. *J. exp. Med.* **39**, 137.

FELTY, A. R. & BLOOMFIELD, A. L. (1924). The relation of vegetative activity of bacteria to pathogenicity. *J. exp. Med.* **40**, 703.

GLADSTONE, G. P. (1948). Immunity to anthrax. Production of the cell-free protective antigen in cellophane sacs. *Brit. J. exp. Path.* **29**, 379.

GRIFFITH, A. S. (1957). The types of tubercle bacilli in lupus and scrofulodermia. *J. Hyg., Camb.* (in the Press).

GRIFFITH, F. (1928). The significance of pneumococcal types. *J. Hyg., Camb.*, **27**, 113.

GRIFFITH, F. (1929). Serological races of pneumococci. Significance of types. *System of Bacteriology, Med. Res. Coun., Lond.*, **2**, 201.

HADLEY, P. (1927). Microbic dissociation. *J. infect. Dis.* **40**, 1.

HOEDEN, J. VAN DER (1955). The epidemiology and epizootiology of leptospirosis in Israel. *J. trop. Med. (Hyg.)*, **58**, 202.

HUDDLESON, I. F. (1955). Biochemical and histopathological reactions in the evolution of bovine brucellosis. *Centennial Symposium Report, Michigan State Univ.*

KALLMANN, F. J. & REISNER, D. (1943*a*). Twin studies on the significance of genetic factors in tuberculosis. *Amer. Rev. Tuberc.* **47**, 549.

KALLMANN, F. J. & REISNER, D. (1943*b*). Twin studies on genetic variations in resistance to tuberculosis. *J. Hered.* **34**, 269, 293.

KILBOURNE, E. D. & HORSFALL, F. L. (1951). Lethal infection with Coxsackie virus of adult mice given cortisone. *Proc. Soc. exp. Biol., N.Y.*, **77**, 135.

LAURENT, E. (1910). *Das Virulenzproblem der pathogenen Bakterien.* Jena: Gustav Fischer.

LURIE, M. B. (1941). Heredity, constitution and tuberculosis. An experimental study. *Amer. Rev. Tuberc.* **44**, Suppl. (Sept.), 1, 68, 80, 112.

McLEOD, J. W. & GORDON, J. (1922). Production of hydrogen peroxide by bacteria. *Biochem. J.* **16**, 499.

MARMOREK, A. (1895). Le streptocoque et le sérum antistreptococcique. *Ann. Inst. Pasteur*, **9**, 593.

MOOSER, H., VARELA, G. & PILZ, H. (1934). Experiments on the conversion of typhus strains. *J. exp. Med.* **59**, 137.

NICOLLE, M. (1906). Morve expérimentale et maladies 'spontanées' des cobayes. *Ann. Inst. Pasteur*, **20**, 801.

ROBERTSON, O. H. & SIA, R. H. P. (1924). Studies on pneumococcus growth inhibition. II. A method for demonstrating the growth-inhibitory and bactericidal action of normal serum-leucocyte mixtures. *J. exp. Med.* **39**, 219.

SKINNER, H. H., HENDERSON, W. M. & BROOKSBY, J. B. (1952). Use of unweaned white mice in foot-and-mouth disease research. *Nature, Lond.*, **169**, 794.

SMITH, H. & GALLOP, R. C. (1956). *B. anthracis.* An extracellular immunizing aggressin isolated from exudates of infected guinea-pigs. *Brit. J. exp. Path.* **37**, 144.

SMITH, H., KEPPIE, J. & STANLEY, J. L. (1955). The chemical basis of the virulence of *Bacillus anthracis.* V. The specific toxin produced by *B. anthracis in vivo. Brit. J. exp. Path.* **36**, 460.

THOMPSON, R. & JOHNSON, A. (1947). The inhibitory action of saliva on the diphtheria bacillus: hydrogen peroxide, the antibiotic agent of salivary streptococci. *J. Bact.* **54**, 53.

TILLETT, W. S. (1927). Studies on Pneumococcus mucosus (Type iii). II. The infectivity of Type iii pneumococcus for rabbits. *J. exp. Med.* **45**, 1093.

TOPLEY, W. W. C. (1942). The biology of epidemics. *Proc. roy. Soc.* B, **130**, 337.

TURRÓ, R. (1908). Toxine du bacille de la morve. *C.R. Soc. Biol., Paris*, **64**, 130.

UEHLINGER, E. & KÜNSCH, M. (1938). Über Zwillingstuberkulose. Untersuchungen an 46 Paaren. *Beitr. Klin. Tuberk.* **92**, 275.

WADSWORTH, A. B. & KIRKBRIDE, M. B. (1918). A study of the changes in virulence of the pneumococcus at different periods of growth and under different conditions of cultivation in media. *J. exp. Med.* **27**, 791.

WEBSTER, L. T. (1925*a*). Further contributions of experimental methods to the study of epidemics. *Amer. J. Hyg.* **5**, 335.

WEBSTER, L. T. (1925*b*). Biology of Bacterium lepisepticum. I. Effects of oxygen tension and the presence of rabbit blood on growth, dissociation, and virulence. *J. exp. Med.* **41**, 571.

WILSON, G. S. (1926). The relation between the age and the virulence of cultures of *B. aertrycke* (mutton). *J. Hyg., Camb.*, **25**, 142.

WILSON, G. S. (1930). The effect on the virulence of *Bact. aertrycke* of cultivation in atmospheres containing varying proportions of oxygen. *J. Hyg., Camb.*, **30**, 433.

WILSON, G. S. & MILES, A. A. (1955). *Topley and Wilson's Principles of Bacteriology and Immunity*, 4th ed. London: Ed. Arnold.

WOO, S. T. (1926). Studies on pneumococcus growth inhibition. V. The relation of virulence to the pneumococcidal activity of normal rabbit serum-leucocyte mixtures. *J. exp. Med.* **43**, 623.

SOME FACTORS INFLUENCING THE SPREAD OF PLANT VIRUSES BY ARTHROPOD VECTORS

KENNETH M. SMITH

Virus Research Unit, Agricultural Research Council, Molteno Institute, Cambridge

INTRODUCTION

The relationship between viruses, and especially plant viruses, and the insects which transmit them (vectors) is a complicated and interesting one. Although a great many facts have been collected we are still very far from a clear understanding of the situation.

A suspicion that there was some sort of connexion between certain diseases of plants and insects is more or less coincident with the discovery of the first virus in 1892. Towards the end of the nineteenth century, Takata (1895), in Japan, showed that the dwarf disease of rice was due to something put into the plant by the leafhopper, *Deltocephalus dorsalis* Motsch. However, this work did not become available to Western workers for many years and, in the meantime, Ball in 1909 had connected the leafhopper *Circulifer* (*Eutettix*) *tenellus* with the disease of sugar beet called curly-leaf, better known as curly-top. A year later Shaw (1910) demonstrated that this leafhopper did in fact infect healthy sugar beet with the curly-top disease. Allard in 1914 is generally credited with the discovery that aphids could transmit plant viruses, and he claimed to have shown that an aphid, known as *Macrosiphum tabaci*, was the vector of tobacco mosaic virus. We know now, however, that aphids do not transmit this virus which does not, apparently, have an insect vector. Possibly Allard was working with a strain of cucumber mosaic virus which can simulate very closely the symptoms of tobacco mosaic virus in tobacco. In 1916 Doolittle and Jagger, working independently, showed that *Aphis gossypii* could transmit the virus of cucumber mosaic.

In 1918 Doolittle & Gilbert transmitted what they thought was cucumber mosaic virus by means of the striped cucumber beetle. There is, however, no case known of an aphid-transmitted virus being carried by a beetle or other mandibulate insect and vice versa. The probable explanation is that Doolittle & Gilbert were working with one of the group of squash-mosaic viruses which are beetle-transmitted as opposed to the aphid-transmitted viruses of the cucumber mosaic group.

Now there are over 300 separate plant viruses described, not all of which by any means are known to have insect vectors. More viruses are transmitted by aphids than by any other type of insect and one aphid species in particular, *Myzus persicae* Sulz., is known to transmit nearly fifty separate viruses. Next in importance come the leafhoppers which are the vectors of many important virus diseases in the Americas. Until just recently no leafhopper-borne viruses were known in Western Europe, but now at least three have been described and more no doubt will be discovered in the near future. A number of species of scale insects, Coccoidea, are concerned in the spread of one particular group of viruses affecting cocoa trees (*Cacao*). There is one virus carried by thrips, that of tomato spotted wilt, and there are nine viruses transmitted by whiteflies (Aleurodidae). Three or four viruses have beetles as vectors and four viruses are borne by Eriophyid mites.

The various kinds of relationships between the viruses and these different types of vectors are discussed in the remainder of this paper.

DIFFERENT TYPES OF INSECT-VIRUS RELATIONSHIPS
Mechanical transmission

In this context mechanical transmission involves the purely passive transfer to the plant of virus contaminating the mouthparts of the insect in question. Unexpectedly enough there appear to be very few instances of this method of virus spread. We have mentioned earlier that no insect vector is known for the virus of tobacco mosaic, a curious fact in view of the extremely infectious nature of this virus. However, this statement needs qualifying slightly because Walters (1952) has shown that the virus can be transmitted by an insect under rather artificial conditions. In his experiments Walters used the large grasshopper, *Melanoplus differentialis*; he allowed the insects to feed on a mosaic tobacco plant and then transferred them immediately to healthy tobacco plants. He did the same thing with two other sap-inoculable viruses, that of tobacco ringspot and potato virus *X*. In each case some successful infections resulted by mechanical transfer of virus, residual on the mouthparts, to the healthy plants during the process of eating the leaves.

Some controversy has centred round the question whether aphids are ever mechanical vectors of plant viruses, as first suggested by Doolittle & Walker (1928). There are several factors which seem to militate against this theory. For example, the specificity of transmission shown by aphids, in which one species can transmit a virus and another species is unable to do so, cannot be explained on the basis of a mere mechanical contamination of the mouthparts. Bradley (1952) tried the experiment of contaminating externally the stylets of the aphid *Myzus persicae* with the viruses of henbane mosaic and tobacco mosaic, but failed to obtain positive transmissions. Furthermore, Watson & Roberts (1940) point out that the aphid *M. persicae*, if transferred rapidly, can transmit the viruses of henbane mosaic, severe etch and potato virus *Y* from tobacco to a number of successive healthy plants. This could hardly happen if the transmission depended on the mechanical cleaning of the stylets. On the other hand, this might be possible if, as suggested by Hoggan (1933), small quantities of virus lodged in the ducts *inside* the stylets of the aphids; under these circumstances more than one feeding puncture might be necessary to remove all the virus. Bradley (1952) suggests that the salivary sheath formed in the plant by the gelling of the salivary material may act as a filter for the aphid's food and its absence during brief feeding punctures may lead to one of the ducts in the stylets becoming obstructed and so cause the aphid to clear it by forcing liquid outwards. This may happen several times, and during the process virus from the previous feeding puncture may pass into the cell.

None of these assumptions, however, explain the non-transmission of certain viruses by aphids nor the specificity of vectors.

Day & Irzykiewicz (1954) have suggested a modified hypothesis of mechanical transmission based on the following points: (1) Short transmission cycle. This may be as short as one minute for both the acquisition and inoculation of virus. (2) Absence of a latent period. (3) Short duration of retention of virus and the rapid loss of infectivity in successive inoculation feeds. (4) Usual absence of vector specificity. (5) Ease with which these viruses can be transmitted mechanically. (6) The absence of retention of virus following a moult. They consider that taken together these six points are conclusive of mechanical transmission.

However, specificity of vectors and selectivity in transmission must still be explained and Day & Irzykiewicz attempt to do this on the assumption of virus inhibitors in the saliva and the different response of viruses to these inhibitors.

In the writer's opinion, however, the case for the mechanical transmission of plant viruses by aphids has not yet been satisfactorily made out.

Aphid-transmitted non-persistent viruses

Aphid-transmitted viruses were first divided into two categories by Watson (1936, 1938) and Watson & Roberts (1939, 1940). 'Non-persistent' viruses are rapidly lost by the vector, usually after a short period of feeding, whilst 'persistent' viruses are retained by the vector for long periods, frequently for the rest of the insect's life, without the necessity for recourse to a fresh source of virus.

A great deal of investigation has been carried out on the conditions governing the non-persistent type of transmission, but the situation is still confused and the exact significance of the various facts is still not understood.

We are assuming, of course, that in a non-persistent virus there is a closer relationship between the virus and the aphid vector than there is in the case of the virus transmitted by purely mechanical means.

The main facts concerning non-persistent viruses in relation to their aphid vectors are as follows:

(1) Vectors are optimally infective when they have fed for only a few minutes on the infected plant.

(2) Virus transmission is improved if aphid vectors are starved for a period before an infection (= acquisition) feed.

(3) After acquisition-feeding infectivity is rapidly lost when the vectors feed on healthy plants.

(4) Infectivity is lost much more slowly when the vectors fast after acquisition-feeding.

Watson & Roberts (1939) consider that the most probable explanation of these effects is that the viruses are inactivated by some substance produced by the aphids when feeding. This hypothesis of an inactivating substance produced by aphids only while feeding can be extended to cover most of the experimental facts, including possibly the specificity of transmission. If such a substance is produced, however, there is no information on where it is produced or where it comes into contact with the virus (Bradley, 1952).

The answer may be in a combination of mechanical and inactivator hypotheses. For purposes of discussion Sylvester (1954) makes the following assumptions: (1) Transmission is mechanical in the sense that virus is carried within the food canal of aphids. (2) Aphids feed in a similar manner and in similar areas during initial stages of penetration, although they may exhibit variations in the rate of penetration. (3) Aphids acquire a similar charge of virus when feeding a short time on a given virus source plant. (4) The action of inactivators which are present in the salivary secretions is not upon the virus but rather upon the host plant cells into which the virus is injected, i.e. the insect renders the host plant cell resistant or practically immune to infection. Sylvester admits that the evidence in support of this 'incompatibility hypothesis' is meagre and goes on to suggest that the implications would be such as to indicate that all viruses such as that of tobacco mosaic, potato virus *X*, etc., are taken up by the aphids when feeding but cannot be demonstrated as being in the insects by transmission tests because the combination of salivary secretions and the contents of inoculated cell is incompatible with the virus to such an extent that transmission is highly improbable.

Regarding the question as to whether the aphid actually picks up a virus which it cannot transmit, the evidence is rather contradictory. It was shown by Bennett & Wallace (1938) that the virus of beet curly-top will persist for a number of days in the aphid, *Myzus persicae*, although the insect is unable to transmit the virus. On the other hand, a recent paper by van Soest & de Meester-Manger Cats (1956) suggests that the aphid *M. persicae* is unable to imbibe the virus of tobacco mosaic from infected plants of *Nicotiana glauca*. It is known that if the stylets of an aphid are severed during the act of feeding, droplets of sap continue to emerge from the cut ends of the stylets, apparently forced out by the turgidity of the plant. Such droplets were tested for the presence of tobacco mosaic virus by (1) inoculation to test plants, (2) examination under the electron microscope, (3) tests by a method of microserology. All these tests gave negative results and lead the authors to the conclusion that the aphid does not imbibe the virus. They suggest that this seems to support the suggestion made by Sukhov (1944) that the salivary sheath, which surrounds the stylets in the plant, acts as a barrier against the tobacco mosaic virus. However, the fact that *Myzus persicae* can easily transmit other rod-shaped viruses such as that of cabbage black ringspot is against Sukhov's hypothesis.

There is slight evidence for the suggestion that inactivators present in the salivary secretions of the aphid act upon the host cell rather than the virus in the work of Kirkpatrick & Ross (1952) on potato leaf-roll. They found that the presence of large numbers of aphids, either infective or non-infective, on a test plant decreased the probability of obtaining an infection, which seems to suggest that the test plant was being modified.

Aphid-transmitted persistent viruses

The chief differences between this type of virus and the foregoing non-persistent viruses are, first, the long period of time, frequently the rest of the life of the aphid, during which the insect retains infectivity. Secondly, the delay in the development of infective power within the aphid, which can be put in another way. Thus in progressive transfers of infective aphids from plant to plant, the non-persistent virus is carried to the first plant and rarely to the second if the feeding periods are of some hours duration, whilst the persistent virus is not transmitted to the first two or three plants but to all the others for a considerable period. Thirdly, there is a greater specificity in the aphid vectors of persistent viruses which are not as a rule transmitted by six or more species as may be the case with some non-persistent viruses. In addition the majority of persistent viruses are not transmissible by mechanical means and the ability of aphid vectors to transmit this type of virus is not affected by preliminary starving.

The delay in the development of infective power in the aphid or, put more shortly, the latent period, varies greatly with the different viruses. The longest latent period, so far discovered, is that of a strawberry virus known as 'Virus 3' transmitted by the aphid, *Capitophorus fragariae* Theob., which takes ten to nineteen days. Aphids left for sixteen days on an infected plant caused infection in the first day of test feeding. It is not known how far the latent period of a persistent virus in the aphid vector is of biological significance, but in some cases it appears to be a function of the test plant. Thus it appears possible to reduce the latent period of the leaf-roll virus in the aphid by the use of host plants of greater susceptibility and in which the virus may be present in higher concentration than in the potato (Kassanis, 1952; Kirkpatrick & Ross, 1952; Klostermeyer, 1953).

The suggestion has been made by Day (1955) that the potato leaf-roll virus may multiply to a limited extent within the aphid. However, experiments carried out by Cadman & Harrison (1956) do not seem to support this. It is known that potato tubers can be freed from leaf-roll virus by keeping them at 36° C. for 3 weeks, and experiments were made to investigate the effects of high temperatures on the persistence of the virus in the aphid *Myzus persicae*. The ability of infective aphids to transmit the virus was greatly decreased by exposing them to 32° C. for 3 or 6 days. The ability to transmit more regularly did not return when the aphids were kept for a further period at 20° C. These results seem to provide no evidence that the virus multiplies in the aphid since, if it did, one would expect the insects to return to their full transmitting power at normal temperatures.

In the complex disease of tobacco known as 'rosette' (Smith & Lea, 1946) the two component viruses are called the 'vein-distorting' and 'mottle' viruses respectively. Experiments show that both viruses persist in the aphid vector for at least 3 weeks, since infection is carried right through twenty serial transfers of 24 hr. feeding on each plant. During these transfers occasional plants developed either the mottle disease only or else the vein-distorting disease only, showing that the flow of virus from the insect is not uniform.

Sylvester (1949 *a, b*) suggests three factors which would aid in classifying a virus as persistent or non-persistent. These are: (1) The period of retention of the virus by the aphid. (2) The effect of a pre-fasting period, prior to the infection-feeding, upon subsequent trans-mission efficiency. (3) The status of sap-transmissibility of the virus. It follows that a typical aphid-borne persistent virus would have these characteristics:

(1) It would be retained by the aphid vector for a relatively long period of time.

(2) The vector efficiency would not be influenced by a prefasting period prior to infection-feeding.

(3) It would not be sap-transmissible with ordinary facility.

A typical non-persistent virus would be opposite in these respects, whilst a virus would be classified as persistent if it had any combination of two or more of the three characteristics in common.

Transmission with multiplication of virus in the insect vector

The question as to whether a plant virus can multiply in an animal, i.e. its insect vector, has long been debated, since it is obviously of considerable interest and it is only comparatively recently that this question has been decided in the affirmative. It has taken many years and the slow accumulation of evidence to show that certain plant viruses do multiply in a certain type of insect vector.

The first to offer some evidence on this point was a Japanese worker (Fukushi, 1933) who studied the dwarf disease of rice and its leafhopper vector, *Nephotettix apicalis* Motsch. He showed that the virus was transmitted from an infective parent insect to the offspring, but only through the female parent. Moreover, the progeny from such an infected parent did not itself become infective until after a period of 9 days from the date of hatching. Fukushi also showed that the virus could be passed through six generations involving eighty-two infective leafhoppers and all derived from a single virus-bearing female without access to a further source of virus. This is strong indirect evidence of multiplication since otherwise the dilution involved would be too great.

Black (1950) carried out similar experiments to those of Fukushi with the virus of clover club-leaf which he has shown to be transmitted through the egg of the vector, a leafhopper *Agalliopsis novella* Say. From a pair of viruliferous (= virus bearing) leafhoppers the breeding was carried out through twenty-one generations over a period of 5 years. The insects were fed throughout on virus-immune lucerne plants without loss of infectivity. Black has calculated that, if multiplication of the virus is not assumed, the dilution of the original virus in the parent insect exceeded $1:2\cdot8\times10^{26}$.

Kunkel (1937) has made an interesting study of the virus of aster yellows and its leafhopper vector, *Macrosteles fascifrons* Stal. He exposed viruliferous leafhoppers to a temperature of 32° C. for varying periods and found that this exposure to high temperatures deprived the insects of their infectivity for a period. The length of this period depended on the length of the exposure to 32° C. If the insects were kept for 1 day at this temperature they regained infectivity within a few hours. If they were kept several days it required 2 days for them to regain infectivity, and if they were kept at 32° C. for 12 days infectivity was entirely lost. Kunkel interpreted these results as indicating that exposure to high temperatures reduced the amount of virus in the insect below the infectivity limit and the delay before the insect again became infective was necessitated by the multiplication of the virus up to a sufficient concentration for infection. Long exposure destroyed the virus altogether and so rendered the insect non-viruliferous. The ability of these insects to regain virus from a fresh source of infection was not apparently affected by the heat treatment. It is instructive to compare the results of this experiment with those of a similar experiment, previously described with the aphid *Myzus persicae* and the virus of potato leaf-roll. Here, unlike the leafhopper, the aphid did not regain normal infectivity when returned to the lower temperature.

Black (1941) approached the problem from a slightly different angle, since he had shown in 1940 that the virus of aster yellows could be inoculated successfully into the leafhopper vector, thus rendering it viruliferous. He colonized a large number of the leafhoppers on a yellowed aster plant for a given time and then removed all the insects to plants of rye which are immune to the aster yellows virus. Thus the leafhoppers received approximately the same dose of virus. Next, a number of the insects were ground up into a paste, made into various dilutions and inoculated into the alimentary canals of virus-free aster leafhoppers. This rather roundabout method had to be employed because the aster yellows virus is not mechanically transmissible to its host plant. Black found that those leafhoppers which had been longest on the rye plants contained most virus since they would withstand the highest dilutions and still produce infectivity in the inoculated leaf-hoppers, the inference being that the virus had multiplied most in those insects which had remained alive longest after the intake of virus in the first place.

A more direct method of measuring multiplication of a virus in an insect vector is by serial inoculations from insect to insect. This was first done by Merrill & TenBroek (1934) who demonstrated the multiplication in the mosquito of the virus of equine encephalomyelitis. Maramorosch (1952) applied this technique and by means of a microsyringe succeeded in carrying the virus serially through ten groups of leafhoppers. He calculated that if the virus was not multiplying the dilution at the 10th passage would have reached 10^{-40}.

In 1938 Trager succeeded in cultivating the virus of equine encephalomyelitis in hanging-drop culture of mosquito tissues and this technique was applied by Maramorosch (1956) to the virus of aster yellows and its leafhopper vector *Macrosteles fascifrons* Stal. In these experiments nymphs of aster leafhoppers were allowed to feed for 2 days on diseased plants of China aster to acquire aster yellows virus. No virus was recovered when juices of these leafhoppers were injected into virus-free leafhoppers on the following day. However, virus was recovered by the same injection method after the nymphs had been cut in pieces and their living tissues incubated for 10 days in a suitable medium in hanging drops. This experiment demonstrates that aster yellows virus can complete its incubation not only in vectors feeding on a constant supply of fresh plant food but also in insect tissues *in vitro*. The experiment also provides additional evidence for multiplication of this plant virus in the tissues of its insect vector.

In the case of another leafhopper-borne virus, that of corn (maize) stunt and its vector, *Dalbulus maidis* Del. & Wol., it was observed by Kunkel (1948) that the lengths of the incubation period of the virus in both host plant and insect vector were the same at optimal temperature.

Maramorosch (1951) inoculated the corn stunt virus, at dilutions of 1:100 insect pulp, into the leafhoppers and found that approximately 6 weeks elapsed after inoculation before the insects became infective. This indicates that the virus was multiplying in the leafhoppers during this period.

Some doubt exists whether the well known virus of beet curly-top does multiply in its vector, the leafhopper *Circulifer tenellus*. There is a certain amount of evidence which supports both views. Thus, leafhoppers frequently lose their ability to transmit the virus but can reacquire it from an infected beet. Moreover, the longer the insects fed on a source of virus the longer they remained infective (Bennett & Wallace, 1938). These facts do not seem to support the idea of virus multiplication. On the other hand, Maramorosch (1955) has developed a new technique for the study of this virus and he considers that his results support the idea of multiplication. Using an improved type of micro-injector he inoculated virus-free leafhoppers with virus-containing juice at dilutions of 1:30 and 1:300. Insects receiving the lower dilution became infective after 1–9 days whilst those receiving the higher dilution only became infective after 5–20 days. This suggests a period of incubation or multiplication of the virus in the insect.

Transmission by mandibulate insects

The transmission of tobacco mosaic virus by means of the grasshopper, which was briefly discussed under the heading of mechanical transmission, is not again dealt with here. Only those cases of transmission by biting insects are discussed where it is considered that some sort of biological relationship exists between vector and virus.

There are at least three instances of virus transmission by biting insects which fall into this category; these are turnip yellow mosaic virus, certain squash mosaic viruses and the virus of cowpea mosaic.

In the case of turnip yellow mosaic virus various species of beetles, beetle larvae, grasshoppers and earwigs (Forficulidae) were all found capable of transmitting the virus (Smith & Markham, 1946; Markham & Smith, 1949). All these different types of insects have one characteristic in common, they regurgitate whilst feeding. This seems to be a necessary corollary to transmission since biting insects which do not regurgitate, such as caterpillars, are unable to act as vectors. The virus is retained for a considerable period by the insect, from 10 to 14 days in the case of turnip yellow mosaic virus, 17–20 days for squash mosaic virus (Freitag, 1956), and 14 days for cowpea mosaic virus (Dale, 1953). Infective larvae of the mustard beetle (*Phaedon cochleariae*) do not retain the virus of turnip yellow mosaic through pupation, nor does the virus overwinter in hibernating adult beetles (*Phyllotreta* spp.). Squash mosaic virus can be recovered in an infective condition from the blood, faeces and regurgitated gut contents of the cucumber beetles, and in this case the virus may possibly overwinter in the hibernating adults (Freitag, 1956).

It is rather difficult to assess the exact relationship between these viruses and their mandibulate vectors. There is no doubt that more is involved than a purely mechanical relationship since the virus is retained by the insects for considerable periods. It may be suggested that transmission only lasts so long as undigested virus material remains in the foregut and can still be regurgitated. The matter, however, is probably not as simple as that, especially when, as in the case of squash mosaic, the virus can be detected in the blood. However, since there is little evidence of multiplication of virus in the insect the eventual explanation may turn out to be a build-up of virus concentration in the insect.

It is interesting to find that though all three beetle-transmitted viruses are also easily sap-inoculable none can be transmitted by sucking insects such as aphids. The reason for this lies presumably in a property of the viruses since they must be easily accessible to the feeding aphid.

Viruses in non-vector insects

It is known in several cases that virus imbibed by or injected into a non-vector insect species does not become immediately inactivated and may in fact persist for long periods. Thus the virus of beet curly-top will persist for 14–21 days in a non-vector species of leafhopper and in an aphid but neither insect is able to transmit the virus (Bennett & Wallace, 1938). Similarly, the virus of curly-top could be recovered from the faeces of flea beetles, and tobacco mosaic virus after ingestion by caterpillars (Smith, 1941). The virus of turnip yellow mosaic is also resistant to the digestive juices of non-vector insects such as caterpillars and even to the digestive enzymes of snails. There must therefore be other reasons for non-transmission than rapid inactivation in the body of the insect.

Maramorosch (1955) studied the duration of retention of the aster yellows virus by vector and non-vector leafhoppers. He inoculated the juices of the two types of leafhoppers, after feeding on a source of aster yellows virus, at a dilution of 1:100, into virus-free aster leafhoppers. He found that it took as long as 66 days for those insects inoculated with the juice of non-vector insects to develop infectivity. Such a long incubation period suggests that the amount of virus was very small. By means of such titrations of the virus recovered from the bodies of the insects it appeared that there was a slow loss of virus from the non-vector species whilst the vector species retained the virus for the rest of their lives.

It may be, of course, that in certain cases non-vector species actually do not imbibe the virus whilst feeding. The reason for this is not clear but some support is given to it by experiments carried out by van Soest & de Meester-Manger Cats (1956) previously mentioned. They were unable to detect the virus of tobacco mosaic in the droplets of plant sap exuding from the cut ends of aphids' stylets in situ in mosaic tobacco plants.

Variations in vector efficiency

Under this heading are discussed variations in the transmitting power of individual insects belonging to the same vector species.

There seems little doubt that there is individual variation among aphid vectors as regards efficiency of transmission with some viruses and Stubbs (1955) suggests that there may exist races of *Myzus persicae* unable to transmit the virus of spinach yellows of which *M. persicae* is the normal vector. The converse of this has been suggested by Bawden & Kassanis (1947) who think there may occur individual aphids capable of transmitting a virus which is not spread by the species as a whole.

An interesting case of transmission by a particular form of an aphid vector has been reported by Paine & Legg (1953), who found that the virus of hop mosaic is transmitted only by the winged form of *Phorodon humuli* Schrank and not by the wingless form.

Cases of differential transmission by developmental stages of insect vectors are also known. The virus of tomato spotted wilt is transmitted by one or two species of thrips (Thysanoptera) but only the larval form can pick up and transmit this virus. The adult thrips can transmit the virus if it has acquired it during its larval life but it cannot acquire the virus *de novo* in the adult stage. The reason for this phenomenon is not certainly known although Bawden (1950) has suggested that the gut wall of the adult insect may be more impermeable to virus than that of the larva. On this assumption virus picked up during the larval stage of the insect would pass through the gut wall and circulate in the blood where it remains for the rest of the insect's life, thus allowing the adult to transmit the virus but not to acquire it.

Kunkel (1926) showed that the virus of aster yellows was transmitted by the adult leafhopper but not by the nymph, the reason for this being the fact that the incubation period of the virus in the insect was longer than the nymphal life of the leafhopper. Kunkel demonstrated this by keeping the larvae at low temperatures; this retarded the development of the nymphs but not the development of infective power. Under these conditions the larval leafhopper becomes infective.

The existence of definite races of the same vector species which were respectively able and unable to transmit a given virus was first demonstrated by Storey (1932) working with the streak virus of maize and the leafhopper vector *Cicadulina mbila* Naude. He named these races *active* and *inactive*, according to their transmitting capacity. No difference in the external morphology of the two races could be detected and there is little doubt that both fall into the one species *C. mbila* Naude. Storey also showed that by the crossing of pure races the ability to transmit is inherited as a simple dominant Mendelian factor, linked with sex. In a later paper (1933) Storey gave results of inoculating and puncturing leafhoppers. This was probably the first record of the successful inoculation of a plant virus into an insect vector to render it infective. By this means it was possible to show that in an active infective leafhopper the virus was present in the contents of the rectum if the insect had fed recently on a diseased plant but not otherwise. It was also present in the general contents of the thorax, abdomen and blood, but not in the naturally voided faeces. The virus appeared in the blood before the insect developed infective power. It was possible to render an inactive insect capable of transmitting the virus if a simple puncture was made in the abdomen. It was necessary, however, for the puncture to be made in some part of the intestine. Inactive races could also be rendered infective by inoculation with the streak virus, although the numbers of successes were significantly less than with active races.

This is probably in no way an isolated phenomenon but may occur with several of the leafhopper-transmitted viruses. Indeed Black (1943) has shown that something of the same sort occurs with the New York strain of potato yellow dwarf virus and the leafhopper *Aceratagallia sanguinolenta* Prov. This case, however, is not so clear cut as the foregoing. In the 'active' races, the virus was transmitted by 80 % of the insects, and by only 2 % in the 'inactive'; whilst of the hybrids 30 % transmitted the virus.

As suggested by Storey, the inability to transmit is probably due to some factor in the intestinal wall which, in the inactive races, resists the passage of the virus and so prevents it reaching the blood and thence the salivary glands.

Kunkel (1954) suggests, as a reason for differences in vector efficiency of the aster leafhopper, that the insects themselves vary in their susceptibility to infection with aster yellows virus. If we accept the suggestion— and the facts now seem to support it—that the infective aster leafhopper is itself diseased, then, of course, efficiency as a vector may depend on a variety of factors. There is the length of life of the transmitting insect, the rate of multiplication of the virus and the concentration inside the insect, and any possible ill-effect of the virus itself upon the insect's own metabolism.

EFFECT OF PLANT VIRUSES UPON THE INSECT VECTOR

The question as to whether a plant virus has any effect, deleterious or otherwise, upon the insect vector is one which has interested virus workers for many years. One of the earliest attempts to investigate the matter was made by Dobroscky (1929) who undertook an intensive study of the salivary glands and alimentary tract of the leafhopper, vector of the aster yellows virus, *Macrosteles fascifrons* Stal., with a view to finding any difference between viruliferous and non-viruliferous insects. Dobroscky was unable to find any difference between the two. The writer has carried out a similar study in conjunction with Dr K. Maramorosch, using the electron microscope to examine thin sections of the salivary glands of *M. fascifrons* with aster yellows virus and of *Circulifer* (= *Eutettix*) *tenellus* Baker with beet curly-top virus. Careful examination was also made of similar material from virus-free leafhoppers. These studies were negative and no difference could be discerned between the viruliferous and virus-free material. The reason for this failure now seems apparent in a recent paper by Littau & Maramorosch (1956) who have made a cytological study with the optical microscope of the aster leafhopper (*M. fascifrons* Stal.). They examined not the salivary glands but the fatbody and found a difference between the viruliferous and virus-free insects. This difference was found in the cells. In the virus-free leafhoppers the nuclei tended to be round or to have smooth contours; only a few were stellate and these were observed in only 36 % of the leafhoppers. The cytoplasm was generally homogenous with a large number of vacuoles of varying size and the cells were intact. In viruliferous insects almost all nuclei of the fatbody cells were stellate (in 95 % of the leafhoppers) and the cytoplasm was reticulate. Many cells seemed abnormal and appeared broken in the sections.

Littau & Maramorosch consider that this is not merely a case of an insect vector of a virus but rather that the insect is an infected host of the aster yellows virus. They state that the persistent transmission of the virus may be a result of progressive deterioration of fatbody cells in which the virus is stored and from which it is being released into the blood. It is rather interesting to consider that the fatbody is the site of multiplication of at least three types of insect viruses, but these involve destruction of the fatbody and rapid death of the infected larva.

A slightly different effect of a plant virus on its insect vector may appropriately be considered here. It has long been known that a type of non-sterile immunity exists between plant viruses and related strains. In other words it is usually not possible to inoculate a virus into a plant already infected with a related virus. The classical example of this is the inability of a 'yellow mottle' strain of tobacco mosaic virus to infect a tobacco plant already infected with a 'green mottle' strain of the same virus. Two strains of aster yellows virus exist, known respectively as aster yellows virus and Californian aster yellows virus. Until recently it has not been possible to test whether a cross-immunity existed between these two viruses because the symptoms produced on the test plants were indistinguishable. Now, however, Kunkel (1955) has found two test plants which react in a different manner to the two viruses. The plants are *Vinca rosea* and *Nicotiana rustica* L. This enabled cross-immunity tests to be carried out which showed that the aster yellows virus protected against the Californian aster yellows virus and vice versa. The discovery of these two differential hosts also enabled Kunkel to carry out experiments designed to show whether a similar cross-immunity existed in the insect vector. Virus-free leafhoppers were fed first on a plant infected with aster yellows virus and then on a plant infected with Californian aster yellows virus. When transferred to healthy plants only the aster yellows virus was transmitted and when the procedure was reversed the plants developed only the Californian aster yellows disease. Kunkel points out that these experiments prove only that leafhoppers, infective for one virus, do not transmit the other. They have not shown that both viruses may not be picked up by the insects. Presumably, however, the virus first acquired is multiplying inside the insect and so the available multiplication sites are occupied, leaving no opportunity for the second virus to reproduce itself.

This seems to be the only case, so far known, of cross-protection of plant viruses in an insect vector. The position seems very different with the aphid-borne viruses; so far as the writer is aware, there is nothing to prevent an aphid vector acquiring consecutively and transmitting any number of allied viruses, such as the different strains of cucumber mosaic virus.

LOCATION AND VISUALIZATION OF VIRUS
IN THE VECTOR

The development of the technique of cutting ultra thin sections for the electron microscope has opened up possibilities of locating and observing plant viruses in the insect vector. So far little seems to have been done in this direction other than some preliminary work by the writer which, as previously pointed out, was entirely negative, probably because the wrong organs were examined. The work of Littau & Maramorosch

(1956) suggests that the fat body rather than the salivary glands is the site of virus multiplication and examination of this by means of thin sections on the electron microscope should prove fruitful.

FEEDING HABITS, ENVIRONMENTAL CONDITIONS AND HOST PLANT SPECIES IN RELATION TO VIRUS TRANSMISSION

In this section are discussed some of the many variable factors which influence the spread of insect-borne plant viruses in the field.

In some cases the intrinsic properties of the virus itself may profoundly affect its spread by the interplay of insect relationships and the weather. Thus, if a virus is of the persistent type, such as that of potato leaf-roll, it can be carried long distances by aphids drifting on the prevailing winds. Aphids can acquire and transmit leaf-roll virus only after feeding periods of some hours, and so spread within the crop is favoured by conditions that restrict frequency of flight. On the other hand, potato virus *Y* is a non-persistent virus and does not remain long infective in the aphid vector, and it spreads mostly in calm, warm weather suitable for flight, particularly early in the season when aphids are colonizing crops (Broadbent, 1953).

Because of the low thermal inactivation point of the aster yellows virus, climate and season have a profound effect upon the ability of the leafhopper *Macrosteles fascifrons* to transmit it. Infective insects that are exposed to high temperatures such as frequently prevail during the summer months in the U.S.A., especially in the South, lose ability to transmit either temporarily or permanently, depending on the length of the hot spell (Kunkel, 1954).

Another combination of circumstances which affects the spread of aphid-borne viruses is the concentration of the virus or viruses in certain leaves and the availability of such leaves to alighting aphids.

There are two common viruses affecting cauliflowers, the cabbage black ringspot and cauliflower mosaic viruses. Both are non-persistent viruses transmitted by the aphid *Myzus persicae* Sulz., yet cauliflower mosaic virus is much more common in fields of cauliflower than is cabbage black ringspot virus which occurs in higher concentration and has a much wider host range than the former. Broadbent (1954) suggests that at least part of the difference between the rates at which the two viruses spread in the field may be accounted for by the different manner in which they are distributed in old infected plants, and the effect this has on transmission by aphids. Cauliflower mosaic virus occurs in high concentration in all the new leaves produced by infected plants. Cabbage black ringspot virus, on the other hand, occurs mainly in the older leaves, and even there is localized in parts that show symptoms. After flying, most aphids alight on the upper parts of plants; they are therefore less likely to acquire cabbage black ringspot virus than cauliflower mosaic virus. The distribution of viruses in different leaf tissues and its influence on virus transmission by aphids has been studied by Bawden, Hamlyn & Watson (1954). These workers consider that some of the anomalies in aphid transmission can be explained by the unequal distribution of readily extractable virus in different tissues of systemically infected leaves and its relatively high concentration in epidermal cells.

In some cases it appears that the aphid can acquire the virus from one tissue in the plant but to secure infection the virus must be injected into another. The beet yellow-net virus can be acquired by the aphid in 5 min., but the inoculation threshold is approximately 15 min. after feeding commences. Sylvester (1949 a) interprets this on the assumption that mesophyll penetration is sufficient to acquire the virus but the phloem is the essential tissue involved in inoculation.

Although the species of plant which acts as the virus source is not known to affect vector efficiency, the species of plant inoculated by the aphid may have some bearing on the matter. Thus in the case of *Brassica nigra* virus, *Myzus persicae* was a more efficient vector to mustard but *Rhopalosiphum pseudobrassicae* was a better vector when transmission was made to Chinese cabbage (*Brassica chinensis* L.) (Sylvester & Simons, 1951).

The behaviour of aphid vectors depends a good deal on the weather and more winged individuals (alatae) develop in the south of the British Isles than in the north (Broadbent, 1953).

Aphids do not sense and make their way towards a favoured crop and, in any case, they move largely by drift since they cannot make any headway against a wind. The alighting response seems to be a non-specific visual one evoked by objects looming up in the path of the flying insects. For example, in 1947, autumn migrants of the peach-potato aphid, *Myzus persicae*, were seen alighting quite indiscriminately on their specific winter host, the peach, and on another tree, spindle, on which they do not overwinter. Thus the aphids exercised their selection between suitable and unsuitable hosts mainly after alighting on them. From this it seems clear that winged migrants do visit and feed on plants which they do not colonize. As the result of these observations Kennedy (1950) suggests that the key considerations affecting the virus-spreading efficiency of a given aphid species are its ability to transmit the virus and the abundance and activity of its winged forms, rather than its potentialities as a direct pest of the crop. Thus among the winged aphids available and capable of transmitting a virus those species also capable of becoming serious pests would be at some disadvantage as virus spreaders compared with species less well adapted to the given plants. In other words, the casual winged insect vector which may alight and feed on a plant before moving off again is a more important agent in the spread of a virus than the vector which alights and remains to colonize the crops.

The feeding habits of an insect may play an important part in determining its role as a vector. For example, the virus of alfalfa dwarf (Pierce's disease of the grape) is transmitted by a number of leafhoppers, all of which belong to the subfamily Tettigellinae. All these insects have one characteristic in common—they are without exception xylem feeders. If they are prevented mechanically from reaching the xylem then they cannot transmit the virus (Houston, Esau & Hewitt, 1947). Two other examples of this occur with the vectors of peach phoney disease (Turner, 1949) and chlorotic streak of sugar cane (Abbott & Ingram, 1942).

On the other hand the leafhopper vector of beet curly-top is a phloem feeder and cannot either transmit the virus or survive if it is unable to reach the phloem (Bennett, 1934). Sometimes the exact area of an infected leaf selected by a potential vector is important. Storey (1938) has shown that the leafhopper *Cicadulina mbila* cannot take up the maize streak virus by feeding on the green areas of the leaf which separate the chlorotic areas induced by the disease.

TRANSMISSION OF PLANT VIRUS COMPLEXES

Three types of differential transmission by aphid vectors of virus complexes are considered here. The first is a straightforward selective transmission; the second is also selective but is contingent upon the latent period of a virus in the insect. In the third type, aphid transmission of a virus is dependent upon the presence in the plant of a second virus.

The first type of differential transmission by aphids of a virus complex can be subdivided into two. Thus, two viruses may occur together in a plant only one of which is aphid-borne. Several examples of this are known, the commonest being the combination of potato X, which is not aphid-transmitted, with potato viruses Y or A which are. Here, of course, the insect virus selects out the virus which it can transmit, leaving the other virus behind. In the other case, a plant may be infected with two aphid-borne viruses and the selective transmission depends upon the aphid species. For example, when the aphids *Myzus persicae* and *Brevicoryne brassicae* L. are colonized upon cauliflower seedlings infected with the cabbage black ringspot and cauliflower mosaic viruses they are able to transmit both, but the aphid *Myzus ornatus* Laing, similarly colonized, picks out the cauliflower mosaic virus, leaving the black ringspot virus behind (Kvicala, 1945). The aphid *M. ascalonicus* Donc., will transmit the viruses of cucumber mosaic and henbane mosaic, but not potato virus *Y* and severe etch virus. This aphid, therefore, will select out cucumber mosaic virus from a plant infected with a mixture of this and potato virus *Y*. In the same way, when fed on leaves containing henbane mosaic and severe etch viruses it transmits only henbane mosaic (Doncaster & Kassanis, 1946).

In discussing the aphid-transmitted persistent viruses we have mentioned the long latent period exhibited by 'Virus 3' of strawberries in the aphid vector *Capitophorus fragariae* Theob., in which 10–19 days elapse before the insect becomes infective. This virus is one component of the strawberry disease known as 'severe crinkle' and Prentice (1949) isolated it by means of the aphid *C. fragariae* which was allowed to feed for several days on a strawberry plant infected with severe crinkle. The aphids picked up the two viruses, the second one being the strawberry mottle virus; this, being of the non-persistent type, was eliminated by transferring the aphids to fresh indicator plants after 24 hr. Thus, by taking advantage of the differences in the times the 'persistent' and 'non-persistent' viruses remain in the aphid vector it is possible to separate out a virus complex.

We turn now to the third type of relationship of aphids with plant virus complexes in which one virus is dependent upon another for aphid transmission. The best known example of this phenomenon is the rosette disease of tobacco (Smith, 1946), which is caused by two viruses, the vein-distorting and mottle viruses, respectively. Both these viruses when together in the plant are of the persistent type and are transmitted with great efficiency by the aphid *Myzus persicae* Sulz.; when separated only the vein-distorting virus is aphid-borne. It appears to be necessary for both viruses to be together in the plant to enable the aphid to pick up the mottle virus; it is not sufficient for the aphid to feed first on a plant with vein-distorting virus and then on a plant with mottle virus. Quite a lot of investigation has been made of this problem but the reason for it is still obscure. The obvious explanation that in the presence of the vein-distorting virus the mottle virus occurs in higher concentration does not seem to be the answer. Another example of the same pheno- menon has been observed by Clinch, Loughnane & Murphy (1936) who state that it is necessary for potato virus *A* to be present in the potato plant to enable the aphid *Myzus persicae* to pick up potato virus *F* (tuber blotch virus) but no experimental data are given.

TRANSMISSION BY ARTHROPODS OTHER THAN INSECTS

There are at least four cases of plant virus transmission by mites (Acarina) and now that this type of vector has been recognized no doubt others will be discovered. The first record was that of the reversion disease of black currants transmitted by the big bud mite, *Phytoptus ribis* (Westw.) Nalepa, (Amos, Hatton, Knight & Massee, 1927; Massee, 1952). Then Slykhuis (1955) demonstrated that the Eriophyid mite *Aceria tulipae* K. was the vector of the virus of wheat streak mosaic and Flock & Wallace (1955) have shown that the virus of fig mosaic is transmitted by the mite *A. ficus* Cotte. Finally, the long-sought-for vector of the American peach mosaic virus has now been identified as a mite (Cochran, Jones & Wilson, 1955).

Not much is known of the relationship between this type of vector and the viruses transmitted. Slykhuis (1955) has shown that when the mite *Aceria tulipae* was reared on wheat infected with streak mosaic all stages except the eggs carried the virus. However, it was found that when virus-free mites in different developmental stages were colonized on diseased wheat the nymphs could acquire the virus but the adults could not. This is a similar phenomenon to that which occurs in the transmission of tomato spotted wilt virus by thrips where the adult insect cannot pick up the virus *de novo*.

DISCUSSION

It can be seen from the foregoing account that a great many facts relating to insects and plant viruses have now been assembled, but the situation is very far from clear. It seems well established, however, that certain plant viruses do multiply in their leafhopper vectors.

It is not known how far the transmission of viruses by other vectors, especially aphids, is a fixed biological relationship. In other words, does the virus mutate so that it becomes insect-borne or can vectors become 'attuned' to transmit plant viruses in a comparatively short time? Viruses which have no known insect vector but have alternative methods of spread, as in the case of tobacco mosaic virus and potato virus *X*, keep going. On the other hand, it can be suggested that plant viruses may appear and then, if no insect vector or alternative method of spread develop, the viruses die out unless propagated artificially in laboratories.

There are several examples of this, the viruses of tomato black ring, *Belladonna* mosaic, *Arabis* mosaic, broken ringspot and lovage mosaic do not now occur in the field. The last-named failed to pass to neighbouring lovage plants over a period of 10 years and indeed was almost impossible to transmit artificially to healthy lovage plants, although it could be passed easily enough by mechanical inoculation to other miscellaneous hosts. The virus of tomato bushy stunt presents an interesting case of the disappearance of a plant virus in the apparent absence of an insect vector. It was first described in England by Smith in 1935, and except for one brief appearance has not been seen since. Now it has turned up again in Italy where it has been found naturally infecting *Petunia*. This is important because it would appear that an insect vector (possibly of the mandibulate type) for the virus must have developed. This seems to be the only explanation of how the virus gets to *Petunia* unless it is soil-transmitted.

Viruses long prevented artificially from having contact with their insect vectors tend to lose their insect-transmissibility (Black, 1953). Is the converse true? If insects, or other arthropods, are bred continuously on virus-infected plants will they eventually become vectors? Why should the virus of turnip yellow mosaic, which is highly infectious, only be transmitted by biting insects, especially the turnip flea beetle, and not by aphids? Why should the virus of fig mosaic be transmitted only by mites? Can the explanation lie in the long association of these arthropods with these two hosts? Fig trees in California are almost universally infected with the fig mosaic virus.

On the other hand, it may happen that an insect which casually visits a virus-infected plant becomes a vector rather than the more common insect fauna of that plant. This would account for sudden outbreaks of new virus diseases. The insect transmission of peach phoney disease and sandal spike seem to be cases in point.

It does not seem possible to correlate physical or other properties of viruses with insect relationships although it is true that many aphid-borne viruses are unstable and occur in low concentration in the host plant.

It may be that in the past too much attention has been paid to the well-known insect fauna of virus-infected plants and not enough to more obscure organisms. Now that consideration has been given to mites as vectors we already have four authentic cases of mite-transmitted plant viruses. There may be other organisms notably in the soil, such as nematode worms, which could act as vectors; or some entirely unsuspected mode of spread may exist. Transmission by the soil needs more investigation; the tobacco necrosis viruses are soil-borne and their method of spread is more like that of fungal or bacterial spores than of a plant virus. The virus of wheat rosette or mosaic is known to be soil-borne but the mechanics of its spread are not understood.

REFERENCES

ABBOTT, E. V. & INGRAM, J. W. (1942). Transmission of chlorotic streak of sugar cane by the leafhopper, *Draeculacephala portola*. *Phytopathology*, **32**, 99.

ALLARD, H. A. (1914). The mosaic disease of tobacco. *Bull. U.S. Dep. Agric.* no. 40.

AMOS, J., HATTON, R. G., KNIGHT, R. C. & MASSEE, A. M. (1927). Experiments in the transmission of reversion in black currant. *Ann. Rep. E. Malling Res. Sta.* **11**, 126.

BALL, E. D. (1909). The leafhoppers of the sugar beet and their relation to the curly-top condition. *Bull. U.S. Dept. Agric. Ent.* **66**, 33.

BAWDEN, F. C. (1950). *Plant Viruses and Virus Diseases*, 3rd ed. Waltham, Mass.: Chronica Botanica Co.

BAWDEN, F. C., HAMLYN, BRENDA M. G. & WATSON, A. MARION (1954). The distribution of viruses in different leaf tissues and its influence on virus transmission by aphids. *Ann. appl. Biol.* **41**, 229.

BAWDEN, F. C. & KASSANIS, B. (1947). The behaviour of some naturally occurring strains of potato virus Y. *Ann. appl. Biol.* **34**, 503.

BENNETT, C. W. (1934). Plant-tissue relations of the sugar beet curly-top virus. *J. agric. Res.* **48**, 665.

BENNETT, C. W. & WALLACE, H. E. (1938). Relation of the curly-top virus to the vector, *Eutettix tenellus*. *J. agric. Res.* **56**, 31.

BLACK, L. M. (1940). Mechanical transmission of aster yellows virus to leafhoppers. *Phytopathology*, **30**, 2.

BLACK, L. M. (1941). Further evidence for multiplication of the aster yellows virus in the aster leafhopper. *Phytopathology*, **31**, 120.

BLACK, L. M. (1943). Genetic variation in the clover leafhopper's ability to transmit potato yellow dwarf virus. *Genetics*, **28**, 200.

BLACK, L. M. (1950). A plant virus that multiplies in its insect vector. *Nature, Lond.*, **166**, 852.

BLACK, L. M. (1953). Loss of vector transmissibility by viruses normally insect-transmitted. *Phytopathology*, **43**, 466.

BRADLEY, R. H. E. (1952). Studies on the aphid transmission of a strain of henbane mosaic. *Ann. appl. Biol.* **39**, 78.

BROADBENT, L. (1953). Aphids and virus diseases in potato crops. *Biol. Rev.* **28**, 350.

BROADBENT, L. (1954). The different distribution of two brassica viruses in the plant and its influence on spread in the field. *Ann. appl. Biol.* **41**, 174.

CADMAN, C. H. & HARRISON, B. D. (1956). Transmission of leaf-roll virus. *3rd. Ann. Rep. Scott. Hort. Res. Inst.* p. 23.

CLINCH, P., LOUGHNANE, J. B. & MURPHY, P. (1936). A study of the aucuba or yellow mosaics of the potato. *Sci. Proc. R. Dublin Soc.* **21**, 431.

COCHRAN, L. C., JONES, L. S. & WILSON, N. S. (1955). Mite vector of peach mosaic. *Agric. Res. U.S.D.A.*, 15 Sept.

DALE, W. T. (1953). The transmission of plant viruses by biting insects with particular reference to cowpea mosaic. *Ann. appl. Biol.* **40**, 384.

DAY, M. F. (1955). Mechanism of transmission of potato leaf-roll by aphids. *Aust. J. Biol. Sci.* **8**, 498.

DAY, M. F. & IRZYKIEWICZ, H. (1954). On the mechanism of transmission of non-persistent phytopathogenic viruses by aphids. *Aust. J. Biol. Sci.* **7**, 251.

DOBROSCKY, I. B. (1929). Is the aster yellows virus detectable in its insect vector? *Phytopathology*, **19**, 11.

DONCASTER, J. P. & KASSANIS, B. (1946). The shallot aphis, *Myzus ascalonicus*, Donc., and its behaviour as a vector of plant viruses. *Ann. appl. Biol.* **33**, 66.

DOOLITTLE, S. P. (1916). A new infectious disease of cucumber. *Phytopathology*, **6**, 145.

DOOLITTLE, S. P. & GILBERT, W. W. (1918). Further notes on cucumber mosaic disease. *Phytopathology*, **8**, 77.

DOOLITTLE, S. P. & WALKER, M. N. (1928). Aphis transmission of cucumber mosaic. *Phytopathology*, **18**, 143.

FLOCK, R. A. & WALLACE, J. M. (1955). Transmission of fig mosaic by the Eriphyid mite, *Aceria ficus*. *Phytopathology*, **45**, 52.

FREITAG, J. H. (1956). Beetle transmission, host range and properties of squash mosaic virus. *Phytopathology*, **46**, 73.

FUKUSHI, T. (1933). Transmission of a virus through the eggs of an insect vector. *Proc. imp. Acad. Japan*, **9**, 451.

HOGGAN, I. A. (1933). Some factors involved in aphid transmission of the cucumber mosaic virus to tobacco. *J. agric. Res.* **47**, 689.

HOUSTON, B. R., ESAU, KATHERINE & HEWITT, W. B. (1947). The mode of vector feeding and the tissues involved in the transmission of Pierce's disease virus in grape and alfalfa. *Phytopathology*, **37**, 247.

JAGGER, I. E. (1916). Experiments with the cucumber mosaic disease. *Phytopathology*, **6**, 148.

KASSANIS, B. (1952). Some factors affecting the transmission of leaf-roll virus by aphids. *Ann. appl. Biol.* **39**, 157.

KENNEDY, J. S. (1950). Aphid migration and the spread of plant viruses. *Nature, Lond.*, **165**, 1024.

KIRKPATRICK, H. C. & ROSS, A. F. (1952). Aphid transmission of potato leaf roll virus to Solanaceous hosts. *Phytopathology*, **42**, 540.

KLOSTERMEYER, E. C. (1953). Entomological aspects of the potato leaf-roll problem in central Washington. *Tech. Bull. Wash. agric. Exp. Sta.* no. 9, p. 1.

KUNKEL, L. O. (1926). Studies on aster yellows. *Amer. J. Bot.* **13**, 646.

KUNKEL, L. O. (1937). Effect of heat on ability of *Cicadula sexnotata* to transmit aster yellows. *Amer. J. Bot.* **24**, 316.

KUNKEL, L. O. (1948). Studies on a new corn virus disease. *Arch. ges. Virusforsch.* **4**, 24.

KUNKEL, L. O. (1954). Maintenance of yellows type viruses in plant and insect reservoirs. *Dynamics of Virus and Rickettsial Infections, International Symposium*, p. 209. New York: Blakiston Co.

KUNKEL, L. O. (1955). Cross-protection between strains of yellows-type viruses. In *Advanc. virus Res.* 3, 251.

KVICALA, B. (1945). Selective power in virus transmission exhibited by an aphis. *Nature, Lond.*, **155**, 174.

LITTAU, V. C. & MARAMOROSCH, K. (1956). Cytological effects of aster yellows virus on its insect vector. *Virology*, **2**, 128.

MARAMOROSCH, K. (1951). Mechanical transmission of corn stunt virus to an insect vector. *Phytopathology* (Abstr.), **41**, 658.

MARAMOROSCH, K. (1952). Direct evidence for the multiplication of aster yellows virus in its insect vector. *Phytopathology*, **42**, 59.

MARAMOROSCH, K. (1955). Multiplication of plant virus in insect vectors. In *Advanc. Virus Res.* 3, 221.

MARAMOROSCH, K. (1956). Multiplication of aster yellows virus in *in vitro* preparations of insect tissues *Virology*, **2**, 369.

MARKHAM, R. & SMITH, K. M. (1949). Studies on the virus of turnip yellow mosaic. *Parasitology*, **39**, 330.

MASSEE, A. M. (1952). Transmission of reversion of black currants. *Ann. Rep. E. Malling Res. Sta.* (1951), p. 162.

MERRILL, H. M. & TENBROECK, C. (1934). Multiplication of equine encephalomyelitis in mosquitoes. *Proc. Soc. exp. Biol., N.Y.*, **32**, 421.

PAINE, J. & LEGG, J. T. (1953). Transmission of hop mosaic by *Phorodon humuli* Schrank. *Nature, Lond.*, **171**, 263.

PRENTICE, I. W. (1949). Resolution of Strawberry Virus complexes. III. The isolation and some properties of Virus 3. *Ann. appl. Biol.* **36**, 18.

SHAW, H. B. (1910). The curly-top of beets. *Bull. U.S. Dep. Agric. Bur. Pl. Ind.* no. 181.

SLYKHUIS, J. T. (1955). Aceria tulipae Keifer (Acarina Eriphyidae) in relation to the spread of wheat streak mosaic. *Phytopathology*, **45**, 116.

SMITH, K. M. (1935). A new virus disease of the tomato. *Ann. appl. Biol.* **22**, 731.

SMITH, K. M. (1941). Some notes on the relationship of plant viruses with vector and non-vector insects. *Parasitology*, **33**, 110.

SMITH, K. M. (1946). The transmission of a plant virus complex by aphids. *Parasitology*, **37**, 131.

SMITH, K. M. & LEA, D. E. (1946). The transmission of plant viruses by aphids. *Parasitology*, **37**, 25.

SMITH, K. M. & MARKHAM, R. (1946). An insect vector of the turnip yellow mosaic virus. *Nature, Lond.*, **158**, 417.

SOEST, W. VAN & MEESTER-MANGER CATS, V. DE (1956). Does the aphid *Myzus persicae* (Sulz.) imbibe tobacco mosaic virus? *Virology*, **2**, 411.

STOREY, H. H. (1932). The inheritance by an insect vector of the ability to transmit a plant virus. *Proc. roy. Soc.* B, **112**, 46.

STOREY, H. H. (1933). Investigation of the mechanism of the transmission of plant viruses. I. *Proc. roy. Soc.* B, **113**, 463.

STOREY, H. H. (1938). Investigations of the mechanism of the transmission of plant viruses by insect vectors. II. The part played by puncture in transmission. *Proc. roy. Soc.* B, **125**, 455.

STUBBS, L. L. (1955). Strains of *Myzus persicae* Sulz. active and inactive with respect to virus transmission. *Aust. J. Biol. Sci.*, **8**, 68.

SUKHOV, K. S. (1944). Salivary secretion of the aphid, *Myzus persicae* (Sulz.) and its ability to form a filtering apparatus. (In Russian.) *C.R. Acad. Sci. U.R.S.S.* **42**, 226.

SYLVESTER, E. S. (1949*a*). Transmission of sugar beet yellow-net virus by the green peach aphid. *Phytopathology*, **39**, 117.

SYLVESTER, E. S. (1949*b*). Beet mosaic virus–green peach aphid relationships. *Phytopathology*, **39**, 417.

SYLVESTER, E. C. (1954). Aphid transmission of non-persistent plant viruses with special reference to the *Brassica nigra* virus. *Hilgardia*, **23**, 53.

SYLVESTER, E. S. & SIMONS, J. N. (1951). Relation of plant species inoculated to efficiency of aphids in the transmission of *Brassica nigra* virus. *Phytopathology*, **41**, 908.

TAKATA, K. (1895). Results of experiments with dwarf diseases of the rice plant. *J. Japan Agric.* **171**, 1.

TRAGER, W. (1938). Multiplication of the virus of equine encephalomyelitis in surviving mosquito tissues. *Amer. J. trop. Med.* **18**, 387.

TURNER, W. F. (1949). Insect vectors of phoney peach disease. *Science*, **109**, 87.

WALTERS, H. J. (1952). Some relationships of three plant viruses to the differential grasshopper, *Melanoplus differentialis* (Thos.). *Phytopathology*, **42**, 355.

WATSON, M. A. (1936). Factors affecting the amount of infection obtained by aphis transmission of the virus Hy. III. *Phil. Trans.* B, **226**, 457.

WATSON, M. A. (1938). Further studies on the relationship between *Hyoscyamus* Virus 3 and the aphis *Myzus persicae* (Sulz.) with special reference to the effects of fasting. *Proc. roy. Soc.* B, **125**, 144.

WATSON, M. A. & ROBERTS, F. M. (1939). A comparative study of the transmission of *Hyoscyamus* Virus 3, Potato Virus *Y* and Cucumber Virus *I* by the vectors *Myzus persicae* (Sulz.), *M. circumflexus* Buckt., and *Macrosiphum gei* (Koch). *Proc. roy. Soc.* B, **127**, 543.

WATSON, M. A. & ROBERTS, F. M. (1940). Evidence against the hypothesis that certain plant viruses are transmitted mechanically by aphids. *Ann. appl. Biol.* **27**, 227.